SOIL DYNAMICS

SOIL DYNAMICS

Shamsher Prakash

Professor of Civil Engineering
University of Missouri-Rolla

McGraw-Hill Book Company

New York   St. Louis   San Francisco   Auckland   Bogotá   Hamburg
Johannesburg   London   Madrid   Mexico   Montreal   New Delhi
Panama   Paris   São Paulo   Singapore   Sydney   Tokyo   Toronto

This book was set in Times Roman by Science Typographers, Inc.
The editors were Julienne V. Brown and Susan Hazlett;
the production supervisor was Phil Galea.
The drawings were done by J & R Services, Inc.
The cover was designed by Charles A. Carson.
Fairfield Graphics was printer and binder.

SOIL DYNAMICS

34567890   FGFG   8987654321

Library of Congress Cataloging in Publication Data

Prakash, Shamsher.
    Soil dynamics.

    Includes bibliographical references and index.
    1. Soil dynamics. 2. Foundations. I. Title.
TA710.P693   624.1′5136   80-23122
ISBN 0-07-050658-2

TO MY FRIEND
Vijaya
in whom I found a brother, philosopher, and sage,
the imprint of whose personality has
influenced every aspect of my life.

CONTENTS

FOREWORD

In his foreword to Mallet and Pacquant's book on earth dams, which appeared in 1951, Terzaghi pointed out that the development of every aspect of civil engineering passes through three stages: the empirical, wherein precedent is the dominant influence; the scientific, wherein great strides are made and overconfidence in the power of science occasionally leads to failures; and the mature, wherein precedent and science combine into a judgment that permits the highest expression of the engineer's calling.

The present state of the art of soil dynamics defies classification into Terzaghi's stages. Rather, soil dynamics is a curious hybrid in which progress has been remarkably uneven. Part of the subject consists of the classical dynamics of elastic continua and the classical theory of damped vibrations, already well advanced and needing only to be adapted to the geometry of practical problems involving the subsoil. The relevant properties of the soils can be ascertained by static or by the simplest of dynamic tests. On the other hand, exclusively dynamic properties unique to soils are dominant in studies of liquefaction, where classical theory plays a minor role.

Uneven progress has resulted also from two other conditions: the differing origins of the loads to be considered in soil dynamics and the relative urgency of obtaining solutions of various practical problems.

Soil-supported structures may on the one hand be acted upon by dynamic forces originating elsewhere than in the soil. Some of the forces are readily calculable, such as those due to rotating or reciprocating machines, the firing of projectiles, or the dropping of weights, whereas others are best evaluated probabilistically, such as those due to wind or waves. In any event, the problem for the engineer is to estimate the ability of the soil to withstand the external loading and to judge the movements, both transitory and permanent, of the soil-supported foundation. If the stresses in the soil are small and the movements essentially elastic, solution is straightforward and the properties of the soil demand very little attention. The solution is by no means so straightforward if the movements are inelastic or if repetitions lead to cumulative displacements.

Still less tractable are problems in which the motions originate, not from external forces acting on a structure but from the supporting soil itself. They are transmitted to the structure which then reacts in accordance with its own characteristics as well as those of the soil. The motion of the soil may be caused by nearby disturbances such as the operation of compressors or pile drivers, or by more distant events such as earthquakes. If the latter, the ground motions themselves cannot be forecast in deterministic fashion; they are postulated by probabilistic means or by such concepts as spectra. Under some circumstances, the ground motions may even induce liquefaction whereupon soil-supported structures will suffer irrespective of their characteristics.

The dependence of the development of various phases of soil dynamics on need, often first perceived by the military, can be illustrated by three examples.

Considerable progress has been made in determining the ultimate bearing capacity of footings and rafts. The impetus for research in this area came largely from the need to design protective structures against the force of high-energy atmospheric blasts. For nonmilitary problems the ultimate bearing capacity is usually of little or no interest in comparison to the movements, particularly when the subsoil is noncohesive and the loads are recurrent as in forges or drop hammers. Although bearing capacity calculations are often made in connection with the design of such facilities, they have slight significance in comparison with estimates of the cumulative settlement, an aspect of soil dynamics still in the empirical stage.

Much of the impetus for obtaining precise knowledge of the elastic properties of soil under low-stress levels came from the need to design tracking radar facilities capable of detecting and locating rapidly moving distant objects. Inertia forces generated by the oscillations of the equipment were of major import. The refinement of the resonant-column test, first found useful in protective structure design, was due in no small way to the specific need to meet the challenge of this problem.

Aseismic design, with concomitant developments in seismology, is a much broader subject than soil dynamics, but one that nevertheless required special developments in some areas of soil dynamics. The economic and social importance of the earthquake problem has fostered the expenditure of much time and talent. Perhaps this aspect of soil dynamics is ready for the mature stage; certainly there has been no lack of scientific development in either theory or experiment, although field verification of design procedures must await information from potentially damaging earthquakes.

The examples could continue. If this book suggests that soil dynamics is far from a homogeneous body of knowledge, that there are major gaps and needed areas of research, and that some problems of practical importance have hardly been addressed whereas others of limited applicability are more thoroughly treated, then the author has succeeded in reflecting the present state of the art. The author is conscious of the gaps and points them out. Thus he introduces the reader to what is presently known, provides an excellent compendium of references to more definitive literature, and suggests wherein further knowledge is urgently needed.

Ralph B. Peck
University of Illinois
Urbana-Champaign

PREFACE

The problems of dynamic loading of soils and foundations have existed ever since the earth came into existence. Earthquakes cause rupture of earth mass and shake everything supported on it.

The study of dynamic behavior of soils and foundations has lagged behind the study of dynamic behavior of structures because it was believed, erroneously, that the superstructure needs to be strengthened more in poor soils than in good soils. However, a large-scale tilting of well-built houses in the Niigata Earthquake of 1964 has focused the attention of the profession on problems of soil dynamics.

However, in Japan and India, pioneering work on these problems was already underway and the author can take legitimate pride in that the first regular graduate course in "soil dynamics" was offered at Roorkee in 1963. This is still one of the most popular courses with students majoring in the study of soils. Ever since, the teaching of soil dynamics has been introduced in almost all of the leading schools throughout the world.

As early as 1960, studies on different aspects of dynamic behavior of soils were initiated at Roorkee. A lot of progress has since been made in the field of liquefaction of soils, dynamic earth pressures, determination of dynamic soil parameters, analysis and design of machine foundations, aseismic design of foundations, piles under earthquake loads, and dynamic soil structure interaction. Progress has also been made in monitoring performance of machine foundations.

The teaching of different aspects of dynamic behavior of soils has till now been done with the help of research material which is scattered among a large number of technical journals. Thus, there was a great need to compile material into a basic text on soil dynamics, which may serve as a starting point for serious studies of this subject. This objective has been kept in view in planning the present text. The text describes the state-of-art on the subject at the time of final compilation as well as provides a basic insight to the reader for whom it may be the first exposure to soil dynamics.

The subject has been developed by introducing the reader to the problems in soil dynamics (Chapter 1); this is followed by theory of mechanical vibrations (Chapter 2). In Chapter 3, wave propagation in elastic medium is discussed while the concepts which have been applied to the determination of soil modulii are discussed in Chapter 4. Also, laboratory and field determination of these constants along with typical data have been included in this chapter. Subsequent chapters are devoted to the stability of retaining walls (Chapter 5), footings (Chapter 6), and pile foundations (Chapter 7), liquefaction of soils (Chapter 8), and machine foundations (Chapter 9).

The material has been arranged logically so that the reader can follow the developmental sequence of the subject with relative ease. Every effort has been made to make the text more-or-less self-contained, so essential for a first text on the subject. A comprehensive bibliography has been added so the interested reader can refer to the details of any work.

The subject of soil dynamics is developing very fast; several analytical techniques and design procedures may change in the near future and may necessitate a revision of the text. This fact has been brought to the attention of the reader at the appropriate places in the text wherein limitations of present-day knowledge on the subject are also mentioned.

In the preparation of this text, several of my colleagues and students helped in a variety of ways. Useful comments were offered by Jai Krishna, Kenji Ishihara, R. W. Stephenson, Masami Fukuoba, Swami Saran, W. D. Liam Finn, and Vijay K. Puri. Solutions to several problems were done by Vijay K. Puri, Jalal Khandoker, and Leo Turek. Vijay K. Puri also assisted in proofreading the entire text.

In the preparation of this text, material has been frequently taken from published journals and books. Thanks are due to the American Society of Civil Engineers for permitting the use of material from their publications. A portion of Article 5.9 and Tables 6.4 and 6.5 and Article 9.18 are reproduced with the permission of the Indian Standards Institution from Indian Standard No. 1893-1975 Third Revision and No. 2974-1969 (Part I) First Revision respectively, to which reference is invited for further details. These standards are available from the ISI, New Delhi.

Acknowledgments to other copyrighted material is given at appropriate places in the text and figures.

Mrs. Margot Lewis typed the manuscript patiently and with great care and her painstaking efforts are acknowledged. Mrs. Barbara Harris assisted in editorial work.

I owe a great deal to my alma mater, Roorkee University, that offered me the wonderful opportunity to experiment in this new area and to develop techniques of testing and analysis, and to the University of Missouri-Rolla where I was afforded an opportunity to synthesize the material collected in Roorkee.

Shamsher Prakash

SOIL DYNAMICS

ONE

INTRODUCTION

1.1 SOIL MECHANICS AND SOIL DYNAMICS

The term "soil mechanics" was coined by Dr. Karl Terzaghi, who is recognized as the "father of soil mechanics." Soil mechanics deals with engineering properties and behavior of soil under stress. A systematic study of soils as construction material was initiated by Terzaghi in the early part of this century. Within a short span of about 20 years, after the publication in 1925 of his first book on soil mechanics in German, the impact of the new science was felt throughout the world.

Soil dynamics is that branch of soil mechanics which deals with engineering properties and behavior of soil under dynamic stress. Even though "stress" meant both static and dynamic stress in the original definition of soil mechanics, only static stress was most often implied by "stress." This is the reason why almost all the texts dealing with soil mechanics make only a passing reference, at best, to behavior of soil under dynamic stress.

1.2 NATURE OF DYNAMIC LOADS

Dynamic loads on foundations and soil structures may act due to earthquakes, bomb blasts, operation of reciprocating and rotary machines and hammers, construction operations, (such as pile driving), quarrying, fast-moving traffic (including landing aircraft), wind, or loading due to wave action of water. The nature of each of these loads is quite different from the nature of the loads in the other cases.

Table 1.1 Magnitudes (M) of earthquakes and energy (E) released†

M (Richter)	5.0	6.0	6.5	7.0	7.5	8.0	8.6
E (10^{20} ergs)	0.08	2.5	14.1	80	446	2500	20,000

Note: Energy released by an earthquake with a magnitude of 6.33 would be on the order of 8×10^{20} ergs.

†Reproduced by permission of Sarita Prakashan, Meerut (UP) India, from *Elements of Earthquake Engineering* by Jai Krishna and A. R. Chandrasekaran (1976).

Figure 1.1 Tilting of building during Niigata earthquake, 1964. *(After Seed and Idriss, 1967.)*

Figure 1.2 Automobile sunk during Niigata earthquake, 1964.

Earthquakes† constitute the single most important source of dynamic loads on structures and foundations. Every earthquake is associated with a certain amount of energy released at its source and can be assigned a magnitude (M) which is just a number (Richter, 1958).

Table 1.1 gives an idea of the energy associated with a particular magnitude.

Due to ground motion during an earthquake, footings may settle, buildings may tilt, soils may liquefy and lose ability to support structures, and light structures may float. Figure 1.1 shows the tilting of a building during the Niigata earthquake (1964). An automobile that sank into the ground and a sewage tank that floated to the surface are shown in Figs. 1.2 and 1.3, respectively. A graphic

Figure 1.3 Sewage treatment tank which floated to surface during Niigata earthquake. *(After Seed and Idriss, 1967.)*

† Vibrations of the earth's surface caused by waves originating from a source of disturbance in the earth mass are called *earthquakes*. An earthquake may be caused by volcanic eruption or by strain-building processes inside the earth's mass. In the latter case, the strain energy that accumulates due to deformation in the earth mass is released when the resilience of the material storing this energy is exceeded. At this stage, slipping of the earth mass occurs.

The point inside the earth mass where slippage or fracture begins is termed the *focus* of the earthquake, and the point just above the focus on the earth's surface is called the *epicenter*.

A measure of the energy released by an earthquake is its *magnitude*. As suggested by Richter (1958), the magnitude of an earthquake equals the logarithm to the base 10 of the maximum amplitude of the ground motion, as recorded in millimeters at a distance of 100 km from the epicenter on standard equipment.

.description of earthquake damage and structural performance in the United States has been presented by Steinbrugge (1970). A listing of selected U. S. earthquakes is also included. Krishna and Chandrasekaran (1976) describe an average of 12 earthquakes, with magnitudes of 7.0 or greater, as occurring somewhere in the world every year.

It is interesting to compare the energy of an earthquake with that of a nuclear explosion. The energy released by a Hiroshima-type atom bomb is 8×10^{20} ergs, equal to that of an earthquake with a magnitude of 6.33. Thus, in terms of energy release, an earthquake of the size ($M = 8.6$) of the Assam earthquake of August 15, 1950, is the equivalent of 2500 such bombs exploded together. A listing of some past Indian earthquakes and their magnitudes is shown in Table 1.2.

It is well known that an earthquake causes random motion in every direction. Figure 1.4a shows the north-south component of the May 18, 1940, El

Table 1.2 Some past Indian earthquakes†

Year	Area	Date	Latitude (degrees north)	Longitude (degrees east)	Magnitude (M)
1819	Kutch	June 16			8.0
1833	Bihar	Aug 26	27.5	86.5	7.7
1897	Assam (Shillong Plateau)	June 12	26.0	91.0	8.7
1900	Palghat (Kerala)	Feb 8	10.7	76.7	6.0
1905	Kangra	Apr 4	32.5	76.5	8.0
1930	Dhubri (ASSAM)	July 3	25.8	90.2	7.1
1934	Bihar	Jan 15	26.6	86.8	8.3
1941	Andamans	June 26	12.4	92.5	8.0
1943	Assam (NE)	Oct 23	26.8	94.0	7.2
1950	Assam (NE)	Aug 15	28.7	96.6	8.6
1956	Anjar	July 21	23.3	70.0	7.0
1956	Bulandsher (UP)	Oct 10	28.1	77.7	6.7
1958	Kapkote (UP)	Dec 28	30.0	80.0	6.3
1960	Delhi	Aug 27	28.3	77.4	6.0
1963	Badgam (Kashmir)	Sept 2	33.9	74.7	5.5
1966	W. Nepal	June 27	29.5	81.0	6.3
1966	Moradabad (UP)	Aug 15	28.0	79.0	5.3
1967	Nicobar	July 2	9.0	93.4	6.2
1967	Koyna	Dec 11	17.4	73.7	6.5
1970	Broach	Mar 23	21.7	72.9	5.7
1970	Bhadrachalam (AP)	Apr 13	17.6	80.6	6.5
1975	Himachal Pradesh	Jan 19	32.5	78.4	6.5

†Reproduced by permission of Sarita Prakashan, Meerut (UP) India, from *Elements of Earthquake Engineering* by Jai Krishna and A. R. Chandrasekaran (1976).

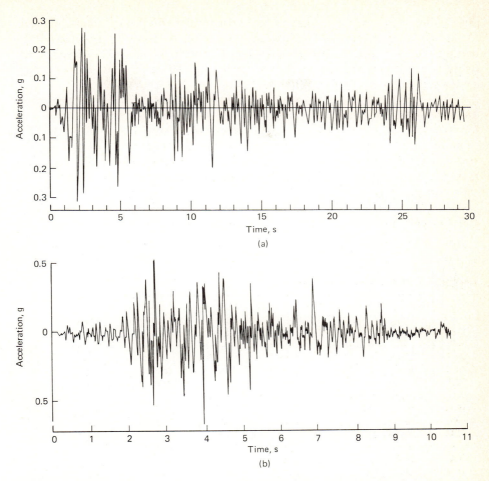

Figure 1.4 (*a*) Accelerogram of El Centro Earthquake of May 18, 1940. NS component. (*b*) Accelerogram of Koyna Earthquake of Dec. 11, 1967. Horizontal component along axis of Koyna Dam.

Centro earthquake, which had a magnitude of 7.1, and Fig. 1.4*b* shows the accelerogram of the Koyna earthquake of December 11, 1967. On the other hand, dynamic loads due to reciprocating and rotary machines are more or less sinusoidal in nature. The impact of a hammer constitutes a transient load on a foundation. Typical dynamic loading diagrams are shown for steady-state motion (Fig. 1.5*a* and *b*), for transient motion (Fig. 1.6), and for pile driving (Fig. 1.7).

The above figures are rather simplified presentations of actual loading conditions. Actual loads in the field may often differ from these simplified

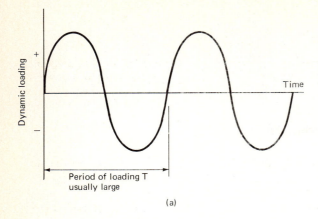

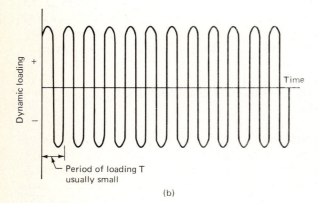

Figure 1.5 Dynamic load due to steady-state vibrations. (*a*) Period of loading *T* usually large; slow-vibrating loading. (*b*) Period of loading *T*, usually small; fast-vibrating loading.

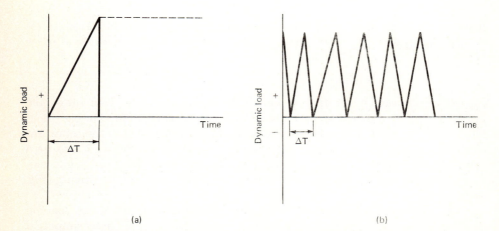

Figure 1.6 Transient dynamic load. (*a*) Single-impulse loading. (*b*) Multiple-impulse loading.

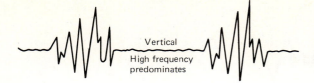

Figure 1.7 Trace of vertical acceleration of ground due to pile driving.

loading diagrams in the following respects:

1. The loading in nature is not truly periodic; that is, the loading cycles are not repeated at equal intervals.
2. The peaks in any two cycles may be different.
3. Purely dynamic loads do not occur in nature. Loads are always combinations of static and dynamic loads. Static loads are caused by the dead weight of the superstructure and the substructure, while dynamic loads may be caused through the sources described above. All loads, other than dead weight, will be considered dynamic loads in the following text unless otherwise stated.

1.3 STRESS CONDITIONS ON SOIL ELEMENTS UNDER EARTHQUAKE LOADING

Loads occur in combination with static and dynamic stresses. If initial static stress is large and additional stresses induced by an earthquake are small, the resulting effect is similar to that shown in Fig. 1.8*a*. In this figure, a symmetrical pulsating stress system is superimposed on an initial sustained stress. If, however, the sustained stress is smaller and the pulsating stress is larger, then the combined effect would be as shown in Fig. 1.8*b*. When a footing is only resting

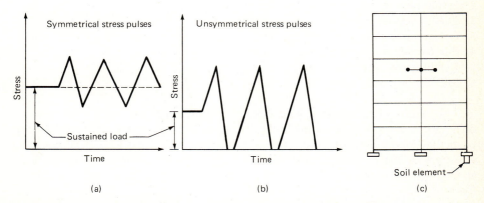

Figure 1.8 One-dimensional loading conditions on soil elements during earthquakes. *(After Seed and Chan, 1966.)*

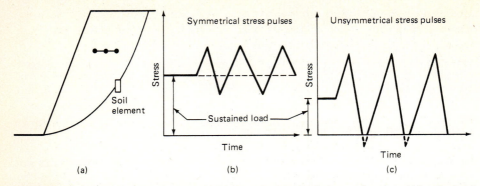

Figure 1.9 Two-dimensional loading conditions on soil elements during earthquakes. *(After Seed and Chan, 1966.)*

on the soil, a negative stress cannot occur on the footing (Fig. 1.8*c*). In such a case, stresses on the soil beneath the footing act only in one direction.

In the case of an embankment, a typical soil element (Fig. 1.9*a*) is subjected to an initial sustained stress before an earthquake. The pulsating stress induced by the earthquake will be superimposed on this sustained stress. Since the soil element can withstand shear stresses in either direction, the resulting pattern will be as shown in Fig. 1.9*b* and *c*.

1.4 PROBLEMS OF DYNAMIC LOADING OF SOILS AND SOIL STRUCTURES

The problems of dynamic loading of soils and soil structures, which will be discussed at length in subsequent chapters, are as follows:

1. Dynamic stress deformation and strength characteristics of soils
2. Earth pressure problems and retaining walls
3. Dynamic bearing capacity and design of shallow footings
4. Pile foundations under dynamic loads
5. Liquefaction of soils
6. Machine foundations

The study of stress strain and strength characteristics of soils poses several difficulties, the most important being the design of an apparatus suitable for a particular job to simulate field loading conditions. No efforts have been made in any part of the civilized world to standardize any tests for the purpose. The same remarks apply to determining other properties of soils under dynamic loads.

In many stability problems, the dynamic force is replaced by a pseudoequivalent static force and solutions are obtained. This may *sometimes* lead to dangerous results. Hence, in such cases, a dynamic analysis is absolutely essential, while in others an estimate of the natural period† of the structure needs to be made to ensure that resonance‡ will not occur.

REFERENCES

Krishna, J., and A. R. Chandrasekaran: "Elements of Earthquake Engineering," Sarita Prakahan, Meerut, UP, India, 1976.

Richter, C. F.: "Elementary Seismology," W. H. Freeman, San Francisco, Calif., 1958.

Steinbrugge, K. V.: Earthquake Damage and Structural Performance in the United States, in R. L. Wiegel (ed): "Earthquake Engineering," Prentice-Hall, Englewood Cliffs, N.J., 1970, chap. 9.

Seed, H. B., and C. K. Chan: "Clay Strength Under Earthquake Loading Conditions," *J. Soil Mech. Found. Div.*, *ASCE*, vol. 92, no. SM 2, pp. 53–78, 1966.

Seed, H. B., and I. M. Idriss: "Analysis of Soil Liquefaction, Niigata Earthquake," *J. Soil Mech. Found. Div.*, *ASCE*, vol. 93, no. SM 3, pp. 83–108, 1967.

† See Chap. 2 for definition.
‡ See Chap. 2 for definition.

CHAPTER TWO

THEORY OF VIBRATIONS

2.1 GENERAL

For a proper understanding and appreciation of the different aspects of design of foundations and soil structures subjected to dynamic loads, it is necessary to be familiar with the simple theoretical concepts of harmonic vibrations. Most of the problems dealt with in subsequent chapters have been solved for the loads acting harmonically. This assumption is reasonably correct for machine foundations, but for complicated motion this is not precisely the case. The departure from reality in such cases will be discussed in appropriate places.

2.2 DEFINITIONS

Period If motion repeats itself in equal intervals of time, it is called a *periodic motion* and the time elapsed in repeating the motion once is called its *period*.

Cycle Motion completed during a period is referred to as a *cycle*.

Frequency The number of cycles of motion in a unit of time is called the *frequency* of vibrations.

Natural frequency If an elastic system vibrates under the action of forces inherent in the system and in the absence of any externally applied force, the frequency with which it vibrates is its *natural frequency*.

Forced vibrations Vibrations that occur under the excitation of external forces are termed *forced vibrations*. Forced vibrations occur at the frequency of the exciting force. The frequency of excitation is independent of the natural frequency of the system.

Degrees of freedom The number of independent coordinates necessary to describe the motion of a system specifies the *degrees of freedom* of the system. A system may in general have several degrees of freedom; such a system is called a *multidegree freedom* system.

Illustration Consider the simple pendulum shown in Fig. 2.1*a*. The displaced position of this system is characterized by θ only. Hence, it constitutes a system

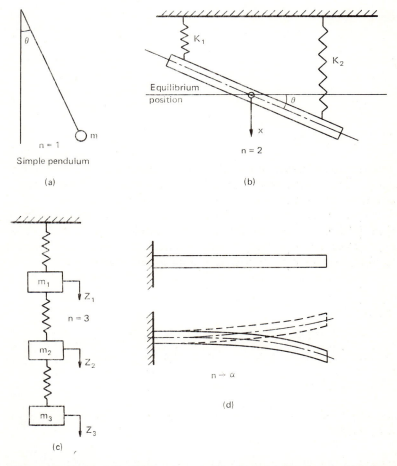

Figure 2.1 Systems with different degrees of freedom. (*a*) One degree of freedom ($n = 1$). (*b*) Two degrees of freedom ($n = 2$). (*c*) Three degrees of freedom ($n = 3$). (*d*) Infinite degrees of freedom ($n \to \infty$).

with one degree of freedom, that is, $n = 1$. In Fig. 2.1b and c, two and three independent coordinates are needed to describe the motion of the systems, respectively. Hence, they constitute systems with two degrees and three degrees of freedom, respectively.

In Fig. 2.1d, the number of coordinates necessary to describe the motion of the elastic cantilever beam is infinite. Hence, this constitutes an infinite degree freedom system.

Resonance If the frequency of excitation coincides with any one of the natural frequencies of the system, *resonance* is said to occur. The amplitudes of motion may be excessive at resonance. Hence, the determination of the natural frequencies of a system is important.

Principal modes of vibration A system with n degrees of freedom vibrates in such a complex manner that the amplitude and frequencies do not appear to follow any definite patterns. Still, among such disorderly motions, there are some special types of simple and orderly motions called *principal modes of vibration*; in a principal mode, each point in the system vibrates with the same frequency.

A system with n degrees of freedom possesses n principal modes with n natural frequencies. More general types of motion can always be represented by the superposition of principal modes.

Normal mode of vibrations When the amplitude of some point of the system vibrating in one of the principal modes is made equal to unity, the motion is then called the *normal mode of vibration*.

2.3 PROPERTIES OF HARMONIC MOTION

The simplest form of periodic motion is *harmonic motion*, which is represented by sine or cosine functions. Let us consider the harmonic motion represented by the following equation:

$$x = X \sin \omega t \tag{2.1}$$

where ω = circular frequency in radians per unit time. We can represent x by the projection on a vertical diameter of a rotating vector of length X, as it moves around a circle with constant angular speed ω (see Fig. 2.2). Since the function repeats itself after 2π rad, a cycle of motion is completed when

$$\omega T = 2\pi \tag{2.2a}$$

or

$$T = \frac{2\pi}{\omega} \tag{2.2b}$$

where T = time period of motion. Frequency f is the inverse of the time period; hence

$$f = \frac{1}{T} = \frac{\omega}{2\pi} \tag{2.3}$$

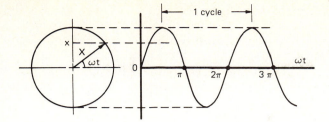

Figure 2.2 Vectorial representation of harmonic motion.

In order to determine the velocity and acceleration of motion, we differentiate Eq. (2.1) with respect to time t:

$$\text{Velocity} = \dot{x} = \omega X \cos \omega t = \omega X \sin\left(\omega t + \frac{\pi}{2}\right) \tag{2.4}$$

$$\text{Acceleration} = \ddot{x} = -\omega^2 X \sin \omega t = \omega^2 X \sin(\omega t + \pi) \tag{2.5a}$$

$$= -\omega^2 X \tag{2.5b}$$

Equations (2.4) and (2.5a) show that both velocity and acceleration are also harmonic and can be represented by vectors ωX and $\omega^2 X$ rotating at the same speed as that of X, i.e., ω rad/unit time. These are, however, leading the displacement vector by $\pi/2$ and π, respectively.

In Fig. 2.3, vertical projections of these vectors are shown plotted against the time axis t. The angles between the vectors are known as *phase angles*. Thus, the velocity vector leads the displacement vector by 90°; the acceleration vector leads the displacement vector by 180° and the velocity vector by 90°.

Example 2.1 We will consider the motion of the piston of a reciprocating machine (Fig. 2.4). The displacement of the piston from the extreme position is

$$S = \ell + r - r \cos \theta - \ell \cos \phi$$

Also

$$\ell \sin \phi = r \sin \theta$$

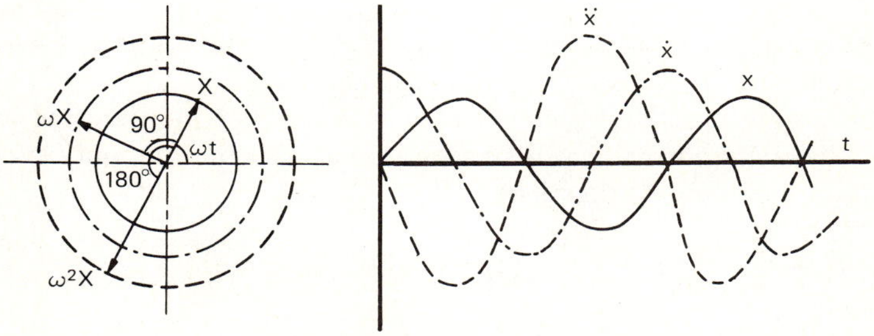

Figure 2.3 Vectorial representation of displacement, velocity, and acceleration.

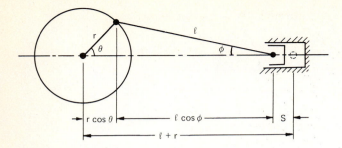

r cos θ — ℓ cos ϕ — S

$\ell + r$

Figure 2.4 Motion of a piston of reciprocating machine.

or
$$\cos \phi = (1 - \sin^2\phi)^{1/2} = \left[1 - \left(\frac{r}{\ell}\right)^2 \sin^2 \theta \right]^{1/2}$$

If we expand the right-hand side by the binomial theorem, we get

$$\cos \phi = 1 - \frac{1}{2}\left(\frac{r}{\ell}\right)^2 \sin^2 \theta - \frac{1}{8}\left(\frac{r}{\ell}\right)^4 \sin^4 \theta$$

$$- \frac{1}{16}\left(\frac{r}{\ell}\right)^6 \sin^6 \theta \cdots$$

or

$$(1 - \cos \phi) = +\frac{1}{2}\left(\frac{r}{\ell}\right)^2 \sin^2 \theta + \frac{1}{8}\left(\frac{r}{\ell}\right)^4 \sin^4 \theta + \frac{1}{16}\left(\frac{r}{\ell}\right)^6 \sin^6 \theta + \cdots$$

Substituting $\cos \phi$ in the expression for S, we get

$$S = r\left[1 - \cos \theta + \frac{1}{2}\frac{r}{\ell}\sin^2 \theta + \frac{1}{8}\left(\frac{r}{\ell}\right)^3 \sin^4 \theta + \frac{1}{16}\left(\frac{r}{\ell}\right)^5 \sin^6 \theta + \cdots \right]$$

The series in brackets contains $\sin^2 \theta$ and even powers of $\sin \theta$. Now

$$\sin^2 \theta = \frac{1}{2}(1 - \cos 2\theta)$$

$$\sin^4 \theta = (\sin^2 \theta)^2 = \tfrac{1}{4}\left(\tfrac{3}{2} - 2\cos 2\theta + \tfrac{1}{2}\cos 4\theta\right)$$

and, substituting ωt for θ, it is seen that S is a function of $\cos \omega t$ and $\cos 2n\omega t$ where $n = 1, 2, \ldots$.

Terms containing circular functions of whole number multiples of ωt are known as *higher harmonics*. It will be seen that, in this motion, only even higher harmonics are present; therefore

$$S = r\left[1 - \cos \theta + \frac{1}{4}\frac{r}{\ell}(1 - \cos 2\theta) + \frac{1}{32}\left(\frac{r}{\ell}\right)^3 \right.$$

$$\left. \times \left(\frac{3}{2} - 2\cos 2\theta + \frac{1}{2}\cos 4\theta \right) + \cdots \right]$$

If $\dfrac{r}{\ell}$ is very small, $\left(\dfrac{r}{\ell}\right)^2$ and higher powers can be neglected. Therefore

$$S = r\left[1 - \cos\omega t + \frac{1}{4}\frac{r}{\ell}(1 - \cos 2\omega t)\right]$$

$$\frac{ds}{dt} = r\omega\left(\sin\omega t + \frac{1}{2}\frac{r}{\ell}\sin 2\omega t\right]$$

and

$$\frac{d^2s}{dt^2} = r\omega^2\left(\cos\omega t + \frac{r}{\ell}\cos 2\omega t\right]$$

2.4 FREE VIBRATIONS OF A SPRING-MASS SYSTEM

Figure 2.5a shows a spring of stiffness k in the undeflected position. If we attach a mass m of weight W, the mass-spring system occupies the position shown in Fig. 2.5b. The deflection δ_{stat} of the spring from the undeflected position is

$$\delta_{\text{stat}} = \frac{W}{k} \tag{2.6}$$

where k is the spring constant, defined as force per unit deflection. The position of the system corresponding to this state is referred to as the *equilibrium position*. If the mass in this position is displaced up or down by z (Fig. 2.5c), then the extreme lower position of the mass will be as shown in Fig. 2.5d. The peak-to-peak displacement is referred to as *double amplitude* (Fig. 2.5e). Figure 2.5f shows the free-body diagram of the mass.

  If the mass is released from the extreme lower position (Fig. 2.5d), it starts to oscillate between the two extreme positions. If there is no resistance to these oscillations, the mass will continue to vibrate (theoretically) indefinitely.

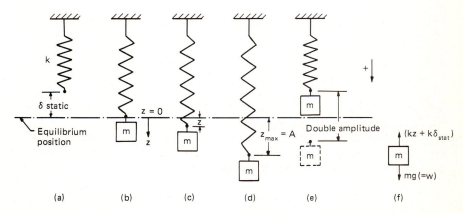

Figure 2.5 Spring-mass system. (*a*) Unstretched spring. (*b*) Equilibrium position. (*c*) Mass in oscillating position. (*d*) Mass in maximum downward position. (*e*) Mass in upward position. (*f*) Free-body diagram of mass corresponding to (*c*).

If the mass of the spring is neglected, the equation of motion can be written as

$$\Sigma F = m\ddot{z} \tag{2.7}$$

where ΣF = summation of all forces in the vertical direction. Using the sign convention shown in Fig. 2.5 and the inertia force acting opposite to acceleration,

$$-(k\delta_{\text{stat}} + kz) + W(= mg) = m\ddot{z} \tag{2.8a}$$

Since $k\delta_{\text{stat}} = W$, we get

$$m\ddot{z} + kz = 0 \tag{2.8b}$$

Equation (2.8b) is a *second-order differential equation*, and its general solution must contain two arbitrary constants, which can be evaluated from initial conditions.

The solution of this equation may be written as

$$z = A \sin \omega_n t + B \cos \omega_n t \tag{2.9}$$

where A and B are arbitrary constants and ω_n is the circular natural frequency of the system.

If we substitute the above solution in the differential equation, we get

$$\left(-\omega_n^2 + \frac{k}{m}\right)z = 0 \tag{2.10}$$

which gives

$$\omega_n^2 = \frac{k}{m} \tag{2.11}$$

When $\omega_n T_n = 2\pi$, one cycle of motion is completed, which gives the expression for natural period as

$$T_n = \frac{2\pi}{\omega_n} = 2\pi\sqrt{\frac{m}{k}} \tag{2.12}$$

The natural frequency of vibration is the number of cycles executed in the unit time and is the reciprocal of the time period T_n. Therefore

$$f_n = \frac{1}{T_n} = \frac{1}{2\pi}\sqrt{\frac{k}{m}} \tag{2.13}$$

Equation (2.13) can also be written in the following form:

$$f_n = \frac{1}{2\pi}\sqrt{\frac{kg}{mg}} \tag{2.14a}$$

Now

$$\frac{mg}{k} = \frac{W}{k} = \delta_{\text{stat}} \tag{2.14b}$$

Therefore

$$f_n = \frac{1}{2\pi}\sqrt{\frac{g}{\delta_{\text{stat}}}} \tag{2.15}$$

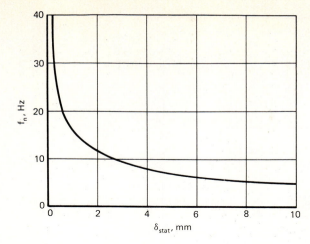

Figure 2.6 Relationship between static deflection and natural frequency.

Equation (2.15) shows that natural frequency is a function of static deflection. Using $g = 981$ cm·s^{-2} and δ_{stat} in millimeters, the frequency in hertz is as shown in Fig. 2.6.

Arbitrary constants in Eq. (2.9) can be determined from the boundary conditions. Let the initial conditions be characterized by the following values:

At $t = 0$, $z = z_0$ and $\dot{z} = v_0$ (2.16)

Substituting these conditions in Eq. (2.9), the complete solution becomes

$$z = \frac{v_0}{\omega_n} \sin \omega_n t + z_0 \cos \omega_n t \tag{2.17}$$

Other types of solutions of Eq. (2.8b) can be written in the following forms

$$z = Z \sin(\omega_n t + \phi) \tag{2.18}$$

and $$z = A \exp i\omega_n t + B \exp -i\omega_n t \tag{2.19}$$

Example 2.2 A mass supported by a spring has a static deflection of 0.5 mm. Determine its natural frequency of oscillation.

SOLUTION

$$f = \frac{1}{2\pi} \sqrt{\frac{g}{\delta_{stat}}} \tag{2.15}$$

$$= \frac{1}{2\pi} \sqrt{\frac{9810}{0.5}}$$

$$= 22.32 \text{Hz}$$

Example 2.3 Determine the spring constant for the system of springs shown in Fig. 2.7.

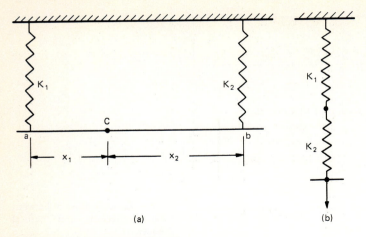

Figure 2.7 Equivalent spring constants.

SOLUTION
(a) Let us consider that a unit load is applied at c. It is shared at a and b in the ratio of $x_2/(x_1 + x_2)$ and $x_1/(x_1 + x_2)$ respectively. The deflection of points a and b are $x_2/(x_1 + x_2) \times 1/K_1$ and $x_1/(x_1 + x_2) \times 1/K_2$ respectively.

Therefore, deflection of point c is

$$\frac{x_1}{x_1 + x_2}\frac{1}{K_2} + \left(\frac{x_2}{x_1 + x_2} \times \frac{1}{K_1} - \frac{x_1}{x_1 + x_2} \times \frac{1}{K_2} \right)\frac{x_2}{x_1 + x_2}$$

$$= \frac{1}{(x_1 + x_2)^2}\left(\frac{x_1^2}{K_2} + \frac{x_2^2}{K_1} \right)$$

Hence, the resulting equivalent spring constant at c is

$$K_{eqv} = \frac{(x_1 + x_2)^2}{x_1^2/K_2 + x_2^2/K_1}$$

If $x_1 = x_2 = x$ and $K_1 = K_2 = K$, then $K_{eqv} = 2K$.
(b) On application of a unit load in Fig. 2.7b, the total deflection is

$$\frac{1}{K_2} + \frac{1}{K_1} = \frac{K_1 + K_2}{K_1 K_2}$$

Hence, equivalent spring constant

$$K_{eqv} = \frac{K_1 K_2}{K_1 + K_2}$$

If $K_1 = K_2 = K$, then $K_{eqv} = K/2$.

2.5 FREE VIBRATIONS WITH VISCOUS DAMPING

If the force of damping F_d is proportional to velocity, it is termed *viscous damping*. Thus

$$F_d = -c\dot{z} \tag{2.20}$$

in which c = coefficient of viscous damping (force per unit velocity, $FL^{-1}T$).

Figure 2.8 shows a spring-mass-dashpot system. If the mass is displaced by z below the equilibrium position, then the free-body diagram is as shown. Using the sign convention shown in this figure, the equation of motion may be written as

$$m\ddot{z} + c\dot{z} + kz = 0 \tag{2.21}$$

Let the solution to this equation be in the form

$$z = e^{st} \tag{2.22}$$

where s is a constant and will be determined later. Substituting this solution in Eq. (2.21), we get

$$\left(s^2 + \frac{c}{m}s + \frac{k}{m}\right)e^{st} = 0$$

which gives

$$s^2 + \frac{c}{m}s + \frac{k}{m} = 0 \tag{2.23}$$

Therefore

$$s_{1,2} = -\frac{c}{2m} \pm \sqrt{\left(\frac{c}{2m}\right)^2 - \frac{k}{m}} \tag{2.24}$$

The general solution can then be written as

$$z = Ae^{s_1 t} + Be^{s_2 t} \tag{2.25}$$

where A and B are arbitrary constants depending upon boundary conditions.

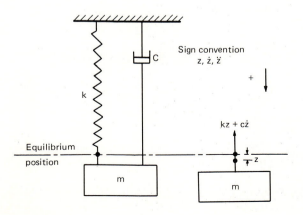

Figure 2.8 Spring-mass-dashpot system.

If the radical in Eq. (2.24) is zero, the damping is said to be *critical damping* c_c, and we get

$$\left(\frac{c_c}{2m}\right)^2 = \frac{k}{m} = \omega_n^2$$

or
$$c_c = 2m\omega_n \tag{2.26}$$

The ratio of actual damping (c) to critical damping (c_c) is defined as the *damping factor* (ξ).

$$\xi = \frac{c}{c_c} \tag{2.27}$$

Now
$$\frac{c}{2m} = \frac{c}{c_c} \cdot \frac{c_c}{2m} = \xi\omega_n \tag{2.28}$$

Substituting the above relationships in Eq. (2.24), we get

$$s_{1,2} = \left(-\xi \pm \sqrt{\xi^2 - 1}\,\right)\omega_n \tag{2.29}$$

Solutions with $\xi = 2$, 1, and 0.2 are shown in Fig. 2.9a. However, a solution of practical significance is one in which the damping is less than critical $(\xi < 1)$. Then

$$s_{1,2} = \left(-\xi \pm i\sqrt{1 - \xi^2}\,\right)\omega_n \tag{2.30}$$

The general solution then becomes

$$z = A \exp\left[\left(-\xi + i\sqrt{1 - \xi^2}\,\right)\omega_n t\right] + B \exp\left[\left(-\xi - i\sqrt{1 - \xi^2}\,\right)\omega_n t\right] \tag{2.31}$$

$$= A \exp(-\xi\omega_n t)\exp\left(+i\sqrt{1 - \xi^2}\,\omega_n t\right) + B \exp(-\xi\omega_n t)\exp\left(-i\sqrt{1 - \xi^2}\,\omega_n t\right)$$

$$= \exp-(\xi\omega_n t)\left(A \cos\sqrt{(1 - \xi^2)}\,\omega_n t + iA \sin\sqrt{1 - \xi^2}\,\omega_n t\right.$$

$$\left. + B \cos\sqrt{1 - \xi^2}\,\omega_n t - iB \sin\sqrt{1 - \xi^2}\,\omega_n t\right)$$

$$= \exp(-\xi\omega_n t)\left(C \cos\sqrt{1 - \xi^2}\,\omega_n t + D \sin\sqrt{1 - \xi^2}\,\omega_n t\right) \tag{2.32}$$

where
$$C = A + B \quad \text{and} \quad D = i(A - B) \tag{2.33}$$

Thus the natural circular frequency ω_{nd} in the viscously damped vibrations equals

$$\omega_{nd} = \omega_n\sqrt{1 - \xi^2} \tag{2.34}$$

Equation (2.32) can then be written as

$$z = Z_0 \exp\left(\frac{-\xi\omega_{nd}t}{\sqrt{1 - \xi^2}}\right)\sin(\omega_{nd}t + \phi) \tag{2.35}$$

in which Z_0 and ϕ are arbitrary constants, depending upon boundary conditions. Fig. 2.9b shows typical damped oscillations for $\xi < 1.0$.

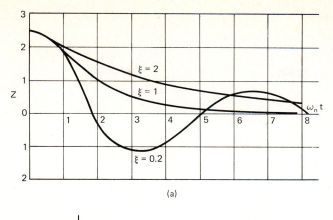

(a)

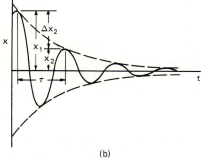

(b)

Figure 2.9 (*a*) Free vibrations with $\xi = 2, 1$, and 0.2. (*b*) Free damped oscillations for $\xi < 1.0$.

If $\xi > 1$, the motion is aperiodic and no oscillation occurs. If $\xi = 1$, the motion is, again, aperiodic. Since this is the minimum damping for aperiodic motion, the system returns to its original position in the minimum time, when critically damped (Fig. 2.9*a*).

2.6 FORCED VIBRATIONS WITH VISCOUS DAMPING

Figure 2.10*a* shows a spring-mass-dashpot system under the action of a force of excitation F such that

$$F = F_0 \sin \omega t \tag{2.36}$$

where ω is the frequency of force of excitation.

The free-body diagram has been shown in Fig. 2.10*b*, and the equation of motion is

$$m\ddot{z} + c\dot{z} + kz = F_0 \sin \omega t \tag{2.37a}$$

The solution to this equation is:

$$z = Z_0 \sin(\omega t - \phi) \tag{2.37b}$$

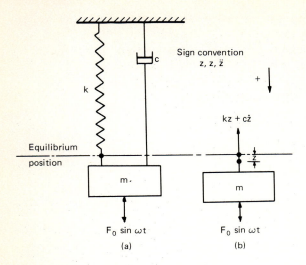

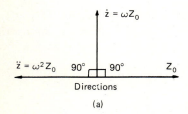

Figure 2.10 Forced vibrations with viscous damping. (*a*) Spring-mass-dash point. (*b*) Free-body diagram.

Then

$$\dot{z} = \omega Z_0 \cos(\omega t - \phi)$$
$$= \omega Z_0 \sin(\omega t - \phi + \pi/2)$$

and

$$\ddot{z} = \omega^2 Z \sin(\omega t - \phi + \pi)$$

Figure 2.11*a* shows z, $\dot{z}$, and $\ddot{z}$ vectors at any particular instant. The force in the spring is opposite to z; hence it can be represented by Oa in Fig. 2.11*b*. Similarly, damping force $c\omega Z_0$ acts in the opposite direction to that of velocity

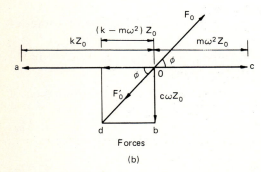

Figure 2.11 Vectorial solution of forced vibrations with viscous damping.

and, hence, is represented by *Ob*. Similarly, *Oc* represents the inertia force $(m\omega^2 Z_0)$, which acts opposite to acceleration. The resultant of these forces is F_0', which must be equal in magnitude and opposite in sign to F_0. Thus, the displacement vector lags the F_0 vector by ϕ. From Fig. 2.11*b*,

$$F_0 = \sqrt{(k - m\omega^2)^2 + (c\omega)^2} \cdot Z_0$$

or

$$Z_0 = \frac{F_0}{\sqrt{(k - m\omega^2)^2 + (c\omega)^2}} \tag{2.38}$$

and

$$\phi = \tan^{-1}\frac{c\omega}{k - m\omega^2} \tag{2.39}$$

Equations (2.38) and (2.39) can be expressed in nondimensional terms as follows:

$$Z_0 = \frac{F_0/k}{\sqrt{(1 - m\omega^2/k)^2 + (c\omega/k)^2}} \tag{2.40a}$$

Now $\dfrac{F_0}{k}$ = static deflection of the system under the action of F_0

$$(\delta_{\text{stat}} \text{ say})$$

Also,

$$\frac{m\omega^2}{k} = \left(\frac{\omega}{\omega_n}\right)^2 = r^2 \quad (\text{say})$$

in which r = frequency ratio, and

$$\left(\frac{c\omega}{k}\right)^2 = \left(\frac{c}{c_c}\frac{c_c\omega}{m\omega_n^2}\right)^2 = \left(\frac{c}{c_c}\frac{2m\omega_n\omega}{m\omega_n^2}\right)^2 = (2\xi r)^2$$

therefore

$$\frac{Z_0}{\delta_{\text{stat}}} = \frac{1}{\sqrt{(1 - r^2)^2 + (2\xi r)^2}} \tag{2.40b}$$

$$\frac{Z_0}{\delta_{\text{stat}}} = \text{magnification factor } (N)$$

Hence

$$N = \frac{1}{\sqrt{(1 - r^2)^2 + (2\xi r)^2}} \tag{2.41}$$

Similarly

$$\phi = \tan^{-1}\frac{2\xi r}{1 - r^2} \tag{2.42}$$

Figure 2.12 is a plot of N and ϕ versus frequency ratio r for r varying from 0 to 5.

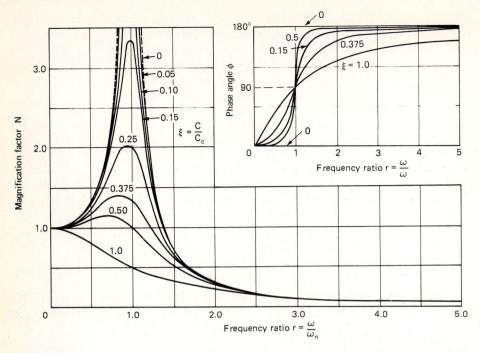

Figure 2.12 Magnification factor and phase angle in forced vibrations. (Reproduced by permission of Prentice-Hall Inc., Englewood Cliffs, N.J., from *Theory of Vibrations with Applications* by W. T. Thomson.)

Particular cases

Effect of frequency ratio r for a particular case when $\xi = 0$

If $r = 0$:	$N = 1$
If $r = 1$:	$N = \infty$
If $r = \infty$:	$N = 0$

At $r = 1$, resonance occurs and amplitudes tend to infinity. The introduction of damping reduces the amplitudes to finite values.

The phase angle ϕ is zero if $r < 1$; the displacement z is in phase with the exciting force F_0 and $\phi = 180°$ if $r > 1$.

Effect of damping factor ξ   As the damping increases, the peak of the magnification factor shifts slightly to the left. This is due to the fact that maximum amplitudes occur in damped vibrations when the forcing frequency (ω) equals the system's damped natural frequency (ω_{nd}), which is slightly smaller than the undamped natural frequency (ω_n).

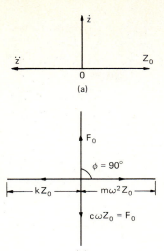

Figure **2.13** Vector diagram. (*a*) Amplitude, velocity, and displacement. (*b*) Forces for forced vibrations at resonance $\left(\dfrac{\omega}{\omega_n} = 1\right)$.

For $r = 1$, the phase angle ϕ is 90° for all values of damping, except when $\xi = 0$. For $r < 1$, the phase angle is less than 90°, and, for $r > 1$, the phase angle is greater than 90°.

The maximum amplitude of motion at $r = 1$ and $\xi > 0$ is (Eq. 2.40*a*)

$$Z_0 = \frac{F_0}{c\omega} \tag{2.43}$$

and the corresponding vector diagram is shown in Fig. 2.13.

The solution in Eq. (2.40*a*) is a steady-state solution, which is important in most of the practical problems. However, there will be transient vibrations initially, corresponding to the solution given by Eq. (2.35). These vibrations will, of course, die out in the first few cycles.

2.7 FREQUENCY-DEPENDENT EXCITING FORCE

In many practical problems of machine foundations, the exciting force depends upon the frequency of machine operation. Figure 2.14 shows such a system mounted on elastic supports, with m representing the unbalanced mass placed at eccentricity e from the center of the rotating shaft. The unbalanced force is $F = (me\omega^2) \sin \omega t$. Therefore, the equation of motion may be written as follows:

$$(M - m)\frac{d^2 z}{dt^2} + m\frac{d^2}{dt^2}(z + e \sin \omega t) = -kz - c\frac{dz}{dt}$$

Rearranging the terms in the above equation, we get

$$M\ddot{z} + c\dot{z} + kz = me\omega^2 \sin \omega t \tag{2.44}$$

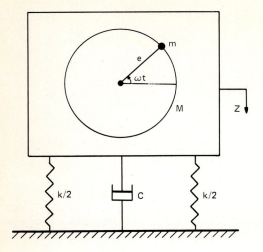

Figure 2.14 Force of excitation due to rotating unbalance.

Here M includes m also. Equations (2.44) and (2.37a) are similar, except that $me\omega^2$ appears in Eq. (2.44) in place of F_0 in Eq. (2.37a). The solution of this equation, therefore, is

$$z = \frac{me\omega^2}{\sqrt{(k - M\omega^2)^2 + (c\omega)^2}} \sin \omega t \qquad (2.45a)$$

Therefore

$$Z_0 = \frac{me\omega^2}{\sqrt{(k - M\omega^2)^2 + (c\omega)^2}} \qquad (2.45b)$$

and

$$\tan\phi = \frac{c\omega}{k - M\omega^2} \qquad (2.46)$$

In nondimensional form, these equations may be arranged as follows:

$$Z_0 = \frac{\dfrac{me\omega^2}{M\omega_n^2}}{\sqrt{\left[1 - (\omega/\omega_n)^2\right]^2 + (2\xi\omega/\omega_n)^2}}$$

or

$$\frac{Z_0}{me/M} = \frac{r^2}{\sqrt{(1 - r^2)^2 + 4\xi^2 r^2}} \qquad (2.47)$$

and

$$\tan\phi = \frac{2\xi r}{1 - r^2} \qquad (2.48)$$

Plots of quantities in Eqs. (2.47) and (2.48) are shown in Fig. 2.15a and b, respectively. These curves are similar in shape to those in Fig. 2.12, with the

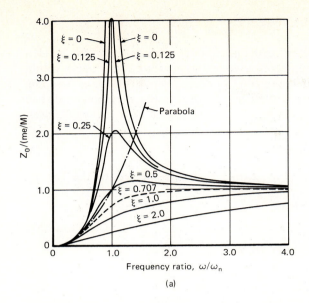

(a)

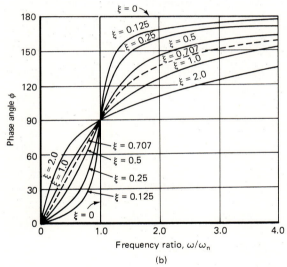

(b)

Figure 2.15 Response of system with rotating unbalances. (*a*) $\dfrac{Z_0}{me/M}$ vs. frequency ratio. (*b*) phase angle ϕ vs. frequency ratio $\dfrac{\omega}{\omega_n}$.

difference being that peak amplitudes occur at

$$\omega_{nd} = \frac{\omega_n}{\sqrt{1 - 2\xi^2}} \tag{2.49}$$

and the value of the ordinate for $r = 1$ in Fig. 2.15a is

$$\frac{Z_0}{me/M} = \frac{1}{2\xi} \tag{2.50}$$

2.8 SYSTEMS UNDER TRANSIENT FORCES

Transient forces may be caused by earthquakes, blasts, impacts, and the sudden dropping of loads. In several such cases, the maximum motion may occur within a relatively short time after the application of force. For this reason, damping may be of secondary importance in transient loads. However, responses due to earthquakes are influenced by damping since they consist of a series of pulses.

Case I. Suddenly Applied Load

Consider a spring-mass system (Fig. 2.16a) that is subjected to the forcing function $F(t)$ in Fig. 2.16b.

The equation for motion of mass m is given by

$$m\ddot{x} + kx = F_0 \tag{2.51}$$

The solution for displacement x is given by

$$x = A \cos \omega_n t + B \sin \omega_n t + \frac{F_0}{k} \tag{2.52}$$

Initially, when $t = 0$, $x = 0$ and $\ddot{x} = 0$; therefore, $A = -F_0/k$ and $B = 0$. Thus, Eq. (2.51) becomes

$$x = \frac{F_0}{k}(1 - \cos \omega_n t) \tag{2.53}$$

If the force F_0 is applied gradually, the static deflection is F_0/k. Thus, magnification of the deflection N is

$$N = \frac{x}{F_0/k} = 1 - \cos \omega_n t \tag{2.54}$$

Magnification versus time has been plotted in Fig. 2.16c. The magnification has a maximum value of 2, which occurs when $\cos \omega_n t = -1$. The first peak is reached when $\omega_n t = \pi$ or $t = T/2$, where T is the natural period of vibration of the system.

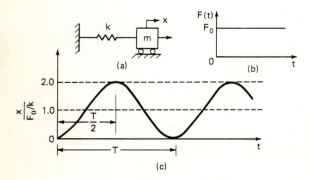

(a)

(b)

(c)

Figure 2.16 Dynamic amplification due to suddenly applied load. (a) One-degree freedom system. (b) Suddenly applied load. (c) Magnification.

Case II. Square Pulse of Finite Duration

Consider that the system shown in Fig. 2.17*a* is subjected to a pulse of uniform intensity for a given duration τ (Fig. 2.17*b*).

For $\tau < T$, the motion is governed by Eq. (2.51). The solution is given by Eq. (2.53).

At $t = \tau$

$$x_\tau = \frac{F_0}{k}(1 - \cos \omega_n \tau) \tag{2.55a}$$

and

$$\dot{x}_\tau = \frac{F_0 \omega_n}{k}(\sin \omega_n \tau) \tag{2.55b}$$

For $t > \tau$, the equation of motion is

$$m\ddot{x} + kx = 0 \tag{2.56}$$

The solution for displacement x is

$$x = A \cos \omega_n t' + B \sin \omega_n t' \tag{2.57}$$

where $t' = t - \tau$.

The values of A and B are determined from the initial conditions in Eq. (2.55) at $t = \tau$ as in Eq. 2.16. Substituting x_τ and $\dot{x}_\tau$ from Eqs. (2.55) in Eq. (2.57) gives

$$x = \frac{F_0}{k}(1 - \cos \omega_n \tau)\cos \omega_n t' + \frac{F_0}{k}\sin \omega_n \tau \sin \omega_n t' \tag{2.58a}$$

$$= \frac{F_0}{k}\left[(1 - \cos \omega_n \tau)^2 + \sin^2 \omega_n \tau\right]^{1/2} \sin(\omega_n t' - \phi)$$

where

$$\phi = \tan^{-1} - \frac{1 - \cos \omega_n \tau}{\sin \omega_n \tau}$$

Therefore

$$x = \frac{F_0}{k}\sqrt{2(1 - \cos \omega_n \tau)}\,\sin(\omega_n t' - \phi)$$

$$= \frac{F_0}{k}(2 \sin \omega_n \tau/2)\sin(\omega_n t' - \phi) \tag{2.58b}$$

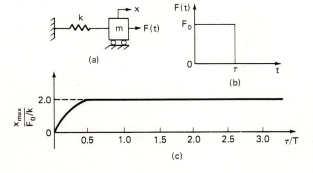

(a)

(b)

(c)

Figure 2.17 Dynamic amplification due to a square pulse. (*a*) One-degree freedom system. (*b*) Square pulse. (*c*) Magnification.

or

$$\frac{x}{F_0/k} = (2 \sin \omega_n \tau/2) \sin (\omega_n' - \phi)$$

The dynamic magnification N is

$$N = \frac{x_{max}}{F_0/k} = 2 \sin \frac{\omega_n \tau}{2} = 2 \sin \frac{\pi \tau}{T} \qquad (2.59)$$

The maximum value is 2 when $\tau/T = \frac{1}{2}$ (see Fig. 2.17c).

If, in Eq. (2.59), we consider the limiting case where τ/T is very small, so that $\sin \pi\tau/T \approx \pi\tau/T$, then

$$X_{max} = \frac{2F_0}{k} \frac{\pi \tau}{T} \qquad (2.60)$$

Now $k = m\omega_n^2$ and $T = 2\pi/\omega_n$. Thus substituting in Eq. (2.60) gives

$$X_{max} = \frac{F_0 \tau}{m\omega_n}$$

Now $F_0 \tau =$ impulse I. Therefore,

$$X_{max} = \frac{I}{m\omega_n} \qquad (2.61)$$

2.9 RAYLEIGH'S METHOD

According to Rayleigh's method, the fundamental frequency† of a continuous elastic system with infinite degrees of freedom can be determined accurately by assuming a reasonable deflection curve for the elastic system. If the true deflection curve of the vibrating system is not known, the use of the static deflection curve of the elastic body gives a fairly accurate fundamental frequency.

In illustrating the application of this method, the energy principle will be used. Expressions will be developed for the kinetic (KE) and potential (PE) energy. Since the total energy is constant,

$$KE + PE = \text{constant}$$

$$\frac{d}{dt}(KE + PE) = 0$$

or

$$\text{maximum KE} = \text{maximum PE}$$

Example 2.4 In Fig. 2.18, the weight of the spring of length L is w per unit length. Determine the natural frequency of the spring-mass system.

---

† Fundamental frequency corresponds to the frequency in the first mode of vibrations.

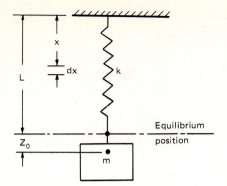

Figure 2.18 System with spring having weight.

SOLUTION Let the displacement of the mass from the equilibrium position be Z_0 and $z = z_0 \cos \omega_n t$. Assuming that the extension of the spring is linear, displacement of the element of spring at distance x from the fixed support is

$$z = \frac{x}{L} Z_0 \cos \omega_n t$$

Velocity of element $dx = \dot{z} = -\frac{x}{L} \omega_n Z_0 \sin \omega_n t$

Maximum KE of the element with mass $(w/g)\,dx$ is

$$d(KE)_{max} = \frac{w}{2g}\,dx\left(\frac{x}{L}\omega_n Z_0\right)^2$$

Integrate the expression above to obtain the maximum kinetic energy of the spring

$$(KE)_{max} = \frac{w}{2g}\left(\frac{\omega_n Z_0}{L}\right)^2 \int_0^L x^2\,dx$$

$$= \frac{1}{2}\frac{wL}{3g}\omega_n^2 Z_0^2$$

The maximum kinetic energy of the rigid mass m is

$$\frac{1}{2}m(Z_0\omega_n)^2 = \frac{1}{2}\frac{W}{g}(\omega_n Z_0)^2$$

The total maximum kinetic energy is

$$\frac{1}{2}\left(\frac{W + \frac{1}{3}wL}{g}\right)\omega_n^2 Z_0^2$$

The maximum potential energy of the spring may be computed as follows:

$$\text{Maximum potential energy} = \int_0^{Z_0} kz\,dz$$

$$= \frac{1}{2}kZ_0^2$$

Since, in a conservative system, maximum kinetic energy equals the maximum potential energy, by equating the two energies we get

$$\frac{1}{2}\left(\frac{W + \frac{1}{3}wL}{g}\right)\omega_n^2 Z_0^2 = \frac{1}{2}kZ_0^2$$

or

$$\omega_n = \sqrt{\frac{kg}{W + \frac{1}{3}wL}}$$

The effect of the weight of the spring can be accounted for by lumping its one-third mass with the concentrated mass of the system.

Example 2.5 Using Rayleigh's method, determine the fundamental frequency of the cantilever beam shown in Fig. 2.19.

SOLUTION The deflected curve of the cantilever beam will be assumed to correspond to that of a weightless beam with the concentrated load P acting at its end. Then

$$y_0 = \frac{PL^3}{3EI}$$

in which EI = flexural stiffness of the beam.

$$\text{Stiffness of beam at the free end } k = \frac{P}{y_0} = \frac{3EI}{L^3}$$

The expression for the deflected shape of the cantilever is

$$y = \frac{1}{2}y_0\left[3\left(\frac{x}{L}\right)^2 - \left(\frac{x}{L}\right)^3\right]$$

$$\text{Maximum potential energy} = \frac{1}{2}Ky_0^2 = \frac{3EI}{2L^3}y_0^2$$

If the weight of the beam is w per unit length and assuming harmonic motion

$$\text{Maximum KE of system} = \frac{w}{2g}\int_0^L (\omega_n y)^2\, dx$$

$$= \frac{w}{2g}\left(\frac{\omega_n y_0}{2}\right)^2 \int_0^L \left[3\left(\frac{x}{L}\right)^2 - \left(\frac{x}{L}\right)^3\right]^2 dx$$

$$= \frac{1}{2}\left(\frac{33wL}{140g}\right)\omega_n^2 y_0^2$$

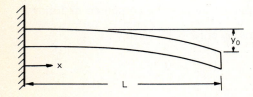

Figure 2.19 Fundamental frequency determination of cantilever beam.

Equating the two energies, the fundamental frequency of vibration is

$$\omega_n = \sqrt{\frac{3EI}{L^3}\frac{g}{\frac{33}{140}wL}} = 3.56\sqrt{\frac{gEI}{wL^4}}$$

The exact solution† would give

$$\omega_n = 3.515\sqrt{\frac{g\,EI}{wL^4}}$$

2.10 LOGARITHMIC DECREMENT

Logarithmic decrement is a measure of the decay of successive maximum amplitudes of viscously damped vibrations and is expressed (Fig. 2.9b) as

$$\delta = \log_e\frac{x_1}{x_2} \tag{2.62}$$

in which x_1 and x_2 are two successive peak amplitudes. If x_1 and x_2 are determined at times $\omega_{nd}t_1$ and $(\omega_{nd}t_1 + 2\pi)$ from Eq. (2.35) and substituted in Eq. (2.62), we get

$$\delta = \log_e\frac{\exp\dfrac{-\xi\omega_{nd}t_1}{\sqrt{1-\xi^2}}}{\exp\dfrac{-\xi(w_{nd}t_1+2\pi)}{\sqrt{1-\xi^2}}} \tag{2.63}$$

$$= \log_e\exp\frac{2\pi\xi}{\sqrt{1-\xi^2}} \tag{2.64}$$

or

$$\delta = \frac{2\pi\xi}{\sqrt{1-\xi^2}} \tag{2.65a}$$

$$\doteq 2\pi\xi \tag{2.65b}$$

where ξ is small.

If the damping is very small, it may be convenient to measure the differences in peak amplitudes for a number of cycles, say n.

In such a case, if x_n is the peak amplitude of the nth cycle, then

$$\frac{x_0}{x_1} = \frac{x_1}{x_2} = \frac{x_2}{x_3} = \cdots = \frac{x_{n-1}}{x_n} = e^\delta$$

---

† See *Mechanical Vibrations*, by W. T. Thomson, Prentice Hall Inc., Englewood Cliffs, N.J., 1958, p. 35.

Also

$$\frac{x_0}{x_n} = \left(\frac{x_0}{x_1}\right)\left(\frac{x_1}{x_2}\right)\left(\frac{x_2}{x_3}\right)\cdots\left(\frac{x_{n-1}}{x_n}\right) = (e^{\delta})^n$$

$$= e^{n\delta}$$

Therefore
$$\delta = \frac{1}{n}\log\frac{x_0}{x_n} \qquad (2.66)$$

2.11 DETERMINATION OF VISCOUS DAMPING

Damping can be determined from either a free-vibration or a forced-vibration test on a system.

In a free-vibration test, the system is displaced from its equilibrium position and a record of the amplitude of displacement is made. Then, from Eqs. (2.65b) and (2.62),

$$\xi = \frac{\delta}{2\pi} = \frac{1}{2\pi}\log\frac{x_1}{x_2} \qquad (2.67)$$

or else, from Eqs. (2.66) and (2.65b),

$$\xi = \frac{\delta}{2\pi} = \frac{1}{2n\pi}\log\frac{x_0}{x_n} \qquad (2.68)$$

In a forced-vibration test, the system may be excited with a constant force of excitation and varying frequencies. A resonance curve is obtained (Fig. 2.20).

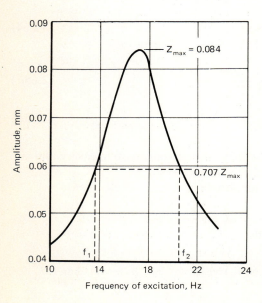

Figure 2.20 Determination of viscous damping in forced vibrations by bandwidth method.

At $r = 1$, from Eq. (2.40*b*),

$$\frac{Z_0}{\delta_{\text{stat}}} = \frac{1}{2\xi}$$ (2.69)

If the frequency ratio is r when the amplitude of motion is 0.707 $(1/2\xi)$, by using Eq. (2.40*b*), we get

$$\frac{0.707}{2\xi} = \frac{1}{\sqrt{(1 - r^2)^2 + 4\xi^2 r^2}}$$

or

$$1 + r^4 - 2r^2 + 4\xi^2 r^2 = 8\xi^2$$

or

$$r^4 - 2r^2(1 - 2\xi^2) + (1 - 8\xi^2) = 0$$

or

$$r_{1,2}^2 = \tfrac{1}{2}\left[2(1 - 2\xi^2) \pm \sqrt{4(1 - 2\xi^2)^2 - 4(1 - 8\xi^2)}\right]$$

$$= \tfrac{1}{2}\left[2(1 - 2\xi^2) \pm \sqrt{4 + 16\xi^4 - 16\xi^2 - 4 + 32\xi^2}\right]$$

$$= (1 - 2\xi^2) \pm 2\xi\sqrt{1 + \xi^2}$$

or

$$r_2^2 - r_1^2 = 4\xi\sqrt{1 - \xi^2}$$

$$\approx 4\xi \qquad \text{if } \xi \text{ is small.}$$

Now

$$r_2^2 - r_1^2 = \frac{f_2^2 - f_1^2}{f_n^2} = \left(\frac{f_2 - f_1}{f_n}\right)\left(\frac{f_1 + f_2}{f_n}\right)$$

$$\approx 2\left(\frac{f_2 - f_1}{f_n}\right) \cdot 1 \qquad \text{since} \qquad \frac{f_1 + f_2}{f_n} \approx 2$$

Therefore

$$\xi = \tfrac{1}{2}\left(\frac{f_2 - f_1}{f_n}\right)$$ (2.70)

This method for determining viscous damping is known as the *bandwidth method*.

2.12 TRANSMISSIBILITY

The system in Fig. 2.14 represents a very practical system that corresponds to a machine foundation with rotating unbalances. We can now compute the forces transmitted to the foundation through the spring and the dashpot.

The maximum force in the spring is kZ_0 and the maximum force in the dashpot is $c\omega Z_0$; the two forces are out of phase at 90° (Fig. 2.11). Hence, the force transmitted F_t to the base is

$$F_t = \sqrt{(kZ_0)^2 + (c\omega Z_0)^2} \qquad (2.71a)$$

$$= kZ_0 \sqrt{1 + \left(\frac{c\omega}{k}\right)^2} \qquad (2.71b)$$

Letting $c\omega/k = 2\xi r$ and substituting Z_0 from Eq. (2.45b), we get transmissibility T_r defined as the ratio of force transmitted to the force of excitation.

$$T_r = \frac{F_t}{m_0 e \omega^2} = \frac{\sqrt{1 + (2\xi r)^2}}{\sqrt{(1 - r^2)^2 + (2\xi r)^2}} \qquad (2.71c)$$

Transmissibility T_r versus frequency ratio ω/ω_n is plotted in Fig. 2.21. It will be seen that for $\xi = 0$, the curve is the same as in Fig. 2.12. Also, all curves pass through $r = \sqrt{2}$. For $r > \sqrt{2}$, all of the curves approach the r axis asymptotically. The higher the frequency ratio, the better the isolation. But there may be excessive amplitudes at the time of starting and stopping a machine when it passes through the zone of resonance. Damping helps to limit these amplitudes to finite values.

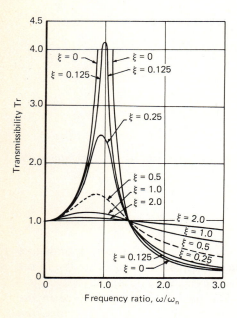

Figure 2.21 Transmissibility (T_r) vs. frequency ratio (r).

2.13 PRINCIPLE OF VIBRATION-MEASURING INSTRUMENTS

Figure 2.22 shows a structure represented as a base undergoing vibrations in the vertical direction.

$$\text{Let } x = X_0 \sin \omega t \tag{2.72a}$$

A vibration-measuring instrument consists of a spring-mass-dashpot system, as shown, mounted on the vibrating base. The relative motion of the mass of the spring is monitored. Let the absolute motion of the mass be y and, neglecting transients,

$$y = Y \sin \omega t \tag{2.72b}$$

Then the equation of motion can be written as

$$M\ddot{y} = -k(y - x) - c(\dot{y} - \dot{x}) \tag{2.73}$$

Letting $y - x = z$ and $\dot{y} - \dot{x} = \dot{z}$ we get

$$M\ddot{z} + c\dot{z} + kz = M\omega^2 X_0 \sin \omega t \tag{2.74}$$

Equation (2.74) is similar to Eq. (2.44). Hence, the solution for Z_0 can be written as in Eq. (2.45b):

$$Z_0 = \frac{M\omega^2 X_0}{\sqrt{(k - M\omega^2)^2 + (c\omega)^2}} \tag{2.75}$$

and

$$\phi = \tan^{-1} \frac{c\omega}{k - M\omega^2} \tag{2.76}$$

or

$$\frac{Z_0}{X_0} = \frac{(\omega/\omega_n)^2}{\sqrt{(1 - r^2)^2 + (2\xi r)^2}} \tag{2.77a}$$

and

$$\phi = \tan^{-1} \frac{2\xi r}{1 - r^2} \tag{2.77b}$$

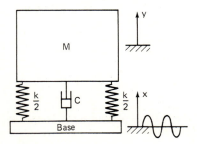

Figure 2.22 A vibration-measuring instrument (seismic instrument) mounted on a vibrating base.

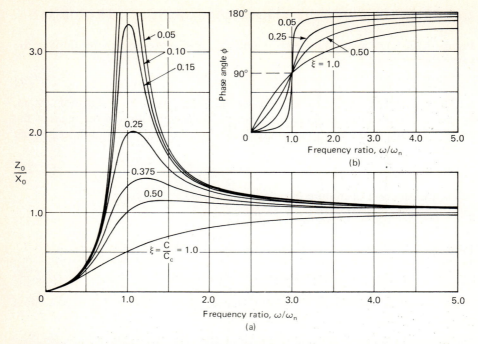

Figure 2.23 Response of a vibration-measuring instrument to a vibrating base. (*a*) Amplitude. (*b*) Phase angle.

A plot of Z_0/X_0 and frequency ratio and the phase angle and frequency ratio is shown in Fig. 2.23.

Displacement Pickup

For large values of $\dfrac{\omega}{\omega_n}(= r)$, and for all values of damping ξ

$$\frac{Z_0}{X_0} = 1$$

Therefore, if the natural frequency of the instrument is so low that the r value is large, then the resulting relative motion Z_0 equals X_0. Therefore, the instrument functions as a displacement pickup.

Acceleration Pickup

Using Eq. (2.77a) and rearranging, we get

$$\frac{Z_0}{\omega^2 X_0} = \frac{1}{\omega_n^2\sqrt{\left[1 - (\omega/\omega_n)^2\right]^2 + \left[2\xi(\omega/\omega_n)^2\right]^2}} = \frac{1}{\omega_n^2\sqrt{D}} \qquad \text{say}$$

$$(2.78)$$

For $\xi = 0.69$, the values of $\sqrt{D}$ in the denominator for different ω/ω_n are

ω/ω_n	0.0	0.1	0.2	0.3	0.4
$\sqrt{D}$	1.000	0.9995	0.9989	1.0000	1.0053

Thus Z_0 is proportional to the absolute acceleration $\omega^2 X_0$ of the vibrating base. The instrument thus functions as an accelerometer. The frequency ratio ω/ω_n in an accelerometer must be small. Therefore, the natural frequency of the instrument must be high.

2.14 SYSTEMS WITH TWO-DEGREES OF FREEDOM (VIBRATION ABSORBER)

Figure 2.24 shows a two-mass–two-spring system. This is a two-degree freedom system. Free-body diagrams of the masses are also shown. The equations for motion of both the masses may be written in the following form:

$$m_1\ddot{z}_1 = F_0 \sin \omega t - k_1 z_1 - k_2(z_1 - z_2) \tag{2.79a}$$

and

$$m_2\ddot{z}_2 = k_2(z_1 - z_2) \tag{2.79b}$$

Let us assume the following solution for the principal modes

$$z_1 = Z_1 \sin \omega t \tag{2.79c}$$

$$z_2 = Z_2 \sin \omega t \tag{2.79d}$$

Substituting these solutions in the equations of motion, we get

$$(-m_1\omega^2 + k_1 + k_2)Z_1 - k_2 Z_2 = F_0 \tag{2.79e}$$

$$(-m_2\omega^2 + k_2)Z_2 - k_2 z_1 = 0 \tag{2.79f}$$

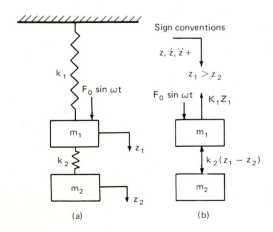

(a) (b)

Figure 2.24 (*a*) Vibration absorber. (*b*) Free-body diagram.

Let the natural circular frequency of the system 1 above be ω_{11}, so that

$$\omega_{11} = \sqrt{\frac{k_1}{m_1}} \tag{2.79g}$$

and the natural circular frequency of system 2 above be ω_{22}, so that

$$\omega_{22} = \sqrt{\frac{k_2}{m_2}} \tag{2.79h}$$

and let

$$Z_0 = \frac{F_0}{k_1} \tag{2.79i}$$

be the static deflection of the mass m_1 due to F_0. Dividing Eq. (2.79e) by k_1 and Eq. (2.79f) by k_2, we get

$$\left[1 + \frac{k_2}{k_1} - \left(\frac{\omega}{\omega_{11}}\right)^2 \right] Z_1 - \frac{k_2}{k_1} Z_2 = Z_0 \tag{2.80a}$$

and

$$-Z_1 + \left[1 - \left(\frac{\omega}{\omega_{22}}\right)^2 \right] Z_2 = 0 \tag{2.80b}$$

To determine the natural frequencies of the system, its free vibrations need to be considered. Let the right side of Eq. (2.80a) be zero and then, from Eq. (2.80a, b), we get

$$\frac{Z_1}{Z_2} = \frac{k_2/k_1}{\left[1 + k_2/k_1 - (\omega/\omega_{11})^2 \right]} = 1 - \left(\frac{\omega}{\omega_{22}}\right)^2$$

or

$$\left[1 + \frac{k_2}{k_1} - \left(\frac{\omega}{\omega_{11}}\right)^2 \right]\left[1 - \left(\frac{\omega}{\omega_{22}}\right)^2 \right] - \frac{k_2}{k_1} = 0 \tag{2.81}$$

The solution of this frequency equation will give the natural frequencies of the system. This may be conveniently rearranged, by letting

$$\frac{k_2}{k_1} = \frac{k_2}{m_2}\frac{m_1}{k_1}\frac{m_2}{m_1} = \mu\left(\frac{\omega_{22}}{\omega_{11}}\right)^2$$

where $\mu = \dfrac{m_2}{m_1}$, as

$$\left[1 + \mu\left(\frac{\omega_{22}}{\omega_{11}}\right)^2 - \left(\frac{\omega}{\omega_{11}}\right)^2 \right]\left[1 - \left(\frac{\omega}{\omega_{22}}\right)^2 \right] - \mu\left(\frac{\omega_{22}}{\omega_{11}}\right)^2 = 0$$

or

$$\left[\frac{\omega_{22}}{\omega_{11}} \right]^2\left(\frac{\omega}{\omega_{22}}\right)^4 - \left[1 + (1 + \mu)\left(\frac{\omega_{22}}{\omega_{11}}\right)^2 \right]\left(\frac{\omega}{\omega_{22}}\right)^2 + 1 = 0 \tag{2.82}$$

This is the general method for solving the natural frequencies of a two-degree freedom system.

In Fig. 2.24, if system 1 constitutes the main system, then system 2 is a *vibrations absorber*, since it can reduce the amplitudes of vibration of the main system appreciably, as will be shown below. From Eq. (2.80b), we get

$$Z_2 = \frac{Z_1}{1 - (\omega/\omega_{22})^2} \tag{2.83}$$

Substituting Z_2 in Eq. (2.80a), we get

$$\left[1 + \frac{k_2}{k_1} - \left(\frac{\omega}{\omega_{11}}\right)^2\right] Z_1 - \frac{k_2}{k_1} \frac{Z_1}{\left[1 - \left(\frac{\omega}{\omega_{22}}\right)^2\right]} = Z_0$$

Therefore

$$\frac{Z_1}{Z_0} = \frac{1 - (\omega/\omega_{22})^2}{\left[1 - (\omega/\omega_{22})^2\right]\left[1 + k_2/k_1 - (\omega/\omega_{11})^2\right] - k_2/k_1} \tag{2.84a}$$

Similarly, when solving for Z_2, we get

$$\frac{Z_2}{X_0} = \frac{1}{\left[1 - (\omega/\omega_{22})^2\right]\left[1 + k_2/k_1 - (\omega/\omega_{11})^2\right] - k_2/k_1} \tag{2.84b}$$

From Eq. (2.84a), it is seen that $Z_1 = 0$, if

$$\omega_{22} = \omega \tag{2.85}$$

Then

$$Z_2 = -X_0 \frac{k_1}{k_2} = -\frac{F_0}{k_2} \tag{2.86}$$

A negative sign indicates that Z_2 and F_0 are in phase opposition. In fact, Z_1 becomes zero at this frequency because the force $k_2 Z_2$ exerted by spring 2 on mass m_1 is equal to and opposite to the force of excitation F_0. The size of the absorber m_2 and its permissible deformation Z_2 depend upon the magnitude of the disturbing force $F_0 (= k_2 Z_2)$.

2.15 SPECTRAL RESPONSE

In Sect. 2.6, the solution for displacement was obtained for a single-degree freedom system with spring, mass, and dashpot, and excited by a forcing function of the form $F_0 \sin \omega t$. The solution can also be expressed in terms of velocity ($\dot{z}$) and acceleration ($\ddot{z}$), all of which are simple harmonic solutions.

If we consider a multidegree freedom system, excited by a forcing function such as ground motion during an earthquake (Fig. 1.4), it is possible to obtain timewise solutions for displacements, velocities, and accelerations. The forcing function is no longer expressed as a mathematical function, and it may be expressed as displacement (of the ground). The quantities that are examined as a result of a forcing function, which may or may not be expressed as a mathematical function, are known as *response quantities*. When examining the vibrations of a column in a building, we can study the stresses, strains, bending moment, or any other desired quantity. Thus, the response of a system can be studied in terms of displacements, velocities, accelerations, stresses, strains, bending moments, shears, and any other parameter that we may choose.

It can be shown that, if a system is not vibrating in one of its principal modes, the complex motion can be represented as a sum of motions corresponding to the principal modes of vibrations as follows:

$$X \sin \omega t = A_{11} X_1 \sin \omega_{n1} t + A_{22} X_2 \sin \omega_{n2} t + A_{33} X_3 \sin \omega_{n3} t$$
$$+ \cdots + A_{nn} X_n \sin \omega_{nn} t \tag{2.87}$$

in which

$X \sin \omega t =$ the resultant motion with X being the maximum response in terms of the desired parameter, say displacement.

$X_1, X_2, \ldots, X_n =$ the parameters of motion in 1st, 2d, ..., nth mode respectively.

$A_{11}, A_{22}, \ldots, A_{nn} =$ the mode participation factor. (This needs some description.)

Let a system have three degrees of freedom with natural frequencies ω_{n1}, ω_{n2}, and ω_{n3}, respectively, in three modes. The displacement response of this system to an excitation function, such as the El Centro earthquake of May 18, 1940, can be worked out in the first, second, and third modes of vibrations. Thus, the maximum displacement in three modes can be determined. The actual displacement of the system is a function of the three maximum values. The 1st mode of vibration contributes the most to the vibrations, and each succeeding higher mode contributes a relatively smaller degree to the final motion. Therefore, the mode participation factor may be regarded as a weighting factor for the maximum response (displacement in this case) in a particular mode for evaluation of the total maximum response of the system. Further, a particular mode may give rise to negative displacements. Therefore, to determine the maximum response of the system, the root mean square value of the response in each mode is usually considered.

Thus, the maximum response of the actual system.

$$X = \sqrt{(A_{11} X_1)^2 + (A_{22} X_2)^2 + \cdots + (A_{nn} X_n)^2} \tag{2.88}$$

A plot of the maximum response of single-degree freedom systems against periods (or frequency) under different dampings is termed the *response spectrum*.

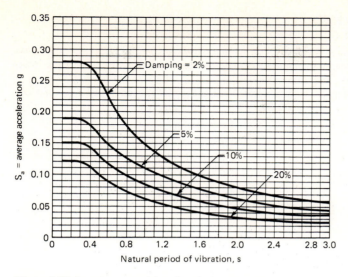

Figure 2.25 Average spectral (acceleration) response curves.

Housner (1959)† prepared the average spectral response curves for four strong earthquakes, including those of El Centro, Taft, California, and Olympia, Washington. These curves may be adopted after corrections if necessary (Fig. 2.25) for designing structures under stress from earthquakes. Periods of structures shall be computed in each mode to determine the corresponding response.

The following relationships may also be used for converting one response quantity to the other.

$$S_d = \frac{S_a}{\omega_n^2} \tag{2.89a}$$

$$S_v = \frac{S_a}{\omega_n} = \omega_n S_d \tag{2.89b}$$

where S = spectral response
a = acceleration
v = velocity
d = displacement
ω_n = natural circular frequency in a particular mode

The above treatment is included only to develop fundamental concepts and is not at all exhaustive. A detailed mathematical treatment of the subject is given by Housner (1959).

---

† G. W. Housner, Behavior of Structures During Earthquakes, *J Eng Mech Div ASCE*, vol. 85, no. EM4, pp. 109–129, 1959.

PRACTICE PROBLEMS

2.1 In Example 2.1, assuming r/ℓ to be small, derive expressions for velocity and acceleration of the piston motion. Determine the maximum velocity and acceleration and the time when these values occur.

2.2 Write the equations of motion for the systems shown in Fig. 2.26a, b, and c and determine their natural frequencies. Determine critical damping in the system in Fig. 2.26b and c.

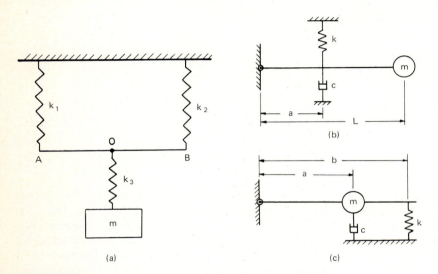

(a)   (b)   (c)

Figure 2.26 Systems with one degree of freedom in Prob. 2.2.

2.3 Set up the equations for motion of the systems shown in Fig. 2.27a, b, c, and d and determine frequency equation and natural frequencies.

2.4 For the system represented by Eq. (2.44), show that the peak amplitude occurs at frequency ratio

$$r = \frac{1}{\sqrt{1 - 2\xi^2}} \quad \text{and} \quad A_{max} = \frac{1}{2\xi\sqrt{1 - \xi^2}}$$

If $\xi > 0.707$, r is imaginary. Discuss the significance of these values with the help of a diagram.

2.5 Determine viscous damping from a free vibration record shown in Fig. 2.9b.

2.6 Show that, in frequency-dependent excitations, the damping factor ξ is given by the following expression:

$$\xi = \frac{1}{2}\left(\frac{f_2 - f_1}{f_n}\right)$$

where f_2 and f_1 are frequencies at which the amplitude is $\dfrac{1}{\sqrt{2}}$ times the peak amplitude.

2.7 Explain what you understand by "average response," "mode participation factor," "degrees of freedom," "principal mode," "natural frequency," "transmissibility," "damping," and "critical damping."

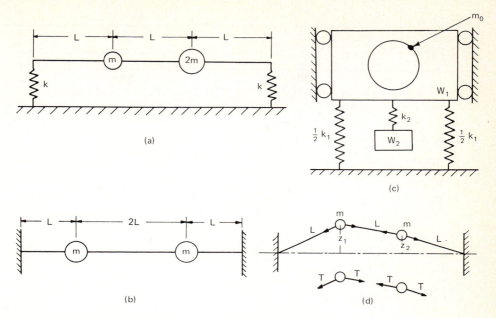

Figure 2.27 Systems with two degrees of freedom in Prob. 2.3.

2.8 An unknown weight W attached to the end of an unknown spring k has a natural frequency of 95 cpm. If 1 kg weight is added to W, the natural frequency is lowered to 75 cpm. Determine the weight W and spring constant K.

2.9 A body weighing 65 kg is suspended from a spring which deflects 1.57 cm under the load. It is subjected to a damping effect adjusted to a value 0.25 times that required for critical damping. Find the natural frequency of the undamped and damped vibrations, and, in the latter case, determine the ratio of successive amplitudes. If the body is subjected to a periodic disturbing force with a maximum value of 25 kg and a frequency equal to 0.75 times the natural undamped frequency, find the amplitude of forced vibrations and the phase difference with respect to the disturbing force.

2.10 A 10-cm-diameter pole with a 10-m length is guided so that it floats vertically in water. The specific gravity of the pole material is 0.81. Find the pole's natural frequency.

THREE

WAVE PROPAGATION IN AN ELASTIC MEDIUM

3.1 INTRODUCTION

Waves are generated in a continuous medium due to a disturbance in the medium. If a pebble is dropped into a large, still pond, waves are generated that travel in all directions. Now, if a small floating object, such as a piece of cork, is introduced on the surface of the still water before dropping the pebble, it will be observed that the piece of cork oscillates about its original position while the waves continue to travel away from the point where the pebble was dropped. It will thus be seen that the waves travel in one direction with a certain velocity, while the piece of cork and, hence, the water oscillate to and fro with a velocity that is different from the velocity of wave travel. This phenomenon is very frequently observed by a child.

In a similar manner, an earthquake produces a motion of the ground by the passage of stress waves that originate from the rupture of the stressed earth mass. Waves may also be generated, both at the surface and within the earth, by artificial means, such as blasting, aircraft landings, and bombardment during war.

Thus, when a load is suddenly applied to a body, the whole body is not disturbed at the instant of loading. The parts closest to the source of a disturbance are affected first, and the deformations produced by the disturbance are subsequently spread throughout the body in the form of stress waves.

The question of wave propagation in an elastic medium is of great importance in geotechnical earthquake engineering since wave velocities depend upon the elastic properties of the medium through which they travel. In this chapter, three problems shall be studied briefly:

1. Wave propagation in elastic rods
2. Wave propagation in an elastic medium
3. Wave propagation in an elastic half space

3.2 WAVE PROPAGATION IN ELASTIC RODS

Three independent kinds of wave motion are possible in rods: longitudinal, torsional, and flexural. Only longitudinal and torsional motions result in the typical wave equation that will be considered here.

Longitudinal Vibration of Rods

Consider the free vibration of a rod with cross-sectional area A, Young's modulus E, and unit weight γ (Fig. 3.1). It is assumed that each cross section remains plane during motion and that the stress is uniform over the area. The stress on a transverse plane at x is σ_x and the stress on a transverse plane at $x + dx$ is $(\sigma_x + \partial\sigma_x/\partial_x \, dx)$. The sum of forces in the x direction can be written as

$$\Sigma F_x = -\sigma_x A + \left(\sigma_x + \frac{\partial\sigma_x}{\partial_x} dx\right) A \tag{3.1}$$

If the displacement of the element in the x direction is designated as u, the equation for motion of the element can then be written by applying Newton's second law as

$$-\sigma_x A + \sigma_x A + \frac{\partial\sigma_x}{\partial x} dx A = dx A \frac{\gamma}{g} \frac{\partial^2 u}{\partial t^2}$$

in which g = acceleration due to gravity

or
$$\frac{\partial\sigma_x}{\partial x} = \frac{\gamma}{g} \frac{\partial^2 u}{\partial t^2} \tag{3.2}$$

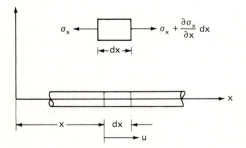

Figure 3.1 Longitudinal vibration of a rod.

The strain in the x direction is $\partial u/\partial x$ and the ratio of stress to strain is Young's modulus; therefore,

$$\sigma_x = E\frac{\partial u}{\partial x} \tag{3.3}$$

Differentiating Eq. (3.3) with respect to x we get

$$\frac{\partial \sigma_x}{\partial x} = E\frac{\partial^2 u}{\partial x^2}$$

Let mass density $\rho = \gamma/g$, and Eq. (3.2) can then be written

$$E\frac{\partial^2 u}{\partial x^2} = \rho\frac{\partial^2 u}{\partial t^2} \tag{3.4a}$$

or

$$\frac{\partial^2 u}{\partial t^2} = \frac{E}{\rho}\frac{\partial^2 u}{\partial x^2} \tag{3.4b}$$

or

$$\frac{\partial^2 u}{\partial t^2} = v_r^2\frac{\partial^2 u}{\partial x^2} \tag{3.4c}$$

in which

$$v_r^2 = \frac{E}{\rho} \tag{3.5}$$

and v_r is defined as the longitudinal-wave-propagation velocity in a rod. Equation (3.4c) is called the one-dimensional *wave equation*. It indicates that during longitudinal vibrations, displacement patterns are propagated in the axial direction at the velocity v_r.

If the wave propagation in a rod is considered at an intermediate point in the rod, it is easy to see that at the instant a wave is generated, there is compressive stress on the face in the positive direction of x and tensile stress on the face in the negative direction of x. Thus, while the compressive wave travels in one direction, the tensile wave travels in the other direction. Initially, only small zones close to these cross sections would feel the stress, but as time passes larger zones would undergo the stress caused by the displacement u.

It is important to distinguish clearly between the velocity of wave propagation v_r and the velocity of particles in the stressed zone $\dot{u}$. Let us consider the stressed zone at the end of the rod in Fig. 3.2a. When a uniformly distributed compressive-stress pulse of intensity σ_x and duration t_n (Fig. 3.2b) is applied to the end of the rod, only a small zone of the rod will undergo compression initially. This compression will be transmitted to successive zones of the rod as time passes. The transmission of the compressive stress from one zone to another occurs at the velocity of a wave propagated in the medium, that is, v_r.

During a time interval Δt, the compressive stress will travel along the rod for a distance $(\Delta x = v_r \Delta t)$. At any time after t_n, a segment of the rod of length $(x_n = v_r t_n)$ will constitute the compressed zone, and the amount of elastic

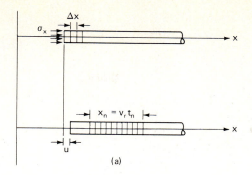

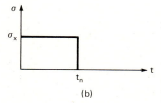

(a)

(b)

Figure 3.2 Velocity of wave propagation and particle velocity in a prismatic rod.

shortening of this zone is given by the displacement of the end of the rod:

$$u = \frac{\sigma_x}{E} x_n = \frac{\sigma_x}{E} v_r t_n$$

or

$$\frac{u}{t_n} = \frac{\sigma_x v_r}{E}$$

Now, the displacement u divided by time t_n also represents the velocity of the end of the rod, or particle velocity. Therefore,

$$\dot{u} = \frac{\sigma_x v_r}{E} \tag{3.6}$$

It is important to note, first, that both wave-propagation velocity and particle velocity are in the same direction when compressive stress is applied and, second, that wave-propagation velocity is the opposite of particle velocity when tensile stress is applied. Another important consideration is that the particle velocity $\dot{u}$ depends on the intensity of the stress or strain induced [Eq. (3.6)], while the wave-propagation velocity v_r is only a function of the material properties.

Torsional Vibration of Rods

The equation for motion of a rod in torsional vibration is similar to that for longitudinal vibrations of rods discussed above.

When x is measured along the length of the rod, the angle of twist $d\theta$ in any length dx of the rod (Fig. 3.3) due to a torque T is

$$d\theta = \frac{T\,dx}{I_p G} \tag{3.7}$$

in which

I_p = polar moment of inertia of the cross-sectional area of the rod
G = shear modulus of the material of the rod
$I_p G$ = torsional stiffness given by the product of the polar moment of inertia I_p of the cross-sectional area and the shear modulus of rod, G

The torques on the two faces of the element are T and T + $(\partial T/\partial x)dx$, as shown in Fig. 3.3. The net torque becomes

$$\Sigma(\text{torque})T = -T + \left(T + \frac{\partial T}{\partial x}\,dx\right) \tag{3.8a}$$

$$= \frac{\partial T}{\partial x}\,dx \tag{3.8b}$$

Applying Newton's second law to the motion of the rod, we get

$$\frac{\partial T}{\partial x}\,dx = \frac{\gamma}{g}I_p\,dx\frac{\partial^2\theta}{\partial t^2} \tag{3.9a}$$

or

$$\frac{\partial T}{\partial x} = \frac{\gamma}{g}I_p\frac{\partial^2\theta}{\partial t^2} \tag{3.9b}$$

Substituting $\dfrac{\partial T}{\partial x}$ from Eq. (3.7) in Eq. (3.9b), we get

$$I_p G\frac{\partial^2\theta}{\partial x^2} = \frac{\gamma}{g}I_p\frac{\partial^2\theta}{\partial t^2} \tag{3.10a}$$

or

$$\frac{\partial^2\theta}{\partial t^2} = G\frac{g}{\gamma}\frac{\partial^2\theta}{\partial x^2} \tag{3.10b}$$

or

$$\frac{\partial^2\theta}{\partial t^2} = v_s\frac{\partial^2\theta}{\partial x^2} \tag{3.10c}$$

where

$$G\frac{g}{\gamma} = \frac{G}{\rho} = v_s^2 \tag{3.11}$$

where v_s is the shear-wave velocity of the material of the rod.

T $\quad$ T + $\frac{\partial T}{\partial x}dx$

$\rightarrow|dx|\leftarrow$

Figure 3.3 Torque acting on element dx of a rod.

Solution of Wave Equation

The solution of Eq. 3.4c for a one-dimensional wave may be expressed in the form

$$u = f(x - v_r t) \tag{3.12}$$

Equation (3.12) represents a function of x traveling at velocity v_r. The derivatives of u with respect to x and t are as follows:

$$\frac{\partial u}{\partial x} = f'(x - v_r t) \qquad \frac{\partial^2 u}{\partial x^2} = f''(x - v_r t)$$

$$\frac{\partial u}{\partial t} = -v_r f'(x - v_r t) \qquad \frac{\partial^2 u}{\partial t^2} = v_r^2 f''(x - v_r t)$$

Substitution of the second derivatives into Eq. (3.4c) yields identical results on both sides, thus satisfying the equation. A more general form of the wave solution is expressed as

$$u = f_1(x - v_r t) + f_2(x + v_r t) \tag{3.13}$$

In the above equation, the first term $f_1(x)$ represents the wave traveling in the positive x direction and the second term $f_2(x)$ represents the wave traveling in the negative x direction.

End Conditions

The conditions at the end of a bar may be studied by making use of the superposition of waves. This is possible because the differential Eq. (3.4c) is linear. Hence, the sum of two solutions is also a solution.

   Consider a wave whose form is described by a step function (Fig. 3.4a). In this figure, a compression wave is traveling in the positive x direction and an identical tension wave is traveling in the negative x direction. In the crossover zone where the two waves pass each other, the portion of the rod in which the two waves are superimposed has zero stress (Fig. 3.4b and c) and the particle velocity is equal to twice the particle velocity in either wave. The particle velocity becomes double in the crossover zone since particle velocity is in the direction of wave travel in a compression wave but is in the opposite direction of wave travel in a tension wave, and the waves are traveling in opposite directions.

   After the two waves pass, the stress and velocity return to zero at the crossover point and the compression and tension waves return to their initial shape and magnitude. It will thus be seen that on the centerline cross section, the stress is zero at all times. This stress condition is the same as that existing at a free end of a rod. If half of the rod is removed, the centerline cross section can be considered a free end (Fig. 3.4d). Therefore, it can be seen that a compression wave is reflected from a free end as a tension wave of the same magnitude

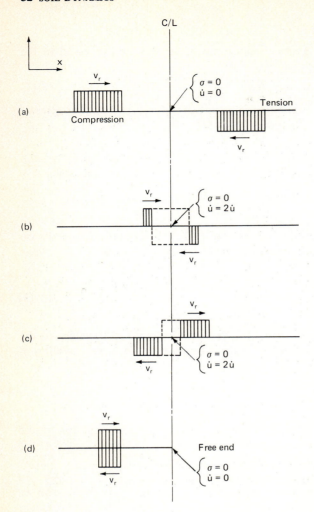

Figure 3.4 Elastic waves in a bar illustrating free end conditions.

and shape. Similarly, it can be shown that a tension wave is reflected as a compression wave of the same magnitude and shape.

Now, let us consider an elastic rod in which a compression wave is traveling in the positive x direction and an identical compression wave is traveling in the negative x direction (Fig. 3.5a). When these two waves pass each other, the cross section through the centerline has stress equal to twice the stress in each wave and zero particle velocity (Fig. 3.5b). After the waves pass each other, they return to their original shape and magnitude (Fig. 3.5c).

The centerline cross section remains stationary during the entire process and, hence, behaves like a fixed end of a rod. Therefore, it can be seen that a compression wave is reflected from a fixed end of a rod as a compression wave of the same magnitude and shape (Fig. 3.5d) and that at the fixed end of a rod the stress is doubled (Fig. 3.5b).

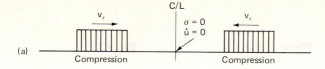

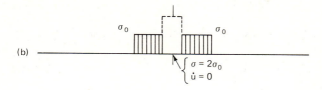

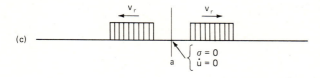

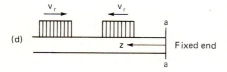

Figure 3.5 Elastic waves in a bar illustrating fixed end conditions.

In the above discussion the waves of constant-stress amplitude were considered. Superposition and reflection of waves of any shape may be studied in a similar manner.

Rods of Finite Length

In the above discussion, it was assumed that the rod is of either infinite or semi-infinite length. In practice, vibration of rods of only finite length is of interest in soil dynamics.

Therefore, if a bar of finite length ℓ is vibrating in one of its normal modes (Fig. 3.6a), the solution to the wave Eq. (3.4c) may be written in the following form:

$$u = U(A \cos \omega_n t + B \sin \omega_n t) \qquad (3.14)$$

where A = constant
  B = constant
  ω_n = natural frequency of the rod
  U = function of x that defines the mode shape of vibrations

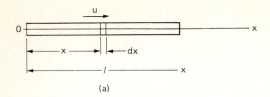

(a)

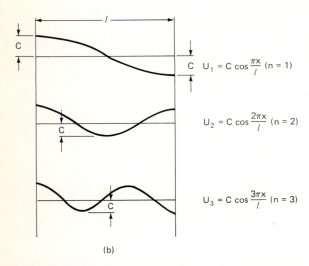

(b)

Figure 3.6 Vibrations of a rod of finite length with free-free end conditions.

Substitution of Eq. (3.14) into Eq. (3.4c) gives

$$\frac{d^2U}{dx^2} + \frac{\omega_n^2}{v_r^2} U = 0 \tag{3.15a}$$

for which the solution is

$$U = C\cos\frac{\omega_n x}{v_r} + D\sin\frac{\omega_n x}{v_r} \tag{3.15b}$$

The constants C and D in Eq. (3.15b) are determined by satisfying the boundary conditions at the end of the bar.

For a rod of finite length, the displacement amplitude U needs to be determined separately for the following three possible end conditions of the rod:

1. Both ends free (*free-free*)
2. One end fixed and one end free (*fixed-free*)
3. Both ends fixed (*fixed-fixed*)

Free-free For the rod of length ℓ in Fig. 3.6, the end conditions for the free-free case are that the stress and strain on the two faces must both be zero. This means that $dU/dx = 0$ at $x = 0$ and at $x = \ell$. Differentiating Eq. (3.15b) with respect to x, we get

$$\frac{dU}{dx} = \frac{\omega_n}{v_r}\left(-C\sin\frac{\omega_n x}{v_r} + D\cos\frac{\omega_n x}{v_r}\right) = 0 \qquad (3.16)$$

Substituting the above boundary conditions in this equation, we get $D = 0$; and

$$C\sin\frac{\omega_n \ell}{v_r} = 0 \qquad (3.17)$$

To satisfy Eq. (3.17),

$$\frac{\omega_n \ell}{v_r} = n\pi$$

or

$$\omega_n = \frac{n\pi v_r}{\ell} \qquad (3.18)$$

where

$$n = 1, 2, 3, \ldots$$

Equation (3.18) is the *frequency equation* by which the frequencies of the normal modes of vibration of the free-free rod are found. By substituting Eq. (3.18) in (3.15b), the distribution of displacement along the rod can be found for any harmonic. The first three harmonics are shown in Fig. 3.6, and the displacement amplitude can be expressed as

$$U_n = C\cos\frac{n\pi x}{\ell} \qquad (3.19)$$

where

$$n = 1, 2, 3, \ldots$$

Fixed-free The end conditions for the rod in Fig. (3.7) are as follows: At the fixed end ($x = 0$), the displacement is zero ($U = 0$); at the free end ($x = \ell$), the strain is zero ($\partial U/\partial x = 0$). Substituting these in Eq. (3.15b), we get

$$c = 0$$

and

$$D\cos\frac{\omega_n \ell}{v_r} = 0$$

which gives

$$\frac{\omega_n \ell}{v_r} = (2n + 1)\frac{\pi}{2}$$

where

$$n = 0, 1, 2, 3, \ldots$$

or

$$\omega_n = (2n + 1)\frac{\pi v_r}{2\ell} \qquad (3.20)$$

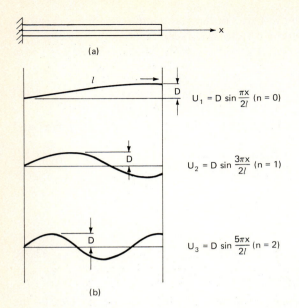

(a)

$U_1 = D \sin \dfrac{\pi x}{2l}$ $(n = 0)$

$U_2 = D \sin \dfrac{3\pi x}{2l}$ $(n = 1)$

$U_3 = D \sin \dfrac{5\pi x}{2l}$ $(n = 2)$

(b)

Figure 3.7 Vibrations of a rod of finite length with fixed-free end conditions.

The displacement amplitude may now be written as

$$U_n = D \sin \frac{\omega_n x}{v_r} = D \sin \frac{(2n+1)\pi x}{2\ell} \qquad (3.21)$$

The first three harmonics described by Eq. (3.21) are shown in Fig. 3.7.

Fixed-fixed The end conditions for the rod in Fig. 3.8 are $U = 0$ at $x = 0$ and at $x = \ell$. Substituting these conditions in Eq. (3.15b), we get $C = 0$ and

$$\sin \frac{\omega_n \ell}{v_r} = 0 \qquad (3.22a)$$

which gives

$$\omega_n = \frac{n\pi v_r}{\ell} \qquad (3.22b)$$

where

$$n = 1, 2, 3, \dots$$

Then we can write

$$U_n = D \sin \frac{n\pi x}{\ell} \qquad (3.23)$$

where

$$n = 1, 2, 3, \dots$$

The first three harmonics described by Eq. (3.23) are shown in Fig. 3.8b.

A rod of finite length in torsional vibrations can be analyzed in an identical manner.

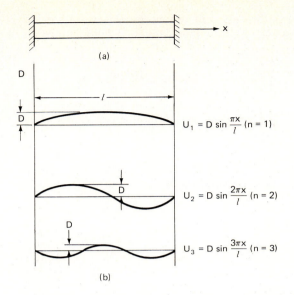

$$U_1 = D \sin \frac{\pi x}{l} \ (n = 1)$$

$$U_2 = D \sin \frac{2\pi x}{l} \ (n = 2)$$

$$U_3 = D \sin \frac{3\pi x}{l} \ (n = 3)$$

Figure 3.8 Vibrations of a rod of finite length with fixed-fixed end conditions.

The concept of a natural frequency of a rod of finite length in a principal mode of vibrations is used in determining the elastic properties of a soil. This is discussed in Chap. 4.

3.3 WAVE PROPAGATION IN AN ELASTIC INFINITE MEDIUM

It will be assumed that the infinite medium through which waves propagate is homogeneous and isotropic. Let us consider a small element of dimensions dx, dy, and dz on which the forces shown in Fig. 3.9 are acting.

Consider the variation in stresses on opposite faces of this element. The stresses on each face of this element are represented by sets of orthogonal

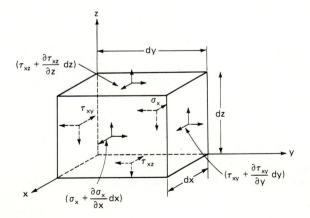

Figure 3.9 Stresses on a small element in an infinite homogeneous, isotropic, and elastic medium.

vectors. Translational equilibrium of this element can be expressed by writing the sum of forces acting parallel to each axis. In the x direction the equilibrium equation is

$$\left(\sigma_x + \frac{\partial \sigma_x}{\partial x} dx\right) dy\, dz - \sigma_x\, dy\, dz + \left(\tau_{xy} + \frac{\partial \tau_{xy}}{\partial y} dy\right) dx\, dz - \tau_{xy}\, dx\, dz$$

$$+ \left(\tau_{xz} + \frac{\partial \tau_{xz}}{\partial z} dz\right) dx\, dy - \tau_{xz}\, dx\, dy = 0$$

$$(3.24)$$

Similar equations can be written for the summation of forces in the y and z directions. Neglecting body forces and applying Newton's second law in the x direction gives

$$\left(\frac{\partial \sigma_x}{\partial x} + \frac{\partial \tau_{xy}}{\partial y} + \frac{\partial \tau_{xz}}{\partial z}\right) dx\, dy\, dz = \rho(dx\, dy\, dz)\frac{\partial^2 u}{\partial t^2} \qquad (3.25)$$

or

$$\rho \frac{\partial^2 u}{\partial t^2} = \frac{\partial \sigma_x}{\partial x} + \frac{\partial \tau_{xy}}{\partial y} + \frac{\partial \tau_{xz}}{\partial z} \qquad (3.26a)$$

Similar equations can be written for the motion in the y and z directions as follows:

$$\rho \frac{\partial^2 v}{\partial t^2} = \frac{\partial \tau_{yx}}{\partial x} + \frac{\partial \sigma_y}{\partial y} + \frac{\partial \tau_{yz}}{\partial z} \qquad (3.26b)$$

$$\rho \frac{\partial^2 w}{\partial t^2} = \frac{\partial \tau_{zx}}{\partial x} + \frac{\partial \tau_{zy}}{\partial y} + \frac{\partial \sigma_z}{\partial z} \qquad (3.26c)$$

in which u, v, and w are displacements in the x, y, and z directions, respectively. The right sides of Eqs. (3.26) may be expressed in terms of displacements, with the help of the following relationships for an elastic medium:

$$\sigma_x = \lambda \bar{\varepsilon} + 2G\varepsilon_x \qquad \tau_{xy} = \tau_{yx} = G\gamma_{xy} \qquad (3.27a)$$

$$\sigma_y = \lambda \bar{\varepsilon} + 2G\varepsilon_y \qquad \tau_{yz} = \tau_{zy} = G\gamma_{yz} \qquad (3.27b)$$

$$\sigma_z = \lambda \bar{\varepsilon} + 2G\varepsilon_z \qquad \tau_{zx} = \tau_{xz} = G\gamma_{zx} \qquad (3.27c)$$

$$G = \frac{E}{2(1 + \nu)} \qquad (3.28a)$$

and

$$\lambda = \frac{\nu E}{(1 + \nu)(1 - 2\nu)} \qquad (3.28b)$$

in which ν = Poisson's ratio

λ, G = Lamé's constants (G is also termed the *shear modulus*)

$\bar{\varepsilon} = \varepsilon_x + \varepsilon_y + \varepsilon_z$

The strain and rotations may be defined in terms of displacements (Timoshenko and Goodier, 1951; Kolsky, 1963) as follows:

Strains

$$\varepsilon_x = \frac{\partial u}{\partial x} \qquad \gamma_{xy} = \frac{\partial v}{\partial x} + \frac{\partial u}{\partial y} \tag{3.29a}$$

$$\varepsilon_y = \frac{\partial v}{\partial y} \qquad \gamma_{yz} = \frac{\partial w}{\partial y} + \frac{\partial v}{\partial z} \tag{3.29b}$$

$$\varepsilon_z = \frac{\partial w}{\partial z} \qquad \gamma_{zx} = \frac{\partial u}{\partial z} + \frac{\partial w}{\partial x} \tag{3.29c}$$

Rotations

$$2\bar{\omega}_x = \frac{\partial w}{\partial y} - \frac{\partial v}{\partial z} \tag{3.30a}$$

$$2\bar{\omega}_y = \frac{\partial u}{\partial z} - \frac{\partial w}{\partial x} \tag{3.30b}$$

$$2\bar{\omega}_z = \frac{\partial v}{\partial x} - \frac{\partial u}{\partial y} \tag{3.30c}$$

where $\bar{\omega}_x$, $\bar{\omega}_y$, and $\bar{\omega}_z$ are rotations about x, y, and z axes, respectively. Now, substituting appropriate expressions from Eqs. (3.27), (3.28), (3.29), and (3.30) in Eq. (3.26a), we get

$$\rho \frac{\partial^2 u}{\partial t^2} = (\lambda + G) \frac{\partial \bar{\varepsilon}}{\partial x} + G \nabla^2 u \tag{3.31}$$

Similarly, Eqs. (3.26b) and (3.26c) give respectively

$$\rho \frac{\partial^2 v}{\partial t^2} = (\lambda + G) \frac{\partial \bar{\varepsilon}}{\partial y} + G \nabla^2 v \tag{3.32}$$

and

$$\rho \frac{\partial^2 w}{\partial t^2} = (\lambda + G) \frac{\partial \bar{\varepsilon}}{\partial z} + G \nabla^2 w \tag{3.33}$$

where ∇^2 (the laplacian operator in cartesian coordinates) is defined as

$$\nabla^2 = \left(\frac{\partial^2}{\partial x^2} + \frac{\partial^2}{\partial y^2} + \frac{\partial^2}{\partial z^2} \right)$$

Equations (3.31), (3.32), and (3.33) are the equations for motion of an infinite homogeneous, isotropic, and elastic medium.

There are two solutions for the above equations. One solution describes the propagation of an irrotational wave while the other describes the propagation of a wave of pure rotation. The first solution is obtained by differentiating Eqs. (3.31), (3.32), and (3.33) with respect to x, y, and z, respectively, and adding all three expressions together. This operation gives

$$\rho \frac{\partial^2 \bar{\varepsilon}}{\partial t^2} = (\lambda + 2G) \nabla^2 \bar{\varepsilon}$$

or

$$\frac{\partial^2 \bar{\varepsilon}}{\partial t^2} = v_c^2 \nabla^2 \bar{\varepsilon} \tag{3.34}$$

This is exactly the form of the wave Eq. (3.4c), where

$$v_c^2 = \frac{\lambda + 2G}{\rho} \tag{3.35a}$$

in which v_c = velocity of compression waves in the infinite medium.

Substituting for λ and G from Eqs. (3.28) in Eq. (3.35a), we get

$$v_c^2 = \frac{E(1 - \nu)}{\rho(1 + \nu)(1 - 2\nu)} = \frac{E_b}{\rho} \tag{3.35b}$$

in which E_b = bulk modulus.

If $\nu = 0$, $V_c^2 = E/\rho$ and equals the velocity of compressive wave propagation in rod v_r, Eq. (3.5). For ν greater than zero, V_c is greater than V_r.

The other solution of the equations for motion can be obtained by differentiating Eq. (3.32) with respect to z and Eq. (3.33) with respect to y and then eliminating $\bar{\varepsilon}$ by subtracting these two equations. Proceeding in this manner, we get

$$\rho \frac{\partial^2}{\partial t^2} \left(\frac{\partial w}{\partial y} - \frac{\partial v}{\partial z} \right) = G \nabla^2 \left(\frac{\partial w}{\partial y} - \frac{\partial v}{\partial z} \right) \tag{3.36}$$

and by using the expression for rotation $\bar{\omega}_x$ from Eq. 3.30a, we get

$$\rho \frac{\partial^2 \bar{\omega}_x}{\partial t^2} = G \nabla^2 \bar{\omega}_x$$

or

$$\frac{\partial^2 \bar{\omega}_x}{\partial t^2} = v_s^2 \nabla^2 \bar{\omega}_x \tag{3.37}$$

Similar expressions can be obtained for $\bar{\omega}_y$ and $\bar{\omega}_z$, which implies that rotation is propagated with velocity

$$v_s = \sqrt{\frac{G}{\rho}} \tag{3.38a}$$

Combining Eqs. (3.35b) and (3.38a) and substituting for G in terms of E from Eq. (3.28a), we get

$$\frac{v_c}{v_s} = \sqrt{2\left(\frac{1 - \nu}{1 - 2\nu} \right)} \tag{3.38b}$$

A plot of V_c/V_s is shown in Figure 3.10. (Richart, 1962).

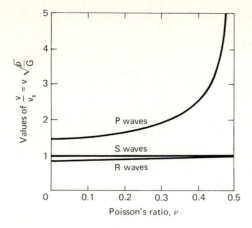

Figure 3.10 Relation between Poisson's ratio ν and velocities of propagation of compression (P), shear (S), and Rayleigh (R) waves in a semi-infinite elastic medium. (*After Richart, 1962.*)

From the above analysis, it can be seen that an infinite elastic medium can sustain two kinds of waves as follows:

1. Compression wave (also called primary wave, P wave, dilatational wave, irrotational wave)
2. Shear wave (also called secondary wave, S wave, distortional wave, equivoluminal wave)

The two waves, which represent different types of body motions, travel at different velocities. It may be noted that the particle motion associated with the compression wave in the rod and the dilatational wave in the infinite medium is the same, but the wave-propagation velocities are different. In the rod, $v_r = \sqrt{E/\rho}$. But in the infinite medium, $v_c = \sqrt{(\lambda + 2G)/\rho}$. This means that the compression wave travels faster in the infinite medium than in a rod because there can be no lateral displacements, while lateral displacements are possible in the rod. The second type of wave motion (distortional) propagates at the same velocity ($v_s = \sqrt{G/\rho}$) in both the rod and the infinite medium.

It will be seen from Eq. (3.35b) that, if $\nu = 0.5$,

$$v_c \to \infty \qquad \text{and} \qquad E_b \to \infty$$

Since water is relatively incompressible as compared to the soil skeleton, the measurements of the velocity of a compression wave in water-saturated soils will not be a representative velocity for soils, but for water. Since water has no shear strength and, hence, has zero value in shear modulus, the velocity of a shear wave in water-saturated soils represents the soil property only. This fact must be considered while planning velocity measurements.

Table 3.1 lists the velocity of wave propagation in compression and shear for different materials.

Table 3.1 Velocities of Compression Waves v_c and Shear Waves v_s†

Soil	ρ, kg $\times$ s^2/cm^4	v_c, m/s	v_s, m/s
Moist clay	1.8×10^{-6}	1500‡	150
Loess at natural moisture	1.67×10^{-6}	800	260
Dense sand and gravel	1.70×10^{-6}	480	250
Fine-grained sand	1.65×10^{-6}	300	110
Medium-grained sand	1.65×10^{-6}	550	160
Medium-sized gravel	1.8×10^{-6}	750	180

† After Barkan (1962).
‡ This value is close to the velocity of wave propagation in water.

3.4 WAVE PROPAGATION IN A SEMI-INFINITE ELASTIC HALF SPACE

In practice, the solutions for wave propagation in an infinite elastic body have little value. Since foundations are supported on the soil, the boundary conditions approximating this situation are those of a semi-infinite half space. It will be assumed, as in Sec. 3.3, that the medium is homogeneous, isotropic, and elastic.

In an elastic infinite medium, it was found that there are two types of body waves, the compression wave and the shear wave. In an elastic half space, it will be seen that another wave, the Rayleigh wave, shows up. The motion of a Rayleigh wave is confined to a zone near the boundary of the half space. The solution for this wave was first obtained by Rayleigh (1885) and later described in detail by Lamb (1904).

The study of waves propagating in a zone close to the surface is of practical interest in the study of the dynamics of bases and foundations. The effect of the free surface of soil on the propagation of waves in soil will be discussed.

The half space may be defined in the xy plane only with z assumed positive in the downward direction (Fig. 3.11). For a plane wave traveling in the x direction, particle displacement is independent of y direction. If u and w are displacements in the x and z directions, respectively, and $v = 0$, then

$$\frac{\partial u}{\partial y} = \frac{\partial w}{\partial y} = 0$$

Then, if the action of body forces is neglected, the equations of wave propagation are the same as Eqs. (3.31) and (3.33):

$$(\lambda + G)\frac{\partial \bar{\varepsilon}}{\partial x} + G\nabla^2 u = \rho\frac{\partial^2 u}{\partial t^2} \tag{3.31}$$

$$(\lambda + G)\frac{\partial \bar{\varepsilon}}{\partial z} + G\nabla^2 w = \rho\frac{\partial^2 w}{\partial t^2} \tag{3.33}$$

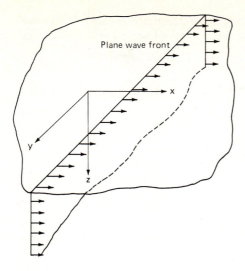

Plane wave front

x

y

z

A general solution of these equations may be written

$$u = \frac{\partial \phi^*}{\partial x} + \frac{\partial \psi^*}{\partial z} \tag{3.39a}$$

$$w = \frac{\partial \phi^*}{\partial z} - \frac{\partial \psi^*}{\partial x} \tag{3.39b}$$

in which ϕ^* and ψ^* are analytic functions. Since the z axis is perpendicular to the soil surface, then for all points in soil, $z > 0$. Considering steady propagation of waves with frequency ω, ϕ^* and ψ^* may be expressed as

$$\phi^* = e^{i\omega t}\phi(x, z) \tag{3.40a}$$

$$\psi^* = e^{i\omega t}\psi(x, z) \tag{3.40b}$$

Then the equations that should be satisfied by the functions ϕ and ψ are as follows:

$$(\nabla^2 + h^2)\phi = 0 \tag{3.41a}$$

$$(\nabla^2 + k^2)\psi = 0 \tag{3.41b}$$

in which

$$h = \frac{\omega}{v_c} \qquad k = \frac{\omega}{v_s} \tag{3.42}$$

since

$$\omega = \frac{2\pi}{T}$$

in which T is the period of the propagated waves, then

$$h = \frac{2\pi}{v_c T} \text{ and } k = \frac{2\pi}{v_s T}$$

However, $v_c T$ and $v_s T$ represent wave lengths of longitudinal and transverse waves. Hence, h and k are reciprocal values of the wave lengths, and k is always larger than h.

Particular solutions of Eqs. (3.41) may be assumed as follows:

$$\phi = Ae^{-\alpha z}e^{i\chi x} \tag{3.43a}$$

$$\psi = Be^{-\beta z}e^{i\chi x} \tag{3.43b}$$

in which

$$\alpha^2 = \chi^2 - h^2 \tag{3.44a}$$

$$\beta^2 = \chi^2 - k^2 \tag{3.44b}$$

A, B, and χ are arbitrary constants determined from boundary conditions.

Let the boundary surface $z = 0$ be subjected to the action of external normal forces distributed over the entire plane; these forces induce normal stress equaling

$$\sigma_z = \sigma_0 e^{i\chi x} \tag{3.45}$$

It is assumed that the tangential stresses on the border plane equal zero; that is,

$$\tau_{zx} = 0 \tag{3.46}$$

Stresses σ_z and τ_{zx} may be expressed through functions ϕ and ψ as follows:

$$\frac{\tau_{zx}}{G} = 2\frac{\partial^2\phi}{\partial x \partial z} - k^2\psi - 2\frac{\partial^2\psi}{\partial x^2} \tag{3.47a}$$

$$\frac{\sigma_z}{G} = -k^2\phi - 2\frac{\partial^2\phi}{\partial x^2} - 2\frac{\partial^2\psi}{\partial x \partial z} \tag{3.47b}$$

By substituting expressions for ϕ and ψ from Eqs. (3.43) in the right parts of Eqs. (3.47), when $z = 0$, we get

$$-2i\chi\alpha A + (2\chi^2 - k^2)B = 0 \tag{3.48a}$$

$$(2\chi^2 - k^2)A + 2i\chi\beta B = \frac{\sigma_0}{G} \tag{3.48b}$$

Hence

$$A = \frac{2\chi^2 - k^2}{F(\chi)}\frac{\sigma_0}{G} \tag{3.49a}$$

$$B = \frac{2i\chi\alpha}{F(\chi)}\frac{\sigma_0}{G} \tag{3.49b}$$

in which

$$F(\chi) = (2\chi^2 - k^2)^2 - 4\chi^2\alpha\beta \tag{3.50}$$

Using Eqs. (3.39), (3.43), and (3.49), we obtain

$$u = i\chi \frac{(2\chi^2 - k^2)e^{-\alpha z} - 2\alpha\beta e^{-\beta z}}{F(\chi)} e^{i\chi x} \frac{\sigma_0}{G} \tag{3.51a}$$

$$w = a \frac{-(2\chi^2 - k^2)e^{-\alpha z} + 2\chi^2 e^{-\beta z}}{F(\chi)} e^{i\chi x} \frac{\sigma_0}{G} \tag{3.51b}$$

In order to transform the exciting force into one acting along the line $x = 0$, $z = 0$ (Fig. 3.11), we assume

$$\sigma_0 = -P\frac{d\chi}{2\pi}$$

Substituting this expression in the right part of Eq. (3.51), and integrating with respect to χ from $-\infty$ to $+\infty$, we obtain the following expressions for the displacements u and w,

$$u = \frac{iP}{2\pi G} \int_{-\infty}^{+\infty} \frac{\chi\left[(2\chi^2 - k^2)e^{-\alpha z} - 2\alpha\beta e^{-\beta z}\right]e^{i\chi x}}{F(\chi)} d\chi \tag{3.52a}$$

$$w = -\frac{P}{2\pi G} \int_{-\infty}^{+\infty} \frac{\alpha\left[-(2\chi^2 - k^2)e^{-\alpha z} + 2\chi^2 e^{-\beta z}\right]e^{i\chi x}}{F(\chi)} d\chi \tag{3.52b}$$

Equation (3.52) corresponds to the forced waves induced by an exciting force acting along the line $x = 0$, $z = 0$.

Velocity of Wave Propagation

Free surface waves occur where the waves are induced by some initial excitement on the border surface. Assuming, for this case, that $\sigma_0 = 0$, constants A and B of Eq. 3.48a and b, may then be determined from the following expressions:

$$-2i\chi\alpha A + (2\chi^2 - k^2)B = 0 \tag{3.53a}$$

$$(2\chi^2 - k^2)A + 2i\chi\beta B = 0 \tag{3.53b}$$

Equation (3.53) will give solutions other than zero for A and B only when the determinant of this system equals zero. Hence, we get

$$F(\chi) = 0 \tag{3.54}$$

Equation (3.54) may be used to determine χ.

Instead of this equation, which contains irrational expressions, we may consider the following equation, which does not contain radical signs (Barkan, 1962):

$$F(\chi)f(\chi) = (2\chi^2 - k^2)^4 - 16(\chi^2 - h^2)(\chi^2 - k^2)\chi^4$$

$$= k^8\left[1 - 8\frac{\chi^2}{k^2} + \left(24 - 16\frac{h^2}{k^2}\right)\frac{\chi^4}{k^4} - 16\left(1 - \frac{h^2}{k^2}\right)\frac{\chi^6}{k^6}\right] = 0$$

$$\tag{3.55}$$

in which

$$f(\chi) = (2\chi^2 - k^2)^2 + 4\chi^2\alpha\beta$$

Since $k > h$, one of the roots of Eq. (3.55) lies between 1 and $+\infty$. It can be shown that the other two roots lie between 0 and h^2/k^2, if they are real.

The first root corresponds to positive values of α and β; therefore, this root does not satisfy the condition $f(\chi) = 0$. The last two roots make α and β positive and imaginary. Therefore, they do not satisfy the equation $F(\chi) = 0$. The latter equation has only one root, $\chi^2 = \lambda^2$,† which is larger than 1. Therefore, $\lambda^2 > k^2$. For a Poisson ratio of 0.5, the real root of Eq. (3.55) is

$$\frac{\lambda}{k} = 1.04678$$

For $\nu = 0.25$, all roots of Eq. (3.55) are real; they are equal to

$$\frac{\chi^2}{k^2} = \frac{1}{4}$$

$$= \frac{1}{4}(3 - \sqrt{3})$$

$$= \frac{1}{4}(3 + \sqrt{3})$$

Of these roots, only the last satisfies the conditions of the problem; its value is

$$\frac{\lambda}{k} = \frac{1}{2}\sqrt{3 + \sqrt{3}} = 1.087664$$

Similarly, in Eq. (3.42), if we designate

$$\lambda = \frac{\omega}{v_R}$$

where v_R is the velocity of propagation of the Rayleigh wave under consideration, it is clear that

$$v_R = \frac{k}{\lambda}v_s$$

For $\nu = 0.5$, $v_R = 0.9553\,v_s$

For $\nu = 0.25$, $v_R = 0.9194\,v_s$

Thus, it is seen that surface waves propagate with somewhat smaller velocity than shear or transverse waves. Thus, v_R is less than v_s. A plot of v_R/v_s for different values of ν is shown in Fig. 3.10 (Richart, 1962).

It is thus seen that there are three principal waves in an elastic half space. These waves have different velocities of propagation. Knowing their velocities, it is easy to predict in which order the waves will arrive at a given point due to a disturbance at another point.

† λ is a root of Eq. (3.55) satisfying the required conditions.

Particle Motion at the Surface

In addition to predicting the order of arrival of waves along the surface, detailed studies were made by Lamb (1904) of surface motion that occurs long distances away from a point source at the surface of an ideal medium.

If a point source acts at the surface of an elastic half space, the disturbance spreads out in the form of symmetrical annular waves. The initial form of these waves will depend on the input impulse; if the input is of short duration, then the characteristic waves shown in Fig. 3.12a will develop (Richart, Hall, and Woods, 1970). These waves have three salient features that correspond to the arrivals of the P wave, S wave, and Rayleigh (R) wave. The horizontal and vertical components of particle motion are shown separately in Fig. 3.12a and b, respectively.

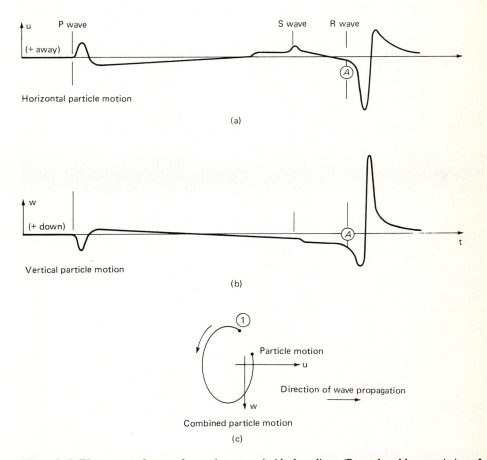

Figure 3.12 Wave system from surface point source in ideal medium. (Reproduced by permission of F. E. Richart, J. R. Hall, Jr., and R. D. Woods, *Vibrations of Soils and Foundations*, Prentice-Hall, Inc., Englewood Cliffs, N. J., 1970, and after Lamb, 1904.)

A particle at the surface first undergoes an oscillatory lateral displacement on the arrival of the *P* wave, followed by a relatively quiet period leading up to another oscillation at the arrival of the *S* wave. This is followed by an oscillation of much larger magnitude when the *R* wave arrives.

The time interval between wave arrivals becomes greater and the amplitude of the oscillations becomes smaller with increasing distance from the source. In addition, *P*-wave and *S*-wave amplitude decays more rapidly than that of an *R* wave. Therefore, the *R* wave is the most significant disturbance along the surface of an elastic half space and, at large distances from the source, may be the only clearly distinguishable wave.

If the horizontal and vertical components of the particle motion starting at point Ⓐ in Fig. 3.12*a* and *b* are combined, the locus of surface-particle motion for the *R* wave can be drawn as shown in Fig. 3.12*c*. The path of the particle motion describes a *retrograde ellipse*.

3.5 WAVES GENERATED BY A SURFACE FOOTING

In practice, a machine foundation may generate waves in a soil mass. An ideal case of a circular footing undergoing vertical oscillations at the surface of an elastic half space will be considered. The energy of the oscillating footing is transmitted away by a combination of *P*, *S*, and *R* waves.

The basic features of this wave field at a relatively large distance from the source are shown in Fig. 3.13 (Woods, 1968). The distance from the source of the waves to each wave in Fig. 3.13 is drawn in proportion to the velocity of each wave for a medium with $\nu = \frac{1}{4}$. The *body waves* (*P* and *S* waves) propagate radially outward from the source along a hemispherical wave front, and the *R* wave propagates radially outward along a cylindrical wave front. All of the waves encounter an increasingly larger volume of material as they travel outward. Therefore, the energy density in each wave decreases with distance from the source. This decrease in energy density, or decrease in displacement amplitude, is called *geometrical damping*. The amplitude of the body waves decreases in proportion to the ratio of $1/r$, where r is the distance from the input source. However, along the surface of the half space, the amplitude decreases as $1/r^2$. The amplitude of the Rayleigh wave decreases as $1/\sqrt{r}$ (Woods, 1968).

The particle motion associated with the compression (*P*) wave is a push-pull motion in the direction of the wave front, and the particle motion associated with the shear (*S*) wave is a transverse displacement that is normal to the direction of the wave front. The particle motion associated with the *R* wave at the surface of a half space, however, is a retrograde ellipse as shown in Fig. 3.12*c*. The shaded zones along the wave fronts for the body waves indicate the relative amplitude of particle displacement as a function of the *dip angle* (the angle measured downward from the surface at the center of the source). The *R* wave can be described by two components, vertical and horizontal, each of which decays with depth but according to separate distributions.

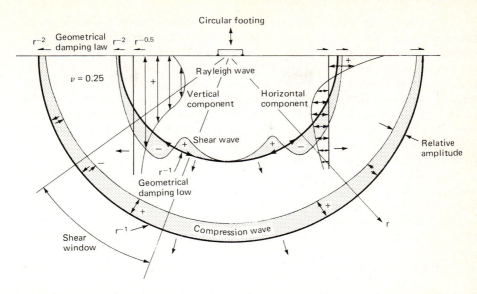

Figure 3.13 Distribution of displacement waves from a circular footing on a homogeneous, isotropic, elastic half space. (*After Woods, 1968.*)

For a vertically oscillating circular energy source on the surface of a homogeneous, isotropic, elastic half space, Miller and Pursey (1954, 1955) determined that the distribution of total input energy among the three elastic waves was 67 percent for the R wave, 26 percent for the S wave, and 7 percent for the P wave. The fact that two-thirds of the total input energy is transmitted away from a surface energy source by the R wave, which decays much more slowly with distance than the body waves, indicates that the R wave is of primary concern for foundations on or near the surface of the ground.

3.6 FINAL COMMENTS

Analytical solutions for the velocity of the propagation of the body waves (P and S waves) and the surface wave (the R or Rayleigh, wave) have been included. There are two major practical applications of these solutions in soil dynamics.

First, the elastic properties of the soil are determined. This may be done by determining the velocity of wave propagation, either in prismatic soil samples or in the soil mass in situ, and by determining the resonance of the vibrating soil sample in the resonant column apparatus. The application of these techniques in particular cases is demonstrated in Chap. 4.

Second, the concept of geometrical damping has great application in proportioning foundations under vibrating footings, as with compressor and reciprocating machines. This topic is discussed in detail in Chap. 9.

In water-saturated soils, only velocities of S-wave propagation must be determined. The P-wave velocity is representative of the modulus of water rather than the modulus of soil.

In the study of wave propagation due to a vibrating footing, the footing was assumed to be circular and placed at the surface of a semi-infinite space. (In practice, a footing is more often rectangular than circular. Also, a footing is always embedded to a certain depth below the ground level.) Nevertheless, the study of the problem as a simplified ideal case does not reduce its practical value. In fact, the departure in the practical results as compared with the analytical predictions based upon simplified assumptions helps either in refining the analytical tools or in generating test data that may be used in developing correction factors to the analytical solutions. In either case, the design and analytical tools are sharpened!

It should also be noted, however, that the soils are neither homogeneous and isotropic nor elastic. Therefore, explanations of the gaps between prediction and actual behavior need to refer to this fact also.

Further, the soils occur in layers. Analytical solutions for elastic waves in layered systems are available (Zoeppritz, 1919; Ewing, Jardetzky, and Press, 1957; Griffiths and King, 1965; and Richart, Hall, and Woods, 1970). The reflection and refraction of waves are used to determine the depth of overburden in exploring soils for civil engineering projects, but these fall outside the scope of this text.

REFERENCES

Barkan, D. D.: "Dynamics of Bases and Foundations," McGraw-Hill Book Co., New York, 1962.
Ewing, W. M., W. S. Jardetzky, and F. Press: "Elastic Waves in Layered Media," McGraw-Hill Book Co., New York, 1957.
Griffiths, D. H. and R. F. King: "Applied Geophysics for Engineers and Geologists," Pergamon Press, New York, 1965.
Kolsky, H.: "Stress Waves in Solids," Dover Publications, Inc., New York, 1963.
Lamb, H.: On the Propagation of Tremors over the Surface of an Elastic Solid, *Philos. Trans. R. S. London*, Ser. A, vol. 203, pp. 1–42, September, 1904.
Miller, G. F., and H. Pursey: The Field and Radiation Impedence of Mechanical Radiators on the Free Surface of a Semi-Infinite Isotropic Solid, *Proc. R. Soc. London*, vol. 223, pp. 521–54, 1954.
_____ and _____: On the Partition of Energy between Elastic Waves in a Semi-Infinite Solid, *Proc. R. Soc. London*, Ser. A, vol. 233, pp. 55–69, 1955.
Rayleigh, L.: On Waves Propagated along the Plane Surface of an Elastic Solid, *Proc. London Math. Soc.*, vol. 17, pp. 4–11, 1885.
Richart, F. E.: Foundation Vibrations, *Trans. ASCE*, vol. 127, part I, pp. 863–898, 1962.
_____, J. R. Hall, Jr., and R. D. Woods: "Vibrations of Soils and Foundations," Prentice-Hall, Inc., Englewood Cliffs, New Jersey, 1970.
Timoshenko, S. and G. N. Goodier: "Theory of Elasticity," McGraw-Hill Book Co., New York, 1951.
_____, D. H. Young, and W. Weaver, Jr.: "Vibration Problems in Engineering," 4th ed., John Wiley and Sons, Inc., New York, 1974.
Woods, R. D.: Screening of Surface Waves in Soils, *J. Soil. Mech. Found. Div., ASCE*, vol. 94, no. SM4, pp. 951–979, July, 1968.
Zoeppritz, K.: *Nachr. Ges. Wiss. Gottingen Math-Phys.*, pp. 66–94, 1919.

DYNAMIC STRESS DEFORMATION AND STRENGTH CHARACTERISTICS OF SOILS

4.1 INTRODUCTION

Several problems in engineering practice require knowledge of the dynamic soil properties. Generally, dynamic foundation problems are divided into either small strain amplitude or large strain amplitude response. For example, foundations for a radar tracking station can tolerate only very small levels of strain while structures in earthquake or blast damage areas must be able to tolerate large strain levels.

A variety of field and laboratory methods have been developed for evaluating dynamic soil properties. The major soil properties that need to be ascertained in soil dynamics and geotechnical earthquake engineering are:

1. Shear strength evaluated in terms of strain rates and stress-strain characteristics
2. Dynamic moduli, Young's modulus, shear modulus, bulk modulus, and constrained modulus
3. Poisson's ratio
4. Damping
5. Liquefaction parameters: cyclic shearing stress ratio, cyclic deformation, and pore-pressure response

In this chapter, conventional static soil tests are summarized first, followed by a detailed discussion of laboratory and field methods used for determining the relevant dynamic soil properties. Values of the dynamic soil moduli for typical soils are presented also.

Liquefaction and parameters associated with liquefaction are discussed in Chap. 8.

4.2 CONVENTIONAL SOIL TESTS UNDER STATIC LOADS

Because diverse rock-weathering processes cause soils to be formed in nature, no human agency has control over the properties of soils. This is the main difference between soils and conventional building materials, such as steel and concrete, whose properties are almost tailor-made.

In addition, soils at any given site are not homogeneous, either areally or with regard to depth. It is therefore absolutely essential that soil tests be performed at all construction sites to evaluate the strength and other pertinent properties of the soils.

In all laboratory strength tests, it is of paramount importance that field loading conditions be reproduced as accurately as possible. This requires that field anisotropy, strain rate, and drainage condition be modeled. Testing problems are more difficult as rates of strain increase as in dynamic problems.

Equipment for testing soils under static loading conditions has been somewhat standardized for a long time. It is desirable to describe briefly the conventional equipment and the types of tests that can be performed.

Although a number of methods are available for shear-testing of soils, the most commonly used are the direct shear test and the triaxial compression test.

Before describing the actual tests and their interpretations, it is necessary to discuss drainage conditions, which have a very important bearing on the shear strength of soils.

4.3 DRAINAGE DURING SHEAR TESTS

Most soil deposits whose shear strengths are to be determined will be saturated at some time during the design life of the structure. Drainage conditions before and during shear influence the shear strength of saturated soils. In shear tests, soils are first subjected to normal or confining stress, which is usually maintained constant. An increasing shear stress is then applied until failure occurs. Shear tests have been devised to measure the shear strength of soils under three different limiting drainage conditions, as discussed below:

1. *Unconsolidated-undrained test or "quick test"*: In these tests, no drainage is permitted under applied normal or confining load, or during shear. Thus, the normal load is not transferred to the soil grains as intergranular pressure but exists as a hydrostatic excess pore pressure. It cannot, therefore, mobilize any frictional resistance. Preventing drainage during shear prevents volume changes that might otherwise take place.

2. *Consolidated-undrained test or "consolidated-quick test"*: In these tests, soils are consolidated (allowed to drain) under applied normal or confining load and no drainage is permitted during shear. Although volume changes can occur during normal loading, these are not possible during shear. This may, however, lead to pore pressures developing during shear.

3. *Drained test or "slow test"*: In these tests, full consolidation (drainage) is allowed under normal or confining loads. Free drainage is also permitted during shear, so that excess hydrostatic pressures do not exist in the soil pores and all stresses are always intergranular.

4.4 DIRECT SHEAR TEST

The direct shear test is the oldest and simplest soil property test. This test is performed in a direct shear apparatus (Fig. 4.1), consisting of an upper, fixed frame and a lower, moveable frame. The test sample is placed in the boxlike apparatus, one-half in each frame. Depending on drainage conditions, porous stones or brass gratings are placed on both the top and bottom of the sample (not shown in the figure).

Spacing screws are used to provide space between the two halves of the shear box. The amount of spacing is governed by the maximum size of soil particles. There should be enough space between the two halves of the box so that the top half will not ride on a soil grain that gets in the space between the two halves, but the space should not be so large that the soil particles will not be supported.

A vertical load, P_n, is then applied and the sample subjected to shearing load, P_h, at the plane of separation, AA. The shearing load is generally measured by a proving ring or a load cell. The relative motion between the upper and

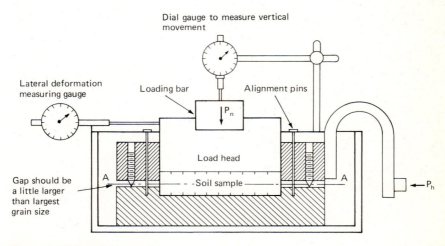

Figure 4.1 Direct shear apparatus.

lower frames (shearing displacement) is measured on a dial gauge or linear variable differential transducer (LVDT).

The vertical displacement is also measured by a dial gauge or LVDT, adjusted at the beginning of the test so that both up and down movements can be observed.

The rate of shearing is between 0.5 and 2.0 mm/min.

The data obtained from direct shear tests are usually plotted as shown in Fig. 4.2a, which shows plots for a dense as well as a loose sand. The upper curve is a plot of the ratio of shearing to normal stress (τ/σ) versus the shearing displacements. The lower curve shows changes in the volume of the sample under shearing displacements. In the case of dense sands, shear stress corresponding to the $(\tau/\sigma)_{peak}$ is a measure of the *peak strength* of the soil. If the shear displacement increases, the shear resistance of the soil is reduced and a nearly constant lower value of τ/σ, corresponding to point B, is obtained. This is called its *ultimate value*. Well-defined peaks are exhibited by dense sands and sensitive and stiff clays only.

The soil samples are tested at different normal stresses. A plot of normal stress σ_n and shear stress τ at failure, is made (Fig. 4.2b). This plot is generally a straight line for sands and normally loaded clays. For precompressed clays, it is curved (curve b) but it is approximated by a straight line. The shear parameters c and ϕ are read from this plot, which is referred to as a *Mohr strength envelope*.

Volume changes take place during shear tests on saturated sands where free drainage is permitted or in dry sands. Loose soils reduce in volume, while dense sands generally expand (dilate) during shear (see Fig. 4.2a). If the initial void ratio of the sand is such that the net volume change from the initial to the final volume at failure is zero, then this void ratio is called the *critical void ratio*.

The concept of the critical void ratio was advanced by Casagrande (1936) and Taylor (1948). However, it was shown that the critical void ratio is not an independent soil parameter but depends on the confining pressure as well. As the normal or confining pressure increases, the void ratio for the zero-net-volume change (critical void ratio) decreases. Thus, the critical void ratio is not a unique property of the sands. This concept is useful in understanding the shear properties of the sands and their liquefaction characteristics.

If a loose saturated sand at a void ratio above the critical void ratio is rapidly deformed, the grains tend to become more compact. For this to occur, water must flow out of the voids. If the loading is so rapid that there is no time for drainage to occur, any load on the soil must be carried instantaneously by the pore water. The pressure between the grains is thus considerably reduced, generating a corresponding reduction in the shear strength. If the strength is reduced to zero by a complete transfer of the initial intergranular stress to the pore water, the sand is said to *liquefy*.

On the other hand, when a saturated sand at a void ratio below the critical void ratio is deformed, the void ratio increases. If the loading is so rapid that there is no time for water to seep into the sand, then water can no longer fill the

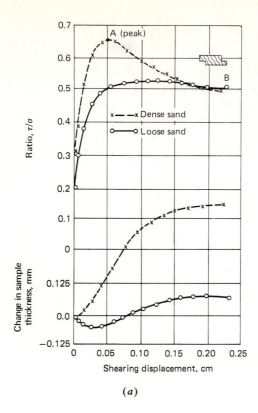

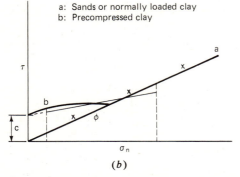

Figure 4.2 (*a*) Typical direct shear data for sands. *(From D. W. Taylor: Fundamentals of Soil Mechanics by permission of John Wiley and Sons, Inc., New York.)* (*b*) Mohr strength envelopes from direct shear test.

voids. As a result, the pore water is put in tension, thereby increasing the resulting pressure between soil grains and causing a temporary increase in strength.

If there is no tendency for the volume to change in drained tests, there is no tendency for water to enter or leave the sand in undrained tests, so the strength would be the same whether or not drainage occurs.

4.5 TRIAXIAL COMPRESSION TEST

Triaxial shear tests, in general, permit better control of stresses and volume changes during shear than direct shear tests do. Figure 4.3 is a diagrammatic sketch showing how a triaxial compression test is set up.

A sample is placed between the porous stones or metal discs. The cylindrical surface of the sample is covered with a thin, impermeable membrane secured to the base and top caps with rubber rings (O-rings). The O-rings and the rubber membrane serve to isolate the water in the pores of the sample from the chamber fluid. The porous stones provide access to the sample for either pore-water drainage or pore-pressure measurements.

Fluid pressure is applied within the chamber containing the sample. The chamber pressure is controlled by a "cell pressure control" and is measured by a pressure gauge. The chamber pressure acts uniformly on the surface of the sample, including the top and bottom loading caps.

Additional vertical load is applied through the loading ram, using a jacking arrangement, and measured by a proving ring or load cell. The axial deformation is usually measured by a dial gauge or LVDT attached to the bottom of the

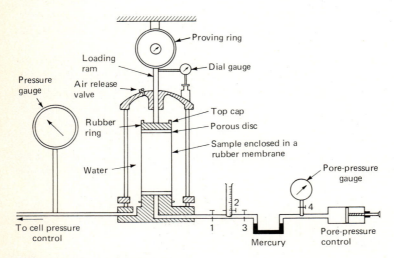

Figure 4.3 Triaxial apparatus.

proving ring and abutting against the top of the chamber. Volume changes in drained tests are measured by the amount of water that flows into or out of a calibrated burette.

In undrained tests, the volume change tendencies of the soil generate pore water pressures. If the drainage system is closed, the pore pressure can be measured by an electronic pressure transducer, manometer, or other pressure gauge.

Different Types of Tests

The tests mentioned in Sec. 4.3 can be performed in a triaxial test machine. Test interpretations are as follows:

Unconsolidated-undrained test on saturated cohesive soil When an overall σ_3 pressure is applied to the soil sample, the entire stress is taken up by pore water since drainage is not permitted ($\Delta u_a = \sigma_3$).

Next, the deviator stress ($\sigma_1 - \sigma_3$) is applied until failure occurs. Drainage is not permitted during this stage of the test, either. The pore pressure at failure is Δu_d.

In Fig. 4.4, circle 1 represents the Mohr circle of total stresses at failure. If an undrained test is repeated on a similar sample with a different confining pressure (circle 2) and the Mohr strength envelope is plotted, it will be a straight line parallel to the σ axis. Since any variation in chamber pressure simply changes the pore pressure while the effective stresses inside the sample remain constant, only one circle of effective stresses will be obtained from such tests.

Consolidated-undrained test on saturated cohesive soil In the consolidated-undrained test, an overall σ_3 pressure is applied and the induced pore pressures are allowed to dissipate (consolidate) so that σ_3 becomes effective pressure. Next, the sample is sheared under undrained conditions. Figure 4.5a shows the variation of the void ratio with σ_3.

In Fig. 4.5b, total and effective stress circles are plotted for two samples that were initially consolidated by chamber pressures of σ_{31} and σ_{32}. The Mohr strength envelopes of total and effective stresses are drawn in continuous and dotted lines, respectively. In this particular case, the magnitude of pore pressure

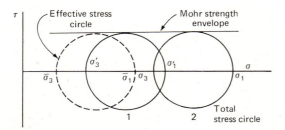

Figure 4.4 Mohr plot for undrained test.

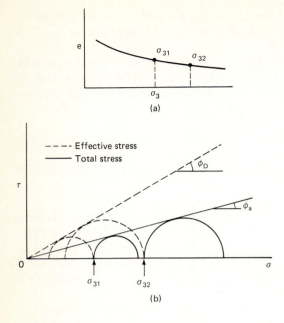

(a)

(b)

Figure 4.5 Mohr plot for consolidated quick tests.

at failure (Δu_d) is approximately equal to the deviator stress. The inclination of the envelope of the Mohr circles of total stresses gives the *apparent angle of internal friction* ϕ_a, and that of the Mohr circles of effective stresses the *"effective" angle of internal friction* ϕ_D. For normally consolidated clays, both envelopes pass through the origin.

Drained tests on saturated cohesive soils In a fully drained triaxial test, the induced pore pressures are allowed to dissipate before the stresses are increased. Therefore, since the pore pressures are zero, all of the stresses in this test are effective stresses.

There is considerable evidence to show that ϕ values obtained from effective stresses, either from the consolidated-undrained or drained tests, are quite comparable although the conditions at failure are quite different in the two tests (Bjerrum and Simons, 1960).

4.6 SPECIAL REQUIREMENTS OF APPARATUS FOR DYNAMIC TESTS

In the static triaxial test described in the previous section, the loads and deformations are read on the load cell and the dial gauge, respectively, while the pore pressures are read on the pore-pressure device. In dynamic tests, records of all these quantities must necessarily be automatic. In the conventional triaxial test, the rate of loading is approximately 1.25 mm/min, and the sample may fail in 10 to 15 min or more. However, because the dynamic loads may be applied in a fraction of a second, the loading device has to be of a special design.

Several different types of apparatus for testing soils under dynamic loading have been designed and fabricated from time to time. The first triaxial apparatus, the pendulum loading apparatus, was assembled at Harvard (Casagrande and Shannon, 1949), followed by an apparatus by Seed and Fead (1959). Subsequently, the oscillatory simple shear apparatus were used (Thiers and Seed, 1968).

In the following sections, a few apparatus and salient test results obtained on typical soils will be discussed.

4.7 PENDULUM LOADING APPARATUS

The first published investigation of the dynamic loading of soils concerned the effect of bomb explosions on the stability of the Panama Canal projects. This, in turn, required knowledge of the stress-deformation and strength characteristics of the pertinent soils and rocks subjected to very rapid loading and unloading (blasts).

Three pieces of equipment were designed by Casagrande and Shannon (1948*b*, 1949) for this purpose. One of the pieces of equipment is the pendulum loading apparatus, shown in Fig. 4.6. This apparatus utilizes the energy of a pendulum which, when released from a selected height, strikes a spring connected to the piston rod of a hydraulic (lower) cylinder. This lower cylinder, in turn, is connected hydraulically to an upper cylinder, which is mounted within a loading frame.

The time of loading† for a pendulum loading apparatus is proportional to the square root of the weight of the pendulum and is inversely proportional to the square root of the spring constant.

In addition, the maximum force is proportional to the first power of the distance the pendulum is pulled back, to the square root of the spring constant, and to the square root of the weight of the pendulum.

This apparatus, with a time of loading of between 0.05 and 0.01 s, was found to be best suited for performing fast transient tests.

Two other apparatus, a falling beam apparatus and a hydraulic loading apparatus, were also designed and fabricated. The loading time for these is from 0.5 to 300 s for the first apparatus and from 0.05 s to any larger desired value for the other.

The load gauge used with this equipment consisted of electric-resistance strain gauges mounted on a metal ring. The strain introduced in the gauges was then in direct proportion to the load. These load gauges can be calibrated under

---

† In these tests, time of loading was defined as the time between the beginning of the test and the point at which the maximum compressive stress is reached (see Fig. 4.7).

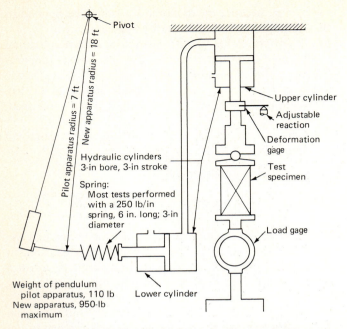

Figure 4.6 Pendulum loading apparatus. *(After Casagrande and Shannon, 1948b.)*

static loads and can be used in a dynamic test. Similarly, a deformation gauge was constructed on a cantilever metal strip with electric-resistance strain gauges mounted on one end while the other end rested on an unmoveable support. The strain introduced in the cantilever was a measure of the deformation of the soil sample.

Two typical soils tested, Cambridge clay and Manchester sand, have the

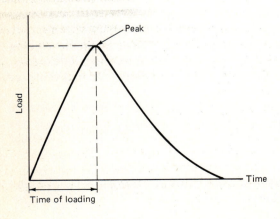

Figure 4.7 Time of loading in transient tests.

following properties:

Cambridge clay

natural moisture content	30 − 50%
liquid limit	37 − 59%
plastic limit	20 − 27%

The tests were performed both in the unconfined and confined state.

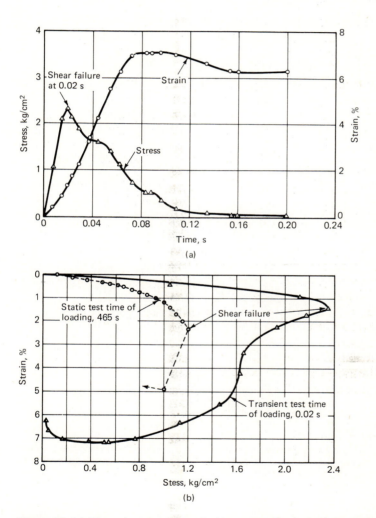

Figure 4.8 (*a*) Time vs. stress and strain in an unconfined transient test on Cambridge clay. (*b*) Stress vs. strain in transient test with time of loading of 0.02 s and a static test on Cambridge clay. (*After Casagrande and Shannon, 1949.*)

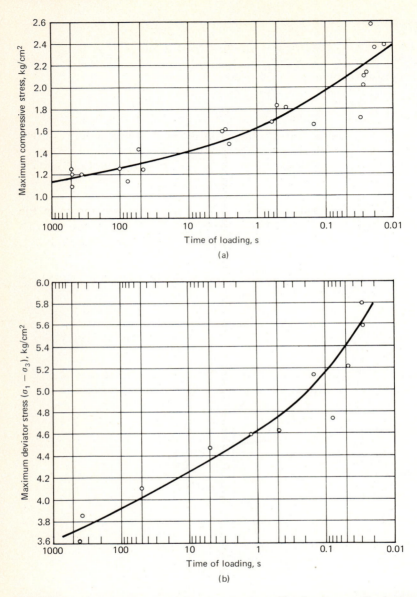

Figure 4.9 (*a*) Maximum compressive stress vs. time of loading in unconfined compression test on Cambridge clay. (*b*) Maximum compressive stress vs. time of loading in confined compression test on Cambridge clay. (*After Casagrande and Shannon, 1949.*)

Manchester sand

grain size   between 0.42 and 0.21 mm

maximum void ratio $e_{max} = 0.88$

minimum void ratio $e_{min} = 0.61$

Figure 4.8*a* shows a simultaneous plot of stress and strain versus time in a test with a time of loading of 0.02 s obtained from an unconfined transient compression test on Cambridge clay. The stress-strain relationship is plotted in Fig. 4.8*b* along with a stress-strain plot for a static test in which time of loading was 465 s.

Typical plots of maximum compressive stress versus time of loading for unconfined and confined transient tests on Cambridge clay are shown in Fig. 4.9*a* and *b*, respectively.

From the typical test data presented above, it may be concluded that:

1. The strength of clays loaded to failure in about 0.02 s is approximately 1.5 to 2.0 times greater than their 10-min static strength.
2. Modulus of deformation, defined as the slope of a line drawn from the origin through the point on the stress-deformation curve and corresponding to a stress of one-half the strength, was about two times in the transient tests.

A typical stress-strain plot of Manchester sand is shown in Fig. 4.10. The principal stress ratio at failure and the time of loading are plotted in Fig. 4.11.

It would be evident from these results that the strength of the sands increased only by about 10 percent while their modulus of deformation was not

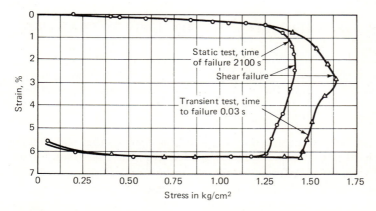

Figure 4.10 Stress vs. strain of Manchester sand in a transient test and static test. *(After Casagrande and Shannon, 1949.)*

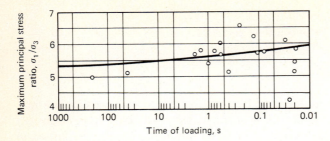

Figure 4.11 Maximum principal stress ratio vs. time of loading of Manchester sand in transient tests. *(After Casagrande and Shannon, 1949.)*

time-dependent. These investigations suffer from the following shortcomings:

1. The dynamic load was not superimposed on a static load (Tschebotarioff, 1949). Certain static shearing stresses are always present in an embankment.
2. At best, the transient loading adopted in these investigations represents only one cycle of earthquake loading. Sometimes there may be as many as 100 peaks in an actual earthquake.
3. Finally, the sands were tested while dry and dense. The effect of dynamic loading on saturated loose sands may induce large pore pressures resulting in loss of strength and consequent partial or complete liquefaction of sands. This aspect of the problem is of great practical importance.

Saturated sands were studied by Seed and Lundgren (1954) under transient loads. Salient results of their investigation shall now be presented.

4.8 BEHAVIOR OF SATURATED SANDS UNDER TRANSIENT LOADING

Seed and Lundgren (1954) investigated the effect of the rate of loading on the strength characteristics of saturated sands. They conducted three types of tests on a uniform sand:

1. Static tests were performed using a constant rate of loading that was chosen so that between 10 and 15 min would be needed to reach a maximum load.
2. Slow transient tests were performed using a constant rate of deformation of 15 cm (6 in)/min. This rate corresponds to a loading time of about 4 s.
3. Rapid transient tests were performed using a constant rate of deformation of about 100 cm (40 in)/s. This rate corresponds to a loading time of about 0.02 s.

In slow transient tests, a testing machine with a platform of a travel rate of up to 15 cm/min was used. An impact testing machine was used to apply loads in rapid transient tests. This impact machine consists of a 22.7-kg (50-lb) weight that is allowed to fall in guides from any desired height onto the test specimen. In these tests, the weight was allowed to fall from a height of 10 cm (4 in) before striking a spring on top of the loading piston. The weight then traveled 2.5 cm (1 in) before its movement was arrested by wooden stops. At the time the weight struck the spring at the piston, it was traveling at a rate of about 300 cm/s (120 in/s). The change in velocity of the weight after striking the loading piston was negligible, and test data indicate that this impact test produced a very nearly constant rate of deformation.

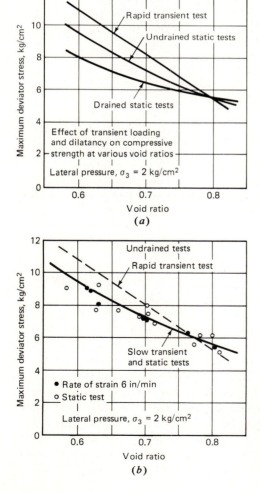

Figure 4.12 Maximum deviator stress vs. void ratio of Sacramento sand. (*a*) Drained static, undrained static, and rapid transient, both drained and undrained. (*b*) Undrained rapid transient and slow transient and static test. (*After Seed and Lundgren, 1954. Reprinted with permission of ASTM, Philadelphia, Pa.*)

Test Results

Figure 4.12a shows a plot of maximum deviator stress versus void ratios for drained static, undrained static, and rapid transient tests in both drained and undrained conditions.

This figure suggests that undrained static strength is greater than drained static strength, since negative pore-water pressures develop in dense sand. As the void ratio increases, the difference in the two strengths reduces, and at $e \approx 0.8$, the two strengths are equal. This value corresponds to the critical void ratio (Casagrande, 1936). Also, it was found that strengths were not materially different in rapid undrained and drained tests. This would seem to indicate that, although provisions were made for drainage to take place in the drained tests, the rate of loading was so fast that there was no time for drainage to occur.

Figure 4.12b shows similar plots for rapid transient, slow transient, and static tests, all undrained. This figure suggests that, within the limits of experimental error, the strengths of specimens of equal void ratios are the same in static and slow transient tests. However, dense specimens have about 15 to 20 percent greater strengths in rapid transient tests than do similar specimens in static or slow transient tests. The strengths of specimens with void ratios larger than about 0.8 are lower in rapid transient tests than the strengths of similar specimens in static tests.

Figure 4.12 also shows that the strengths of dense specimens are considerably greater in rapid transient tests than the strengths of similar specimens in static drained tests. Thus, the strength increase in rapid transient tests comes from two sources: the development of negative pore-water pressure due to dilatancy effects and the strength increase due to the high rate of loading.

It was also found that modulus of deformation at 1 percent strain and 2 percent strain is about 30 percent greater in rapid transient tests than that determined in static tests.

4.9 EFFECT OF STATIC STRESS LEVEL AND NUMBER OF PULSES ON STRENGTH OF COHESIVE SOILS

As discussed previously, the application of a transient load is simply analogous to the first pulse of an earthquake. Under this pulse, the soil may mobilize enough additional strength to prevent failure or even to prevent any appreciable permanent deformation of the soil. However, with subsequent reversals and continued stress, the soil may be sufficiently deformed to cause either a reduction in soil strength or such larger shear displacements that deformations are readily apparent even though failure has not occurred. Seed (1960) used the apparatus shown in Fig. 4.13 to study the effect of number of stress reversals and other factors on the deformations in soils. In this apparatus, soil specimens are dynamically loaded using a pneumatic system and are subjected to confining pressure in a triaxial cell (Seed and Fead, 1959).

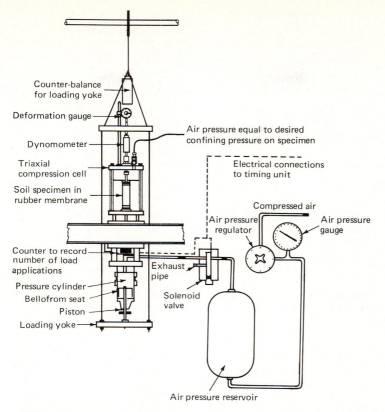

Figure 4.13 Apparatus for oscillatory triaxial test. *(After Seed and Fead, 1959. Reprinted with permission of ASTM, Philadelphia, Pa.)*

Test Procedure and Results

The stress-strain curve from a conventional static test is shown in Fig. 4.14. A series of specimens of Vicksburg silty clay of identical composition were prepared by static compaction to a degree of saturation of about 95 percent.

One specimen was loaded to a stress equal to 66 percent of this strength, corresponding to a factor of safety of 1.5, and allowed to come to equilibrium over a period of 30 min. At this stage, 100 transient stress pulses, corresponding to an initial stress change of ±35 percent, were applied, and the resulting deformations of the samples were recorded. The stress-strain relationship for the sample is plotted in Fig. 4.14. For purposes of comparison, the strength of the soil, when loaded to failure by a single transient stress application, is also shown.

Although the maximum applied stress, including the earthquake stress, is less than the normal strength of the soil (in fact, the lowest safety factor was 1.12 based on the normal strength and 1.52 based on the transient strength), the soil nevertheless deformed almost 11 percent during the transient stress applications.

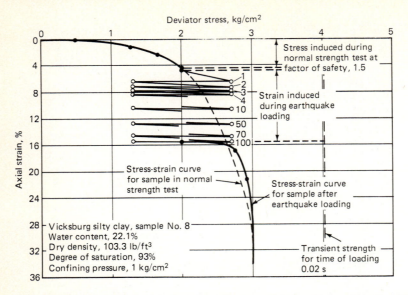

Figure 4.14 Stress vs. strain for Vicksburg silty clay under applied static and oscillatory stress in triaxial test. *(After Seed, 1960.)*

The effects of the initial static stress level (or factor of safety) and the transient pulses corresponding to 20, 40, and 60 percent of the initial sustained stress were also studied. Figure 4.15 presents data for one-directional loading on three samples of an undisturbed saturated silty clay of medium sensitivity [San Francisco Bay mud, liquid limit (LL) = 88, plastic limit (PL) = 43]. Stress levels equal to 100, 80, and 60 percent of the normal strength of the clay (that is, the strength determined in a conventional undrained test) were applied to the three samples. The samples were able to support these stresses for different numbers of stress reversals, but ultimately each sample failed completely. The number of pulses causing failure can readily be determined from Fig. 4.15. It is interesting to note that, even for a stress level of as low as 60 percent of the normal strength of the soil, 900 transient applications induced failure of this material.

From the data presented in Fig. 4.15, a determination was made of the relationship between the magnitude of the pulsating stress and the number of stress pulses required to cause failure for the special case of no sustained stress (Seed and Chan, 1966). This relationship is shown by the upper curve in Fig. 4.16. Failure was induced by any desired number of pulses by using different stress levels to complete the full range of this relationship.

Three samples were also subjected to a sustained stress equal to 47 percent of their normal strengths, and, when creep movement had essentially stopped, different levels of pulsating stresses were superimposed. In this case, the pulsating stress levels used were 115, 60, and 40 percent of the normal strength; they induced failure after 1, 9, and 88 stress applications, respectively. Plotting this data leads to a second curve in Fig. 4.16.

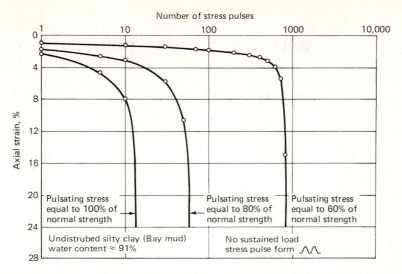

Figure 4.15 Soil deformation under pulsating stress applications in one-directional loading. *(After Seed and Chan, 1966.)*

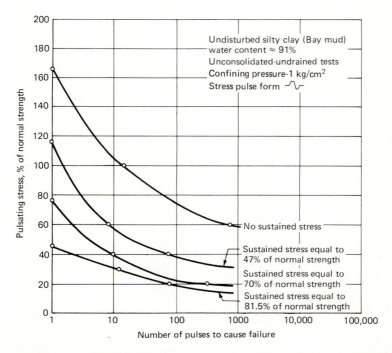

Figure 4.16 Relationship between stress level and number of pulses causing failure in one-directional loading. *(After Seed and Chan, 1966.)*

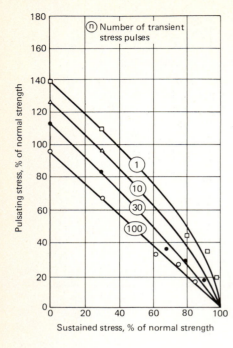

Figure 4.17 Combination of sustained and pulsating stress intensities causing failure in Vicksburg silty clay. *(After Seed and Chan, 1966.)*

Tests similar to those in Fig. 4.16 were performed on different soils. Figure 4.17 presents a relationship between combinations of sustained stress level and pulsating stress level that produces failure in Vicksburg silty clay by various selected stress applications.

The possibility of failure occurring under any combination of sustained and pulsating stress conditions with any reasonable number of stress pulses can be determined directly from a family of curves of this type. Similar curves for San Francisco Bay mud and a compacted silty clay were also obtained by Seed and Chan (1966).

Figure 4.18a compares combinations of sustained and pulsating stresses that induce failure in soft and compacted clays in one transient pulse. The total stress† required to cause failure was greater than the normal strength of each soil. Also, the strength exhibited by undisturbed silty clay was greater than that displayed by compacted soils.

As the number of pulses increases to 30, failure occurs in sensitive soil at a considerably lower stress level than that in compacted soils (Fig. 4.18b).

Symmetrical stress pulses of two-directional loadings‡ resulted in a reduction in strength of all three soils tested. Typical results with San Francisco Bay mud are shown in Fig. 4.19. Below the dotted line drawn at 45° from the origin,

---

† Defined as sustained stress + pulsating stress.
‡ See Sec. 1.3.

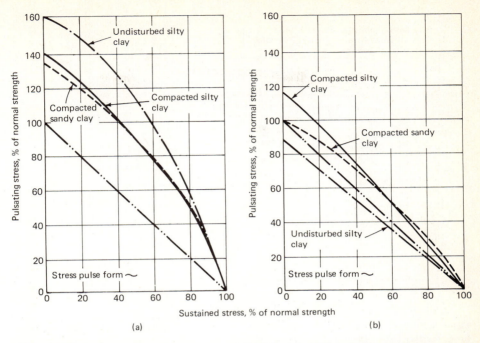

Figure 4.18 Comparison of stress conditions causing failure for different soils. (*a*) 1 pulse. (*b*) 30 pulses. (*After Seed and Chan, 1966.*)

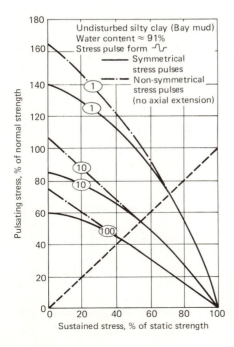

Figure 4.19 Combinations of sustained and pulsating stresses causing failure—one- and two-directional loading in San Francisco Bay mud. (*After Seed and Chan, 1966.*)

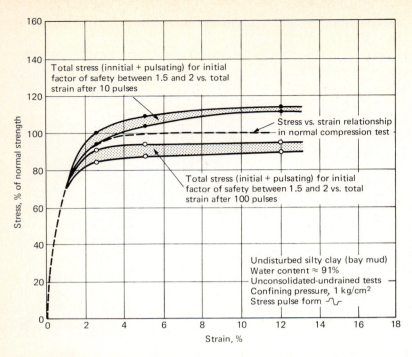

Figure 4.20 Relationship between total stress and total strain under pulsating load conditions in San Francisco Bay mud. *(After Seed and Chan, 1966.)*

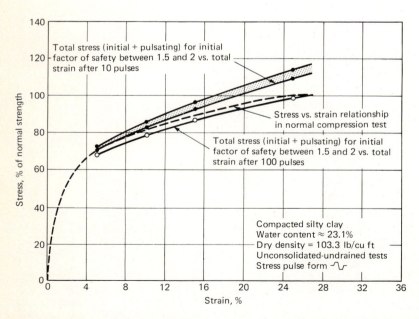

Figure 4.21 Relationship between total stress and total strain under pulsating load conditions in Vicksburg silty clay. *(After Seed and Chan, 1966.)*

note that the stress conditions in one- or two-directional loadings are the same since the pulsating stress is either smaller than or equal to the sustained stress.

The effects of wave form of loading and anisotropic consolidation on total stresses causing failure were not appreciable. Total stress and total strain under pulsating loads are plotted in Fig. 4.20 for San Francisco Bay mud and in Fig. 4.21 for Vicksburg silty clay. For comparison, the stress-strain relationships for these soils have also been plotted from a normal strength test.

The general forms of the total-stress–total-strain relationships are similar despite the wide variation in the properties of the two soils. In situations involving 10 stress pulses, total stress versus total strain is somewhat higher than the stress-strain relationship of a normal test; if there are 100 stress pulses, this is slightly below the normal plot. Therefore, it may be concluded that in all cases, where the safety factor is between 1.5 and 2 and the number of stress pulses is between 10 and 100, the stress-strain from a normal strength test approximates the static stress-strain curve.

4.10 FACTORS AFFECTING STRESS-DEFORMATION AND STRENGTH CHARACTERISTICS OF COHESIVE SOILS UNDER PULSATING LOADS

Based upon the studies described above, the variables on which stress-deformation and strength characteristics of the cohesive soils depend are summarized below:

1. Type of soil and its properties (for example, water content, γ_d, and state of disturbance)
2. Initial static (sustained) stress level
3. Magnitude of pulsating stress
4. Number of repetitions of this stress
5. Frequency of loading
6. Shape of wave form of loading
7. One-directional or two-directional loading

4.11 OSCILLATORY SIMPLE SHEAR TEST

Stress in a triaxial compression test does not adequately simulate the field loading condition. For many deposits, a major part of the soil deformation may be attributed to the upward propagation of shear waves from underlying layers. A soil element, as in Fig. 4.22 at xx, may be considered to be subjected to a series of cyclic shear strains or stresses that may reverse many times during an earthquake, as shown in Fig. 4.23. In the case of a horizontal ground surface, there are no shear stresses on the horizontal plane before the earthquake. During the earthquake, the normal stresses on this plane remain constant while cyclic shear stresses are induced during the period of shaking.

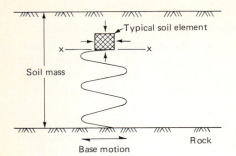

Figure 4.22 Transmission of shear waves from rock base into the overlying soil.

Other field conditions that differ from those developed in triaxial compression tests are as follows (Peacock and Seed, 1968):

1. In the field, there is a cyclic reorientation of the principal stress directions. The major principal stress is initially vertical and rotates through some angle θ, to the right and left of its initial position. In a triaxial compression test, the major principal stress can act only in either the vertical or horizontal direction.
2. In the field, the soil element is initially consolidated to k_0 condition.
3. In the field, deformations are presumed to occur under plane-strain conditions, while in a triaxial compression test, the intermediate principal stress is either equal to minor principal stress during axial compression or equal to major principal stress during lateral compression.

The simple shear device consists essentially of a simple box, an arrangement for applying a cyclic load to the soil, and an electronic recording system. The box of Roscoe (1953), which contains a square sample with a side length of 6 cm and a thickness of about 2 cm, is provided with two fixed side walls and two hinged end walls so that the sample may be subjected to deformations of the type shown in Fig. 4.23. A schematic diagram in Fig. 4.24 illustrates how the end walls rotate simultaneously at the ends of the shearing chamber to deform the soil uniformly (Peacock and Seed, 1968). Kjellman (1951), Hvorslev and Kaufman (1952), Bjerrum and Landra (1966), and Prakash, Nandkumaran, and Joshi (1973) have described the apparatus fabricated respectively at their centers.

Test data from simple shear tests have been analyzed to determine shear parameters, soil moduli, and damping, as well as the liquefaction potential of loose sands (Chap. 8). Prakash, Nandkumaran, and Bansal (1974) reported test

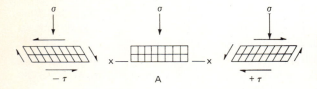

Figure 4.23 Idealized stress condition for element of soil below ground surface during an earthquake.

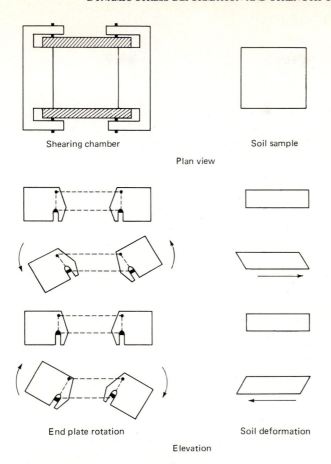

Shearing chamber   Soil sample

Plan view

End plate rotation   Soil deformation

Elevation

Figure 4.24 Schematic diagram illustrating rotation of hinged end plates and soil deformation in oscillatory simple shear. *(After Peacock and Seed, 1968.)*

data on three *artificial* soils (a mixture of sand and bentonite) compacted at their optimum moisture content in quick tests. Figure 4.25 shows time-dependent records of strains respectively in displacement gauge and the load gauge.

    Figure 4.26 is a plot of the number of cycles versus horizontal deformation for sample 1. Plots are made for dynamic shear stress intensities of 0.182, 0.375, and 0.542 kg/cm^2. For all tests, the normal stress was 0.292 kg/cm^2 and the dynamic shear stress frequency was 0.175 Hz.

    Figure 4.27 plots dynamic shear stress and horizontal displacement on sample 1 after 30 cycles of oscillatory stress under various normal stresses. Similar data were obtained for other samples and at frequencies of 0.35 Hz and 0.70 Hz.

    Assuming that failure corresponds to 12-mm displacement, as for a direct shear test under static loads, Mohr strength envelopes for all three soils are

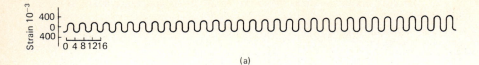

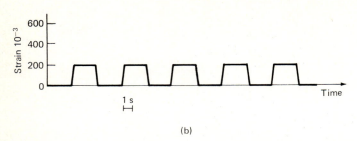

(a)

(b)

Figure 4.25 Timewise record of strain in (*a*) load gauge (*b*) displacement gauge. *(After Prakash, Nandkumaran, and Joshi, 1973.)*

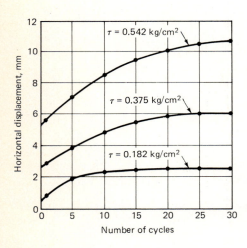

$\tau = 0.542$ kg/cm^2

$\tau = 0.375$ kg/cm^2

$\tau = 0.182$ kg/cm^2

Figure 4.26 Number of cycles vs. horizontal displacement in oscillatory simple shear in sample no. 1 ($\sigma_n = 0.292$ kg/cm^2, $f = 0.175$ Hz). *(After Prakash, Nandkumaran, and Bansal, 1974.)*

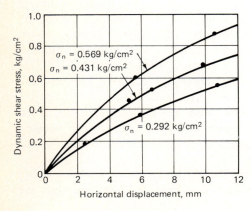

$\sigma_n = 0.569$ kg/cm^2

$\sigma_n = 0.431$ kg/cm^2

$\sigma_n = 0.292$ kg/cm^2

Figure 4.27 Dynamic shear stress vs. horizontal displacement in 30 cycles in sample no. 1. *(After Prakash, Nandkumaran, and Bansal, 1974.)*

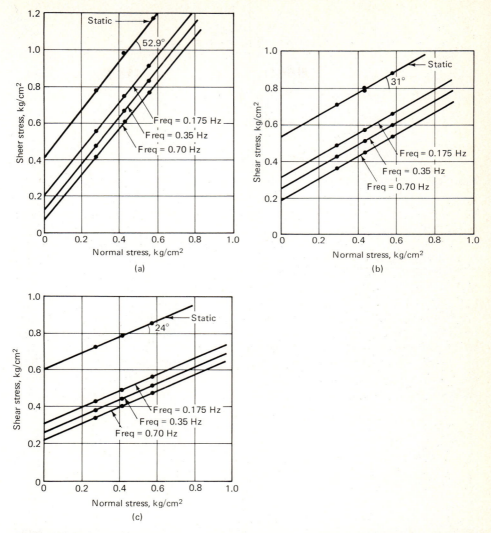

Figure 4.28 Mohr envelopes for static and dynamic stresses. (*a*) SM (*b*) CL (*c*) CH (*After Prakash, Nandkumaran, and Bansal, 1974.*)

plotted in Fig. 4.28. It can be seen from this figure that the strength parameter *c* is reduced under oscillatory tests while the angle of internal friction remains almost constant. The cohesion intercept decreases with increasing frequency. Also, the more compressible a soil, the larger the reduction in the cohesion parameter.

The shear-stress–shear-strain relationship may be as shown in Fig. 4.29*a*. The soils exhibit nonlinear stress-strain characteristics from the very beginning of the loading cycle. For purposes of analysis, this behavior may be represented

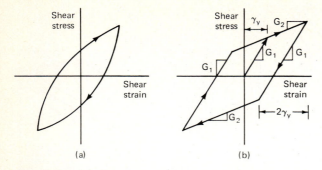

Figure 4.29 (*a*) Stress-strain curve of a soil and (*b*) bilinear model. *(After Thiers and Seed, 1968.)*

by a bilinear model as in Fig. 4.29*b* (Thiers and Seed, 1968). The bilinear model is defined by three parameters:

1. Modulus G_1 until a limiting strain γ_γ
2. Modulus G_2 beyond strain γ_γ
3. Strain γ_γ

When the direction of strain is reversed, behavior is again determined by the modulus G_1 until a strain change of $2\gamma_\gamma$ has developed and the modulus G_2 again controls the behavior. This pattern then continues throughout the cycle.

Typical stress-strain plots from simple shear testing of San Francisco Bay mud were obtained from the records of deformation and load versus time for different cycles of loading. Figure 4.30 shows such plots for cycle 1, cycle 50,

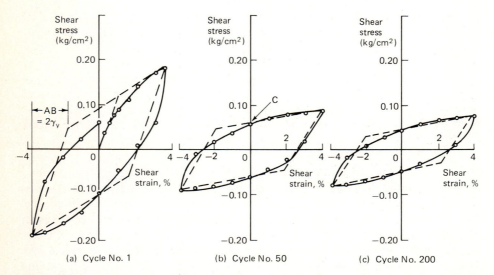

Figure 4.30 Stress-strain curves and bilinear models in San Francisco Bay mud. (*a*) Cycle no. 1. (*b*) Cycle no. 50. (*c*) Cycle no. 200. *(After Thiers and Seed, 1968.)*

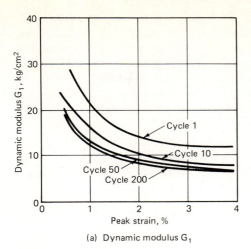

(a) Dynamic modulus G_1

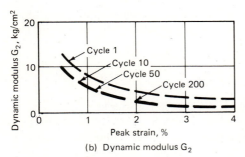

(b) Dynamic modulus G_2

Figure 4.31 Effect of cyclic loading on dynamic moduli. (*a*) Dynamic modulus G_1 (*b*) Dynamic modulus G_2. (*After Thiers and Seed, 1968.*)

and cycle 200, with about 4 percent shearing strain. The decrease in peak load as the number of cycles increases is reflected by the progressive flattening of the stress-strain curves. Similar tests were performed at different peak strains, and plots of dynamic modulus G_1 and G_2 versus peak strain are shown in Fig. 4.31.

Thiers and Seed (1968) also studied the reduction in static shear strength and static secant modulus at 1 percent strain due to 200 cycles of peak strains of different magnitude up to 4 percent and found that while strength reduction was only about 20 percent at 4 percent peak cyclic strain, the static modulus after cyclic loading decreased to about 50 percent of its initial value.

4.12 RESONANT COLUMN APPARATUS

The resonant column test for determining modulus and damping characteristics of soils is based on the theory of wave propagation in prismatic rods† (Richart, Hall, and Woods, 1970). Either compression waves or shear waves can be

† See Chap. 3.

propagated through the soil specimen. Previously solid samples were used. Recently hollow samples have been used with advantage. In such an apparatus, the exciting frequency is adjusted until the specimen resonates. The modulus is computed from the resonant frequency and the geometric properties of the specimen and the driving apparatus. Damping is determined by switching off the driving power at resonance and recording the amplitude of the decaying vibrations from which the logarithmic decrement can be calculated.

Woods (1978) presented chronological development of the use of resonant column apparatus in geotechnical earthquake engineering. Currently, more than 80 resonant column devices are available in 60 countries around the world, the latest being the one fabricated for the first time in India at Roorkee (Prakash and Srivastava, 1979).

4.13 FIELD TESTS

Several types of field tests have been developed to measure shear modulus, damping, and Poisson's ratio. Descriptions of the most widely used tests are given below.

Cross-Bore Hole Wave Propagation Method

In the cross-bore hole method (Stokoe and Woods, 1972), the velocity of wave propagation from one subsurface boring to a second subsurface boring is measured. At least two bore holes are required, one for the impulse and one or more for sensors. As shown in Fig. 4.32, the impulse rod is struck on top, causing an impulse to travel down the rod to the soil at the bottom of the hole. The shearing between the rod and the soil creates shear waves that travel horizontally through the soil to the vertical motion sensor in the second hole; the time required for a shear wave to traverse this known distance is measured.

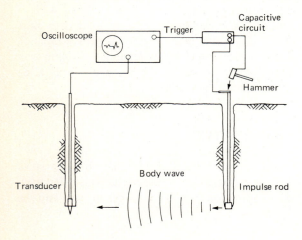

Figure 4.32 Sketch showing cross-bore hole technique for measurement of velocity of wave propagation.

There are four sources of major concern in conducting cross-bore hole shear tests: the bore holes, the seismic source, the seismic receiver, and the recording and timing equipment.

Although a minimum of two bore holes must always be used, for extensive investigations and for increased accuracy, whenever possible, three or more bore holes are suitable. If bore holes are installed in a straight line, wave velocities can be calculated from the intervals of time required for passage between any two bore holes. Thus, the necessity for precisely recording the triggering time is eliminated (Stokoe and Hoar, 1978). In addition, the bore holes must be vertical to properly measure travel distance. In general, any bore hole 10 m or more deep should be surveyed using an inclinometer or another logging device for determining verticality (Woods, 1978).

Although both impulsive and steady-state seismic sources are in use, impulsive sources predominate. The major criteria for a seismic source are:

1. It must be capable of generating predominantly one kind of wave.
2. It must be capable of repeating desired characteristics at a predetermined energy level.

Velocity transducers (geophones) that have natural frequencies of 4 to 15 Hz are adequate for detecting (receiving) the shear waves as they arrive from the source. The receivers must be oriented in the shearing mode and should be securely coupled to the sides of the boring.

The recording equipment should be able to resolve arrival times of up to 0.2 ms or 5 percent of the travel time. Storage oscilloscopes are often used for this as well.

Up-hole or Down-hole Wave-Propagation Methods

Up-hole and down-hole tests can be performed by using only one bore hole. In the up-hole method, the sensor is placed at the surface and shear waves are generated at various depths within the bore hole. In the down-hole method, the excitation is applied at the surface and one or more sensors are placed at different depths within the hole (Fig. 4.33). Both the up-hole and the down-hole methods give average values of wave velocities for the soil between the excitation and the sensor if one sensor is used, or between the sensors, if more than

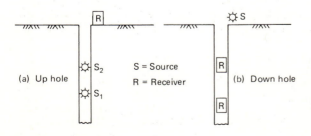

(a) Up hole   S = Source   (b) Down hole

R = Receiver

Figure 4.33 (*a*) Up-hole and (*b*) down-hole techniques for measurement of velocity of wave propagation.

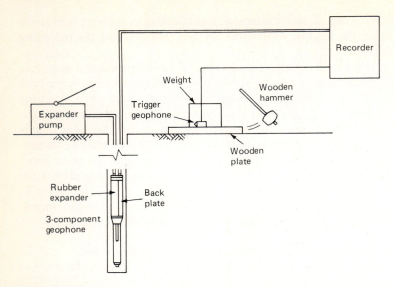

Figure 4.34 Equipment and instrumentation for down-hole survey. *(After Imai and Yoshimura, 1975.)*

one is used in the bore hole (Richart, 1977). Figure 4.34 is a schematic diagram of the down-hole survey with all principal elements included (Imai and Yoshimura, 1975).

Surface-Wave-Propagation Method

Rayleigh waves and Love waves can be used to determine shear modulus of soils near the surface (Chap. 3). The Rayleigh wave (R wave) travels in a zone close to the surface. An electromagnetic or other harmonic vibrator can be used to generate a steady-state R wave, and the ground surface can be deformed as shown in Fig. 4.35. According to Indian Standard (IS 5249-1978), a mechanical oscillator is set to work at approximately 10 Hz. One ray is drawn away from the center line of the oscillator. One of the geophones connected to the horizontal plates of the oscilloscope is fixed 30 cm away from the oscillator along a ray drawn so that the sensing axis of the geophone is vertical. A similar geophone, connected to the vertical plates of the oscilloscope, is moved along this ray, away from the oscillator. The sensing axis of the geophone is kept vertical until

Figure 4.35 Deformed shape of a half-space surface. *(After Woods, 1978.)*

the Lissajous figure on the oscilloscope screen becomes a circle. The two signals are at the same frequency and 90° out of phase. However, if the phase angle is different than 90°, the Lissajous figure is an ellipse, and for zero phase angle it is a straight line (Doebelin, 1966). The distance between the two geophones is measured. This distance is then a measure of the wave length of the generated Rayleigh wave. The test is repeated with the oscillator's other frequencies of operation. The test can also be conducted by using a phase meter in place of an oscilloscope.

In cases where uniform soils extend to infinite depths and the Lissajous figure is a circle, the wavelength λ of propagating waves is given by:

$$\lambda = 4S \tag{4.1}$$

in which S is the measured distance between geophones.

Velocity of shear waves v_s is given by:

$$v_s = \lambda f \tag{4.2}$$

in which f is the frequency of vibration at which the wavelength has been measured.

When the test is conducted by using a phase meter, the phase angles corresponding to different distances between geophones are recorded and curves are plotted of the phase angles versus the distances. From the curves, the distances S between the geophones are determined for a phase difference of 90°. The remaining computations remain unaltered.

The elastic modulus E and the modulus G of the soil medium are calculated as follows:

$$E = 2\rho v_s^2(1 + \nu) \tag{4.3}$$

$$G = (v_s^2 \rho) \tag{4.4}$$

in which ρ = mass density of soil
           v_s = velocity of shear waves
           ν = Poisson's ratio of soil

Table 4.1 gives representative values for Poisson's ratios that can be used in lieu of measured values.

The effective depth of the R wave has been empirically related to one-half λ (Fry, 1963; Ballard, 1964).

Table 4.1 Representative values of Poisson's ratio (ν)

Type of soil	ν
Clay	0.5
Sand	0.3–0.35
Rock	0.15–0.25

Although Indian Standard recommends that the mechanical oscillator be mounted on a standard block, wave velocities can be studied just as well without the block, provided the oscillator force is not so large that the system jumps from the ground. It should be noted that larger forces are required to study soils at greater depths. Therefore, some dead weights may be used on the oscillator in the absence of a block.

The Indian Standard method also recommends the use of a hammer test for determining the velocity of wave propagation. In the hammer test, radial lines are ranged out from a point for a distance of 30 to 40 m. Points are marked on these lines at 2-m intervals. A velocity pickup or a geophone is embedded 150 mm deep in the ground at the origin of the radial lines. Waves are generated near this point by the impact of a 5-kg hammer falling from a height of 2 m on a 150-mm steel plate resting on the ground. Another geophone is similarly fixed at a known distance along one of the radial lines. The time taken by the waves to travel a known distance is obtained by feeding the output of the pickups to a timer. The test is then repeated for the different known distances between the pickups along each of the marked lines. The test may be performed at different locations to obtain a representative value of wave velocities in the area being investigated.

The values of the travel times of compression waves and the corresponding distances along selected lines at selected locations are plotted, and straight lines are drawn through these points. The value of the average velocity is obtained as:

$$v_c = \frac{S}{t} \qquad (4.5)$$

in which v_c = velocity of compression waves

S = distance

t = corresponding time of travel of waves

Elastic modulus E is determined by equation:

$$E = v_c^2 \rho \frac{(1 + \nu)(1 - 2\nu)}{(1 - \nu)} \qquad (4.6)$$

Depending upon the nature of the medium involved, the arrivals of compression and shear waves may be distinguishable from the records, if the distances between pickups are large enough. In this case, both E and G can be determined independently.

Block Resonance Test

Indian Standard (IS 5249-1978) recommends the block resonance test for determining modulus and damping values. A standard block $1.5 \times 0.75 \times 0.70$ m high is cast either at the surface or in a pit 4.5×2.75 m at a suitable depth (Fig. 4.36) and is excited in both horizontal and vertical modes.

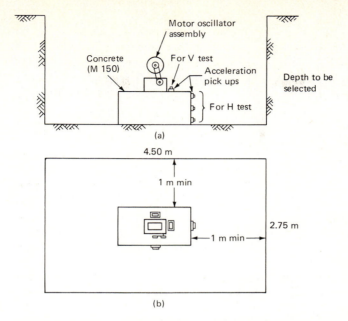

Figure 4.36 Setup for a block-resonance test. (*a*) Section. (*b*) Plan view.

Forced-vertical-vibration test   For the vertical-vibration mode, two acceleration pickups are fixed on top of the block as shown in Fig. 4.36*b*, so that they can sense vertical motion of the block. The mechanical oscillator, which works on the principle of eccentric masses mounted on two shafts rotating in opposite directions (see Chap. 8), is mounted on the block so that it generates purely vertical sinusoidal vibrations. The line of action of the vibrating force passes through the center of gravity of the block. After a suitable dynamic force value is chosen, the oscillator is operated at a constant frequency. The oscillator frequency is increased in steps of small values, say, from 1 cycle up to the maximum frequency of the oscillator, and the signals are recorded. The same procedure is repeated for the various dynamic force values. At any force level and frequency, the dynamic force should not exceed 20 percent of the total mass of the block and motor-oscillator assembly. A form for recording results of this test is shown in Table 4.2.

Longitudinal horizontal-vibration tests   For the longitudinal horizontal-vibration test, the mechanical oscillator is mounted on the block so that horizontal sinusoidal vibrations are generated in the direction of the longitudinal axis of the block. Three acceleration pickups are mounted on the block with one on top, a second at the bottom, and the third in the middle along the vertical center line of the transverse face of the block to sense horizontal vibrations, as shown in Fig. 4.36*a*. The oscillator is excited in several steps, starting from rest. The signal

Table 4.2 Resonance test: vertical/horizontal excitation

Site:
Calibration of pickup: millimeters (K) for 2 g* (2×9810 mm/s^2) at chart multiplication factor 1000
Paper speed (S): _____ mm/s

Block size:

Serial no.	Chart multiplication factor (λ)	Length of record, mm (L)	No. of cycles (n)	Frequency (f), Hz $\dfrac{n \times S}{L}$	f^2	$4\pi^2 f^2$	Acceleration on record peak-to-peak mm (a)	Absolute acceleration $9810 \times \left(\dfrac{a}{1000} \times \dfrac{\lambda}{K}\right)$	Amplitude $\dfrac{Col.\,9}{Col.\,7}$	Remarks
1	2	3	4	5	6	7	8	9	10	11

*Acceleration due to gravity.

of each acceleration pickup is amplified and recorded. The remainder of the procedure is the same as that described for vertical vibrations.

Determination of coefficient of elastic uniform compression of soil In the case of forced-vertical-vibration tests, the amplitude of vibration A_z at a given frequency f is given by

$$A_z = \frac{a_z}{4\pi^2 f^2} \tag{4.7}$$

in which a_z represents the vertical acceleration of vibration, in millimeters per second squared, of the block at frequency f, and f is the frequency in hertz.

Amplitude-versus-frequency curves are plotted for each force level to obtain the natural frequency of the soil and the foundation block tested (Fig. 4.37). The natural frequency at different force levels will be different because different forces cause different strain levels below the block and this is accounted for when choosing appropriate design parameters.

The coefficient of elastic uniform compression (C_u)† of soil is given by the following equation:

$$C_u = \frac{4\pi^2 f_{nz}^2 M}{A} \tag{4.8}$$

in which f_{nz} = natural frequency in vertical vibrations
M = mass of the block, oscillator, and motor
A = contact area of the block with the soil

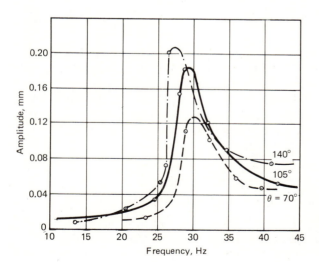

Figure 4.37 Amplitude-vs.-frequency plot from vertical resonance test at raw mill site in Bhutan. (*Prakash et al., 1976.*)

† C_u is defined as the slope of stress versus elastic settlement curve of a plate-load test (see Sec. 9.5, Chap. 9); C_u and E are related [see Eq. (4.11)].

From the value of C_u in Eq. (4.8) for the test block of contact area A, the value of C_{u1} for another area A_1 may be obtained from the equation:†

$$C_{u1} = C_u \sqrt{\frac{A}{A_1}} \tag{4.9}$$

Relationship between shear modulus, Young's modulus, and coefficient of elastic uniform compression Values of shear modulus G and Young's modulus E are related to each other by the equation (Barkan, 1962):

$$G = \frac{E}{2(1 + \nu)} \tag{4.10}$$

in which ν = Poisson's ratio.

C_u can be obtained from E by the equation:

$$C_u = \frac{1 \cdot 13E}{(1 - \nu^2)\sqrt{A}} \tag{4.11}$$

in which A = area of contact.

Determination of coefficient of elastic uniform shear of soil In a horizontal-vibration test, the amplitude of horizontal vibrations (A_x) can be obtained by the equation:

$$A_x = \frac{a_x}{4\pi^2 f^2} \tag{4.12}$$

in which a_x = horizontal acceleration in the direction under consideration and f = frequency in horizontal vibrations in hertz. Amplitude versus frequency curves are plotted for each force level to obtain the natural frequency f_{nx} of the soil and block tested as in Fig. 4.37. A plot of amplitude with height of block determines its mode of vibrations. The coefficient of elastic uniform shear (C_τ)‡ of soil is then determined by the following equation:

$$C_\tau = \frac{8\pi^2 \gamma f_{nx}^2}{(A_0 + I_0) \pm \sqrt{(A_0 + I_0)^2 - 4\gamma A_0 I_0}} \tag{4.13}$$

† This relation is valid for small variations in the base area of the foundations and may be used for areas up to 10 m². For areas larger than 10 m², the value of C_u obtained for 10 m² may be used.

‡ C_τ is defined as the slope of shear stress versus the elastic lateral displacement curve of a plate. C_τ is approximately $\frac{1}{2} C_u$ for the block under consideration. For detailed discussion, see Chap. 9. (Use the positive sign when f_{nx} is the second natural frequency and the negative sign when f_{nx} is the first natural frequency.)

in which $\quad \gamma = \dfrac{M_m}{M_{mo}}$

$f_{nx} =$ horizontal resonant frequency of block soil system

$A_0 = \dfrac{A}{M}$

$I_0 = 3.46(\dfrac{I}{M_{mo}})$

$M_m =$ mass moment of inertia of the block, oscillator, and motor about the horizontal axis passing through the center of gravity of the block and perpendicular to the direction of vibration

$M_{mo} =$ mass moment of inertia of the block, oscillator, and motor about the horizontal axis passing through the center of the contact area of the block and soil and perpendicular to the direction of vibration

$I =$ moment of inertia of the foundation contact area about the horizontal axis passing through the center of gravity of the area and perpendicular to the direction of vibration

The coefficient of elastic uniform shear (C_{τ_1}) for an area of the foundation (A_1) is given by the following equation:

$$C_{\tau_1} = C_\tau \sqrt{\dfrac{A}{A_1}} \qquad (4.14)$$

Indian Standard also recommends that free vibration tests be performed by pulling the block and releasing it in a longitudinal direction or by hitting it with a hammer for vertical excitation. From the natural frequency, the C_τ, C_u, and E and G values can then be determined.

Damping In forced-vertical vibration tests, the value of damping coefficient ξ of soil is given by the following equation:

$$\xi = \dfrac{f_2 - f_1}{2 f_{nz}} \qquad (4.15)$$

in which

$f_2, f_1 =$ two frequencies on the amplitude frequency plot at which the amplitude is equal to $x_m / \sqrt{2}$

$x_m =$ maximum amplitude

$f_{nz} =$ frequency at which amplitude is maximum (resonant frequency) (Fig. 4.38)

The logarithmic decrement and hence the damping in the system from the free-vibration record are easily determined in a free-vibration test (see Sec. 2.10 Chap. 2).

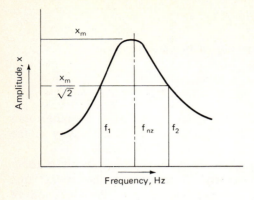

Figure 4.38 Determination of damping from forced-vertical-vibration test.

Cyclic-Plate-Load Test

The equipment for a cyclic-plate-load test is similar to that used in a static-plate-load test. It is assembled according to details given in IS 1888-1971 and Barkan (1962) or in textbooks on foundation engineering.

    After the equipment has been set up and arranged, the initial readings of the dial gauges are noted and the first increment of static load is applied to the plate. This load is kept constant for some time until no further settlement occurs or until the rate of settlement becomes negligible. The final readings of the dial gauges are then recorded. The entire load is removed and the plate is allowed to rebound. When no further rebound occurs, the readings of the dial gauges are again noted. The load is then gradually increased until its magnitude is equal in value to the next higher proposed stage of loading; the load is maintained constant and the final dial gauge readings are noted. The entire load is then reduced to zero and final dial gauge readings are recorded when the rate of rebound becomes negligible.

    The cycles of loading, unloading, and reloading are continued until the estimated ultimate load has been reached; the final values of dial gauge readings are noted each time.

    The magnitude of the load increment is such that the ultimate load is reached in five to six increments.

    The elastic rebound of the plate corresponding to each intensity of loading can be obtained from the data obtained during cyclic-plate-load tests, as shown in Fig. 4.39a. The load intensity versus the elastic rebound is plotted as shown in Fig. 4.39b.

    The value of C_u can be calculated from the equation given below:

$$C_u = \frac{p}{S_e} \text{ kg/cm}^3 \tag{4.16}$$

in which p = corresponding load intensity in kilograms per square centimeter and S_e = elastic rebound corresponding to p in centimeters.

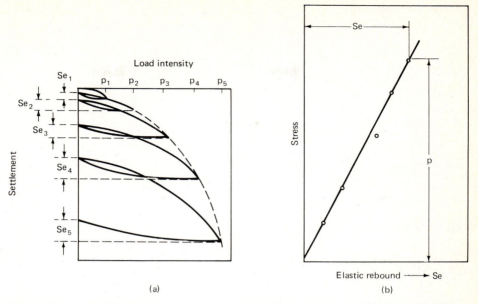

Figure 4.39 (*a*) Load intensities vs. settlement in a cyclic-plate-load test. (*b*) Load intensity vs. elastic rebound from cyclic-plate-load test.

4.14 TYPICAL VALUES OF SOIL CONSTANTS

A large amount of data on the values of soil constants has been collected. Factors affecting the soil constants have been identified and equations have been developed relating the soil constants and the factors affecting them. Hardin (1978) discussed in detail a mathematical formulation of soil elasticity and soil plasticity in terms of effective stresses. On this basis the maximum value of shear modulus, $G_{\max}$, is expressed by Eq. (4.17) (Hardin and Black 1969):

$$G_{\max} = 1230\,\mathrm{OCR}^k \frac{(2.973 - e)^2}{1 + e} \bar{\sigma}_0^{0.5} \qquad (4.17)$$

in which $\mathrm{OCR} =$ overconsolidation ratio

           $\bar{\sigma}_0 =$ effective all-around stress, psi

           $e =$ void ratio

           $k =$ a factor that depends upon the plasticity index of clays

Hardin (1978) recommends that this equation be used for the anisotropic state of stress by taking $\bar{\sigma}_0 = (\bar{\sigma}_1 + \bar{\sigma}_2 + \bar{\sigma}_3)/3$, the mean effective principal stress. The parameter k, given in Table 4.3, is related to the plasticity index, PI.

Table 4.3 Values of k

PI	k
0	0
20	0.18
40	0.30
60	0.41
80	0.48
> 100	0.50

Equation (4.17) can be expressed in a more convenient form as follows:

$$G_{max} = \frac{A \, OCR^k}{F(e)} (p_a)^{1-n} (\bar{\sigma}_0)^n \tag{4.18}$$

By introducing p_a,† the parameter A is dimensionless, whereas $\bar{\sigma}_0$ and G_{max} in Eq. (4.17) are in lb/in^2 and the constant 1230 has the dimensions $(lb/in^2)^{0.5}$. It is also desirable to change the form of the void ratio function in Eq. (4.17) by letting

$$F(e) = 0.3 + 0.7e^2 \tag{4.19}$$

in Eq. (4.18). The function $F(e)$ is less complicated than the void ratio function in Eq. (4.17), but gives about the same effect as e in the range $0.4 < e < 1.2$. For very large values of e, Eqs. (4.18) and (4.19) give monotonically decreasing values of G_{max} while Eq. (4.17) gives $G_{max} = 0$ for $e = 2.973$, with G_{max} increasing for $e > 2.973$. Equations (4.18) and (4.19) will approximate Eq. (4.17) for $0.4 < e < 1.2$ by taking $n = 0.5$ and $A = 625$. Figure 4.40‡ shows a plot of $[G_{max}/(OCR)^k(p_a\bar{\sigma})^{0.5}]$ versus the void ratio from laboratory and field measurements (Hardin, 1978).

The elastic parameters required for computation of soil constant are k, n, and ν. For most purposes, it will suffice to use $\nu = 0.12$, $n = 0.5$, and values of k in Table 4.3. For preliminary analysis, Fig. 4.40 can be used as a guide (Hardin, 1978).

For clean sands, it was found that G is dependent on $\bar{\sigma}_0$ and e (Richart, 1977). Analytical expressions were presented for the shear modulus of clean sands as

$$G_{max} = 700 \frac{(2.17 - e)^2}{1 + e} (\bar{\sigma}_0)^{0.5} \tag{4.20}$$

for round-grained sands ($e < 0.80$) and

$$G_{max} = 326 \frac{(2.97 - e)^2}{1 - e} (\bar{\sigma}_0)^{0.5} \tag{4.21}$$

† p_a stands for atmospheric pressure.
‡ In this figure, s is a dimensionless elastic stiffness parameter in Hardin's (1978) proposed stress-strain relation for inherent isotropy. For clean sands, s varies from 1200 to 1500 and for silts and clays, s varies from 700 to 2000.

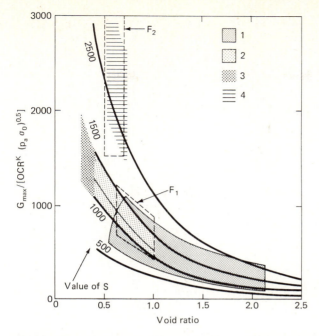

Figure 4.40 Elastic stiffness from laboratory and field measurements: 1—lab, silty sands, silts, and clays; 2—lab, clean sands; 3—lab, dense, well-graded gravel-sand with some fines; 4—lab, relatively uniform clean gravels; F_1—field, silty sands, silts, and clays at Ferndale, Cholame, and El Centro sites by SW-AA (1971); F_2—field, sands, silts, and clays at Anderson et al. (1978) sites A, B, and C. *(After Hardin, 1978.)*

for angular-grained sands. In Eqs. (4.20) and (4.21), G and $\bar{\sigma}_0$ have units of kilograms per square centimeter. Both equations were originally established to correspond to shearing strains of 10^{-4} or less. Equation (4.20) gave values slightly lower than those obtained by pulse tests (Whitman and Lawrence, 1963). Iwasaki and Tatsuoka (1977) recently determined experimentally that

$$G_{max} = 900 \frac{(2.17 - e)^2}{1 + e} (\bar{\sigma}_0)^{0.38} \qquad (4.22)$$

from tests on clean sands ($0.61 < e < 0.86$ and $0.2 < \sigma_0 < 5$ kg/cm^2) at shearing strain amplitudes of 10^{-6}. For shearing strains for 10^{-4}, their results agreed with Eq. (4.20).

Comparison of G from Different Tests

Several comparisons have been made among G_{max} values obtained by different tests in the field and in the laboratory.

Cunny and Fry (1973) reported on laboratory and field evaluations of G_{max} at 14 sites which contained a variety of soils. The steady-state surface vibration

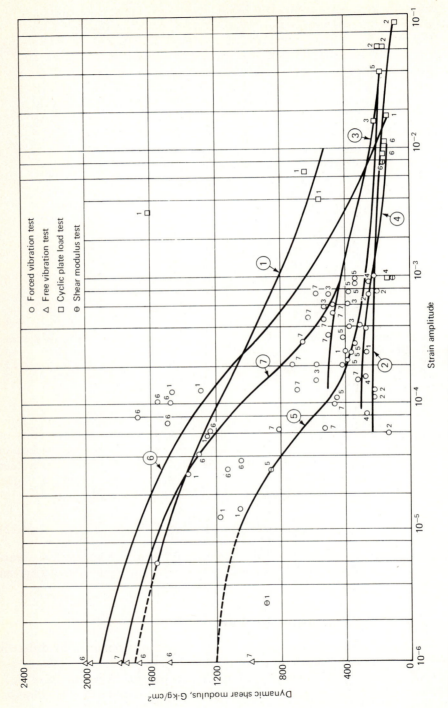

Figure 4.41 Dynamic shear modulus vs. strain. *(After Prakash and Puri, 1980.)*

method (Rayleigh-wave method) was used for evaluating G_{max} in the field. The resonant column test was used in the laboratory. From evaluation of test data, the laboratory-determined shear and compression moduli were found to range within ± 50 percent of the in situ moduli. It was pointed out that the cross-hole method should give better values of v_s at depths from which undisturbed samples were taken, and that inclusion of the secondary time effect would bring the laboratory cohesive-soil values nearer to the field values. The secondary time effect is negligible for sands. Stokoe and Richart (1973) and Iwasaki and Tatsuoka (1977) found agreement between the resonant column and the cross-hole field test values. Prakash and Puri (1980) reported in situ data on dynamic soil constants for several sites from resonance tests on blocks, as per Indian Standards, the shear modulus test, the wave propagation test, and the cyclic-plate-load test. The modulus (G) values were reduced to a mean effective confining pressure $(\bar{\sigma}_0)$ of 1 kg/cm^2 using Eq. (4.23):

$$\frac{G_1}{G_2} = \left(\frac{\bar{\sigma}_{01}}{\bar{\sigma}_{02}}\right)^{0.5} \tag{4.23}$$

The relationship between C_u and G, as recommended by Barkan (1962), was used to calculate G:

$$G = \frac{C_u(1 - \nu)\sqrt{A}}{2.26} \tag{4.24}$$

in which A = area of contact and ν = Poisson's ratio.

The detailed values of shear moduli for the seven sites are shown in Table 4.4. A plot of G versus strain is shown in Fig. 4.41. A plot of normalized

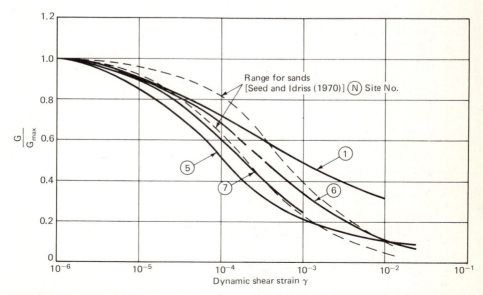

Figure 4.42 Normalized shear modulus (G/G_{max}) vs. shear strain. *(After Prakash and Puri, 1980.)*

Table 4.4 Values of dynamic shear modulus from field tests at different sites*

Site no.	Description	Soil type†	Type of test	Size of block or plate	Dynamic shear modulus G, kg/cm² from test	Dynamic shear modulus G, kg/cm² for confining pressure of 1 kg/cm²	Associated strain level	Remarks (location)
1	2	3	4	5	6	7	8	9
1	Forging hammer foundation, HAL Koraput, India	Lateritic soil silty sand $S_s = 2.67$ $\gamma = 1.93$ $e = 0.59$ $\phi = 32°$ $\omega_c = 15.2\%$	Forced-vertical-vibration test	Block: 1.5 × 0.75 × 0.7 m high	382.4 498.0 451.7 502.6 466.5	1055.0 1373.0 1246.0 1478.0 1288.0	1.5×10^{-4} 2.8×10^{-5} 5.6×10^{-5} 1.2×10^{-4} 1.2×10^{-4}	1 2 3 4 5
			Shear modulus test	Block: 1.5 × 0.75 × 0.7 m high	347.0 616.0 460.0	892.0 1586.0 1183.0	2.8×10^{-6} 5.6×10^{-6} 1.26×10^{-5}	2 3 4
	(Prakash, Basavanna, and Arya, 1968)		Cyclic-plate-load test	Plate: 30.5 × 30.5 cm	1672.0 338.1 2928.5 544.1	1613.0 553.0 3146.0 639.0	3.1×10^{-3} 3.9×10^{-3} 1.3×10^{-3} 6.5×10^{-3}	1 2 3 4
2	Heavy vibration equipment fertilizer, Kanpur, India	Stiff, brown-gray, silty clay (about 1 m) under lain by medium to dense sandy silt and silty fine sand (about 9.0 m)	Forced-horizontal-vibration test	Block: 1.5 × 0.75 × 0.70 m high	69.3 76.5 55.5 80.1	191.2 210.9 154.0 221.5	8.6×10^{-4} 1.26×10^{-4} 6.0×10^{-5} 1.1×10^{-4}	1 2 3 4
	(Arya, Prakash, and Gupta, 1967)		Cyclic-plate-load test	Plate: 30.5 × 30.5 cm	130.3 223.4 209.72 130.8	77.5 132.7 124.5 77.53	1.049×10^{-1} 6.2×10^{-2} 6.2×10^{-2} 4.26×10^{-1}	1 2 3 4

No.	Site	Soil	Test	Size				
3	Aeroengine test beds, AEF, Chandigarh, India	Silty sand $S_s = 2.61$ $\gamma = 1.80$ $e = 0.72$ $\phi = 30.5$ $\omega_c = 18.6\%$	Forced-vertical-vibration test	Block: $1.5 \times 0.75 \times 0.7$ m high	136.9	368.0	4.0×10^{-4}	A
					152.4	420.5	2.0×10^{-4}	B
					212.8	587.0	1.5×10^{-4}	C
			Forced-horizontal-vibration test	Block: $1.5 \times 0.75 \times 0.7$ m high	190.0	524.0	5.8×10^{-4}	A
					137.3	379.0	6.1×10^{-4}	B
					171.4	489.0	7.2×10^{-4}	
			Cyclic-plate-load test	Plate: 30.5×30.5 cm	200.2	186.9	1.63×10^{-2}	
	(Prakash and Basavanna, 1968)							
4	Diesel power house, Sirhind, India	Fine to medium sand with some silt $S_s = 2.47$ $\gamma = 1.75$ $e = 0.72$ $\phi = 30°$ $\omega_c = 22.2\%$	Forced-vertical-vibration test	Block: $1.5 \times 0.75 \times 0.70$ m high	93.3	257.2	8.6×10^{-5}	$\theta\ddagger = 35°$
					94.3	260.0	1.6×10^{-4}	$\theta = 70°$
					96.9	267.0	3.06×10^{-4}	$\theta = 105°$
					104.1	276.0	3.6×10^{-4}	$\theta = 140°$
			Forced-horizontal-vibration test	Block: $1.5 \times 0.75 \times 0.7$ m high	111.0	306.0	4.2×10^{-4}	$\theta = 35°$
					97.2	268.0	7.5×10^{-4}	$\theta = 70°$
					87.4	240.8	9.0×10^{-4}	$\theta = 105°$
					104.1	210.2	1.0×10^{-3}	$\theta = 140°$
			Cyclic-plate-load test	Plate: 30.5×30.5 cm	80.77	131.8	1.8×10^{-2}	
	(Prakash and Gupta, 1971)							

Table 4.4 (Continued)

Site no.	Description	Soil type†	Type of test	Size of block or plate	Dynamic shear modulus G, kg/cm² from test	Dynamic shear modulus G, kg/cm² for confining pressure of 1 kg/cm²	Associated strain level	Remarks (location)
1	2	3	4	5	6	7	8	9
5	Diesel power house, Nakodar, India	Medium sand $S_s = 2.58$ $\gamma = 1.79$ $e = 0.718$ $\phi = 30$ $\omega_c = 19.2$	Forced-vertical-vibration test	Block: $1.5 \times 0.75 \times 0.70$ m high	162.6 141.2 132.4 122.9	448.4 390.0 365.0 122.9	1.1×10^{-4} 2.2×10^{-4} 2.8×10^{-4} 3.0×10^{-4}	$\theta = 35°$ $\theta = 70°$ $\theta = 105°$ $\theta = 140°$
			Forced-horizontal-vibration test	Block: $1.5 \times 0.75 \times 0.70$ m high	146.5 135.0 126.1 125.0	404.0 371.5 347.9 344.3	3.6×10^{-4} 7.7×10^{-4} 9.0×10^{-4} 9.8×10^{-4}	$\theta = 35°$ $\theta = 70°$ $\theta = 105°$ $\theta = 140°$
			Shear modulus test	Block: $1.5 \times 0.75 \times 0.70$ m high	312.0	867.3	3.0×10^{-5}	
			Cyclic-plate-load test	Plate: 30.5×30.5 cm	198.3	166.0	3.9×10^{-2}	

(Prakash and Gupta, 1970)

No.	Site	Soil description	Test type	Size				
6	Cement factory, Rajban, India	Boulder deposits with matrix of medium to coarse silty sand; properties of the matrix material $S_s = 2.70$ $\gamma = 2.15$ $e = 0.605$ $\phi = 32.5$ $w_c = 28\%$	Forced-vertical-vibration test	Block: $3.0 \times 1.5 \times 1.0$ m high	579.9	1310.8	4.2×10^{-5}	RB$_1$
					574.9	1255.0	4.6×10^{-5}	RB$_1$
					521.6	1143.0	3.06×10^{-5}	RB$_2$
					494.0	1082.8	3.6×10^{-5}	RB$_2$
			Forced-horizontal-vibration test	Block: $3.0 \times 1.5 \times 1.0$ m high	683.3	1498.0	7.2×10^{-5}	RB$_1$
					770.0	1688.0	7.6×10^{-5}	RB$_1$
					697.7	1562.0	1.0×10^{-4}	RB$_2$
					691.2	1480.0	1.06×10^{-4}	RB$_2$
			Free-vertical-vibration test	Block: $3.0 \times 1.5 \times 1.0$ m high	762.1	1674.0	1.0×10^{-6}	RB$_1$
					683.3	1498.0	1.0×10^{-6}	RB$_2$
			Free-horizontal-vibration test	Block: $3.0 \times 1.5 \times 1.0$ m high	1114.3	2443.0	1.0×10^{-6}	RB$_1$
					967.1	2120.0	1.0×10^{-6}	RB$_2$
			Cyclic-plate-load test	Plate: 60×60 cm	232.3	155.0	9.1×10^{-3}	VP$_1$
					204.4	136.3	1.03×10^{-2}	VP$_2$
					297.3	198.4	7.1×10^{-3}	VP$_3$
					223.0	148.8	1.1×10^{-2}	VP$_4$
7	University of Roorkee (Prakash, et al., 1973)	Poorly graded fine silty sand up to 5.0 m $S_s = 2.63$ $\gamma = 1.83$ $e = 0.69$ $\phi = 30°$	Forced-vertical-vibration test	Block: $1.5 \times 0.75 \times 0.7$ m	293.0	805.5	6.4×10^{-5}	$\theta = 35°$
					251.0	692.1	1.24×10^{-4}	$\theta = 70°$
					191.8	529.2	1.45×10^{-4}	$\theta = 105°$
					174.1	480.4	1.58×10^{-4}	$\theta = 140°$
				Block: $1 \times 1 \times 1$ m	206.2	538.1	6.4×10^{-5}	$\theta = 35°$
					180.8	472.0	1.0×10^{-4}	$\theta = 70°$
					145.0	372.0	1.3×10^{-4}	$\theta = 105°$
					129.0	322.3	1.5×10^{-4}	$\theta = 140°$

Table 4.4 (Continued)

Site no.	Description	Soil type†	Type of test	Size of block or plate	Dynamic shear modulus G, kg/cm² from test	Dynamic shear modulus G, kg/cm² for confining pressure of 1 kg/cm²	Associated strain level	Remarks (location)
1	2	3	4	5	6	7	8	9
		ω_c = 17.6% Depth of water table, 4.2 m; followed by a layer of silty clay up to 17.75 m	Forced-horizontal-vibration test	Block: 1.5 × 0.75 × 0.70 m	274.3	757.0	2.0×10^{-4}	$\theta = 35°$
					242.4	668.8	3.0×10^{-4}	$\theta = 70°$
					225.0	621.0	4.6×10^{-4}	$\theta = 105°$
					210.0	578.2	7.3×10^{-4}	$\theta = 140°$
				Block: 1 × 1 × 1 m	221.7	573.6	2.1×10^{-4}	$\theta = 35°$
					193.2	504.0	3.4×10^{-4}	$\theta = 70°$
					180.8	471.7	5.0×10^{-4}	$\theta = 105°$
					168.1	438.5	6.0×10^{-4}	$\theta = 140°$
			Free-vertical-vibration tests	Block: 1.5 × 0.75 × 0.70 m high	647.5	1786.0	1.0×10^{-6}	
				Block: 1 × 1 × 1 m	687.6	1798.0	1.0×10^{-6}	
			Free-horizontal-vibration tests	Block: 1.5 × 0.75 × 0.7 m high	725.3	2001.0	1×10^{-6}	
				Block: 1 × 1 × 1 m high	379.4	990.0	1.0×10^{-6}	

Puri (1969)

* Prakash and Puri (1980).
† S_s = specific gravity of particles; γ = bulk density of soil; e = void ratio; ϕ = angle of internal friction; ω_c = water content.
‡ θ = angle of setting of eccentric masses.

modulus (defined as G-value at a particular strain, divided by G-value at strain of 10^{-6}) and strain is shown in Fig. 4.42. A similar plot for sands and clays was also made by Richart (1977), who presented a good summary of correlations between dynamic constants and shear strain.

4.15 FINAL COMMENTS

Stress deformation and strength characteristics of soils under static and dynamic loads depend on soil characteristics, such as void ratio, relative density, stress history, and preconsolidation pressure, and on initial static stress level, pulsating stress level, number of stress pulses, and, to a lesser degree, the frequency of loading and the shape of the wave form.

In silts and clays, with an initial safety factor of 1.5 or 2.0 and between 10 and 100 stress pulses, the total stress (static plus dynamic) versus total strain curve is very close to the stress-strain plot under static loading.

The study of shear parameters in oscillatory simple shear shows that cohesion intercepts decrease appreciably in more plastic clays under oscillatory loads and the angle of internal friction remains constant.

Several laboratory and field methods are available for determining soil modulus. The laboratory methods are oscillatory simple or triaxial shear, and resonant column apparatus. A laboratory apparatus to measure the ultrasonic longitudinal and shear wave velocities was reported by Stephenson (1977). The field methods include cross-bore hole tests, up-hole or down-hole tests, surface-wave techniques, block resonance test, and cyclic-plate-load test.

Simple equations have been developed to use available data to make preliminary estimates of the soil modulus at low strain amplitudes for sands and clays. Also, certain noncohesive deposits from in situ tests were studied to determine variations of soil modulus with strains. Therefore, depending upon the strain value associated in a particular problem, a reasonable estimate of the soil modulus can be made. Ishihara (1971) suggested values of strain levels from several field and laboratory tests and the corresponding state of soil (Fig. 4.43). However, it is recommended that the soil modulus be determined for a wide range of strain levels; a suitable value may then be picked. A correction for confining pressure differences between field and test conditions also needs to be made, as per Eq. (4.23).

Woods (1978) compiled a table of advantages and disadvantages of field techniques discussed in the chapter (Table 4.5).

The effect of a high confining pressure on the dynamic soil modulus has not been investigated to any extent. The problem is of great importance in seismic analysis of high earth and rockfill dams, such as the Tehri and Kishau Dams, which are proposed to be built in the Himalayas and will each be about 300 m high. Preliminary work in this direction has been initiated at Roorkee.

In actual analysis of substructures, it is convenient to express the stress-strain curve in a mathematical form. For monotonic loading, Kondner's (1963) hyper-

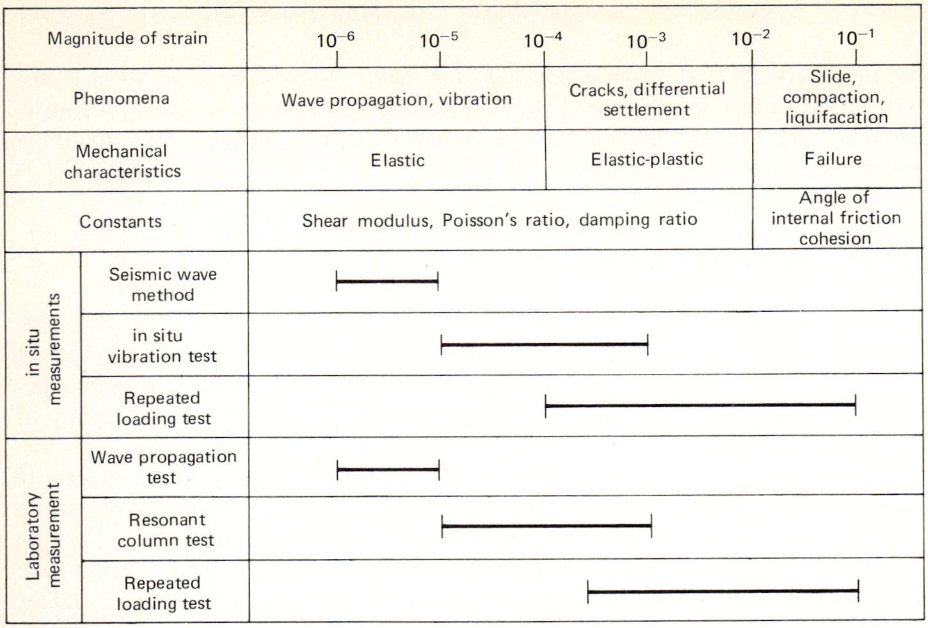

Magnitude of strain	10^{-6} 10^{-5} 10^{-4} 10^{-3} 10^{-2} 10^{-1}		
Phenomena	Wave propagation, vibration	Cracks, differential settlement	Slide, compaction, liquifacation
Mechanical characteristics	Elastic	Elastic-plastic	Failure
Constants	Shear modulus, Poisson's ratio, damping ratio		Angle of internal friction cohesion

in situ measurements	Seismic wave method
	in situ vibration test
	Repeated loading test
Laboratory measurement	Wave propagation test
	Resonant column test
	Repeated loading test

Figure 4.43 Strain level associated with different in situ and laboratory tests. (*After Ishihara, 1971.*)

Table 4.5 Field techniques for measuring dynamic soil properties*

Field technique	P-wave velocity	S-wave velocity	Other measurements	Advantages	Disadvantages
Refraction	X	X	Depths and slopes of layers	Reversible polarity Works from surface Samples large zone Preliminary studies	Misses low velocity zones Low strain amplitudes Properties measured are for thin zones near boundaries
Cross-hole	X	X		Known wave path Reversible polarity Works in limited space	Need two or more holes Need to survey holes for verticality
Down-hole or up-hole	X	X		One hole only Reversible polarity Finds low velocity Works in limited space	Measures average velocities Ambient noise near surface Low strain amplitude
Surface		X	Attenuation of R wave	Work from surface	Uncertain about effective depth Needs large vibrator
SPT			Empirical correlation with liquefaction	Widely available Widely used in past	Needs "standardization"
Resonant footing			Modulus of near-surface soils	Works from surface	Limited depth of influence

*After Woods (1978).

bola has been adopted in several cases. However, for cyclic stress-strain, Richart (1977) and Desai and Christian (1977) recommend the use of the Ramsberg-Osgood (1943) model. The detailed treatment of the subject is beyond the scope of this text.

PRACTICE PROBLEMS

4.1 List and discuss the factors affecting shear strengths of cohesive soils under static and dynamic loads.

4.2 Differentiate between the structure of undisturbed and remolded soils. Draw stress-strain curves for both. If an undisturbed clay sample is vibrated, what type of structure do you expect after the vibrations have ceased?

4.3 What do you understand by a "stress control" and "strain control" type of shear testing device?
(*a*) Is the pendulum loading apparatus a stress control type or a strain control type?
(*b*) Is Seed's apparatus for repetitive load applications "stress" or "strain" controlled?

4.4 Describe the effects of the following on the strength of clayey soils:
(*a*) Number of pulses of loading
(*b*) Wave form of pulsating load
(*c*) One-dimensional and two-dimensional loading
(*d*) Drainage conditions
(*e*) Loading time

4.5 A clay sample, 3.8 cm in diameter and 8 cm long, is subjected to one-dimensional pulsating stress. The frequency of load application is 2 Hz and sustained load is zero.
Draw a typical dynamic stress versus total strain for this sample. Superimpose on this diagram the static stress versus strain in an unconfined test on this sample.
How does this plot differ from the one in Fig. 4.21?

4.6 List and discuss the methods for determining dynamic soil modulus of soils.

4.7 List and discuss the factors on which the soil moduli depend. In a given case, how are corrections for the variations in these factors applied to determine the value for your problem?

4.8 List and discuss the provisions of the Indian Standards for determining dynamic soil modulus. If you were to write a standard of your own, how would you revise these provisions?

4.9 The following tests were performed at the ground surface to determine the value E, the Young's modulus, and C_u, the coefficient of elastic uniform compression for the design of a compressor foundation at a site.

Table 4.6 Vertical-vibration test data

Serial no.	Angle of settling of eccentric masses	f_{nz}, Hz	Amplitude at resonance mm
1	15	35.0	0.06375
2	30	32.0	0.150
3	45	31.0	0.210
4	60	29.5	0.30
5	120	28.0	0.525
6	140	27.0	0.620

(*a*) A vertical vibration test was made on an M-150 concrete block $1.5 \times 0.75 \times 0.7$ m high, using different eccentricities of the rotating mass of the oscillator. The data obtained are given in Table 4.6.

(*b*) A cyclic-plate-load test was made on a plate 70×70 cm. The elastic settlement corresponding to a load intensity of 2.5 kg/cm^2 was 6.00 mm.

(*c*) A wave-propagation test gave an average value of travel time of compression waves as 0.02 s, corresponding to a distance between geophones of 6 m.

The water table at the proposed location is 2.0 m below the proposed depth of the foundation of 3.0 m. The base contact area of the foundation is 10×8 m. Compute the values of E and C_u.

REFERENCES

Anderson, D. G., C. Espana, and V. R. McLamore: Estimating In-Situ Shear Moduli at Competent Sites, *Proc. ASCE Specialty Conference on Earthquake Engineering and Soil Dynamics*, Pasadena, vol. 1, pp. 181-197, June 1978.

Arya, A. S., S. Prakash, and D. C. Gupta: "Report on Soil Characteristics for Heavy Duty Vibrator Equipment of Fertilizer Project, Kanpur," Earthquake Engineering Studies, School of Research and Training in Earthquake Engineering, University of Roorkee, Roorkee, India, 1967.

Ballard, R. F., Jr.: "Determination of Soil Shear Moduli at Depth by In-Situ Vibratory Techniques," W. E. S., Misc. Paper No. 4-691, December 1964.

Barkan, D. D.: "Dynamics of Bases and Foundations," McGraw-Hill Book Co., New York, 1962.

Bjerrum, L., and A. Landra: Direct Simple Shear Tests on a Norwegian Quick Clay, *Geotechnique*, vol. 26, no. 1, pp. 1-20, March 1966.

_____ and N. E. Simmons: "Comparison of Shear Strength Characteristics of Normally Consolidated Clays," Research Conference on Shear Strength of Cohesive Soils, ASCE, Boulder, CO pp. 711-726, June 1960.

Casagrande, A.: Characteristics of Cohesionless Soils Affecting the Stability of Slopes and Earth Fills, *J. Boston Soc. Civ. Eng.*, vol. 23, p. 13, 1936.

_____ and W. L. Shannon: Stress Deformation and Strength Characteristics of Soils under Dynamic Loads, *Proc. Second Int. Conf. Soil Mech. Foundation Engin.*, vol. 5, pp. 29-34, 1948*a*.

_____ and _____: "Research on Stress Deformation and Strength Characteristics of Soils and Soft Rocks Under Transient Loading," Harvard Soil Mechanics Series No. 31, 1948*b*.

_____ and _____: Strength of Soils Under Dynamic Loads, *Trans. ASCE*, pp. 755-72; Discussion, p. 825, 1949.

Cunny, R. W., and Z. B. Fry: Vibratory In-Situ and Laboratory Soil Moduli Compared, *J. Soil Mech. Found. Div.*, ASCE, vol. 99, no. SM 12, pp. 1055-1076, 1973.

Desai, C. S., and J. T. Christian: "Numerical Methods in Geomechanics," McGraw-Hill Book Co., New York, 1977.

Doebelin, E. O.: "Measurement Systems: Application and Design," McGraw-Hill Book Co., New York, 1966.

Drnevich, V. P., J. R. Hall, Jr., and F. E. Richart, Jr.: Effect of Amplitudes of Vibration on Shear Modulus of Sand, *Proceedings of the International Symposium on Wave Propagation and Dynamic Properties of Earth Materials*, Albuquerque, NM, 1967.

Fry, Z. B.: "Development and Evaluation of Soil Bearing Capacity, Foundations of Structures," W. E. S., Technical Report No. 3-622, rept. no. 1, July 1963.

Hardin, B. O.: The Nature of Stress-Strain Behavior of Soils, State of the Art Report, *Proc. ASCE Specialty Conference on Earthquake Engineering and Soil Dynamics*, Pasadena, pp. 3-90, June 1978.

_____ and W. L. Black: Closure to Vibration Modulus of Normally Consolidated Clays, *J. Soil Mech. Found. Div.*, ASCE, vol. 95, no. SM 6, pp. 1531-1537, November 1978.

_____ and V. P. Drnevich: Shear Modulus and Damping in Soils: Measurement and Parameter Effects, *J. Soil Mech. Found. Div.*, ASCE, vol. 98, no. SM 6, pp. 603-624, 1972*a*.

_____ and _____: Shear Modulus and Damping in Soils: Design Equations and Curves, *J. Soil Mech. Found. Div.*, *ASCE*, vol. 98, no. SM 7, pp. 667-692, 1972*b*.

Hvorslev, M. J., and R. I. Kaufman: "Torsion Shear Apparatus and Testing Procedure," USAE Waterways Experiment Station, Bulletin No. 38, May 1952, 76 pp.

Imai, T., and M. Yoshimura: "The Relation of Mechanical Properties of Soils to P- and S-Wave Velocities for Soil Ground in Japan," Report RD-477, TN-07 Urawa Research Institute, Oya Corp., 1975.

Indian Standard Method of Load Test on Soils, IS 1888-1971, 1st rev., Indian Standards Institution, New Delhi.

Indian Standard Method of Test for Determination of Dynamic Properties of Soil, IS 5249-1978, 1st rev., Indian Standards Institution, New Delhi.

Indian Standard on Identification and Classification of Soils for General Engineering Purposes, IS 1498-1971, 1st rev., Indian Standards Institution, New Dehli.

Ishihara, K.: Factors Affecting Dynamic Properties of Soils, *Proc. Fourth Asian Regional Conference on Soil Mechanics and Foundation Engineering*, Bangkok, vol. 2, August 1971.

Iwasaki, T., and F. Tatsuoka: Dynamic Soil Properties with Emphasis on Comparison of Laboratory Tests with Field Measurements, *Proc. Sixth World Conference on Earthquake Engineering, New Delhi*, vol. 1, pp. 153-158, January 1977.

Kjellman, W.: Testing of Shear Strength in Sweden, *Geotechnique*, vol. 2, pp. 225-232, 1951.

Kondner, R. L.: Hyperbolic Stress-Strain Response: Cohesive Soils, *J. Soil Mech. Found. Div.*, *ASCE*, vol. 89, no. SM 1, pp. 115-143, 1963.

Leet, L. D.: Earth Motion from the Atomic Bomb Test, *Am. Sci.*, vol. 34, pp. 198-207, 1946.

Park, T. D., and M. L. Silver: Dynamic Triaxial and Simple Shear Behavior of Sand," *J. Geot. Engg. Div. ASCE*, vol. 101, no. GT 6, pp. 513-529, June 1975.

Peacock, W. H., and H. B. Seed: Sand Liquefaction Under Cyclic Loading Simple Shear Conditions, *J. Soil Mech. Found. Div.*, *ASCE*, vol. 94, no. SM 3, pp. 689-708, May 1968.

Prakash, S.: "Introductory Soil Testing," Asia Publishing House, Bombay, 1968.

_____ and B. M. Basavanna: "Report on Soil Characteristics for Heavy Aero Engine Beds, AEF, Chandigarh," Earthquake Engineering Studies, School of Research and Training in Earthquake Engineering, University of Roorkee, Roorkee, 1968.

_____, _____, and A. S. Arya: "Report on Soil Characteristics for Heavy Duty Forging Hammer Foundation of Hindustan Aeronautics Ltd., Koraput," Earthquake Engineering Studies, School of Research and Training in Earthquake Engineering, University of Roorkee, Roorkee, India, 1968.

_____ and M. K. Gupta: "Report on Dynamic Properties of Soil for Diesel Power House Nakodar," Earthquake Engineering Studies, School of Research and Training in Earthquake Engineering, University of Roorkee, Roorkee, India, 1970.

_____ and _____: "Report on Dynamic Properties of Soils for Diesel Power House Sirhind," Earthquake Engineering Studies, School of Research and Training in Earthquake Engineering, University of Roorkee, Roorkee, India, 1971.

_____ and P. Nandkumaran: "Behavior of Sand Clay Mixture in Oscillatory Shear," *Symposium on Repeated Loading of Soils with Particular Reference to Road Pavements, University of New South Wales, Sydney*, 1975.

_____, _____, and V. K. Bansal: Behavior of Soils Under Oscillatory Shear Stresses, *Proc. Fifth Symposium on Earthquake Engineering, Roorkee*, vol. 1, pp. 127-134, November 1974.

_____, _____, and V. H. Joshi: Design and Performance of an Oscillatory Shear Box, *J. Indian Geotech. Soc.*, vol. 3, no. 2, pp. 101-112, April 1973.

_____ and V. K. Puri: Natural Frequency of Block Foundations Under Free and Forced Vibrations, *J. Indian Geotech.*, vol. 2, no. 4, October 1972.

_____ and _____: Dynamic Properties of Soils from In-situ Tests, unpublished report, University of Missouri-Rolla, MO, July 1980.

_____, G. Ranjan, P. Nandkumaran et al.: "Report on Soil Investigations for Cement Factory at Rajban (H.P.)," Studies carried out at the Civil Engineering Department, and the School of Research and Training in Earthquake Engineering, University of Roorkee, Roorkee, India, 1973.

_____, _____, S. Saran, et al.: "Report on Geotechnical Investigations for Penden Cement Authority, Cement Factory at Gomtu, Bhutan," Geotechnical Engineering Studies, University of Roorkee, Roorkee, India, 1976.

_____ and P. Srivastava: "Design and Performance of a Resonant Column Device," *J. Indian Geotech.*, vol. 9, no. 4, pp. 313-327, October 1979.

Puri, V. K.: "Natural Frequency of Block Foundations under Free and Forced Vibrations," A dissertation submitted in partial fulfillment of the requirements for the degree of Master of Engineering in Soil Mechanics and Foundation Engineering, University of Roorkee, Roorkee, India, 1969.

Ramsberg, W., and W. T. Osgood: "Description of Stress Strain Curves by Three Parameters," Tech. Note 902, National Advisory Committee on Aeronautics, Washington, D.C., 1943.

Richart, F. E., Jr.: Dynamic Stress-Strain Relations for Soils, State of the Art Report, *Proc. Ninth International Conference on Soil Mechanics and Foundation Engineering, Tokyo*, vol. 2, pp. 605-612, 1977.

_____, J. R. Hall, and R. D. Woods: "Vibrations of Soils and Foundations," Prentice-Hall, Inc., Englewood Cliffs, N.J., 1970.

Roscoe, K. H.: An Apparatus for the Application of Simple Shear to Soil Samples, *Proc. Third Int. Conf. Soil Mech. Found. Engin.*, vol. 1, pp. 186-191, 1953.

Seed, H. B.: Soil Strength During Earthquakes, *Proc. Second World Conf. Earthquake Engg.*, vol. 1, pp. 183-194, 1960.

_____ and C. K. Chan: Clay Strength Under Earthquake Loading Conditions, *J. Soil Mech. Found. Div., ASCE*, vol. 92, no. SM 2, pp. 53-78, March 1966.

_____ and J. W. N. Fead: "Apparatus for Repeated Load Tests on Soils," *Special Technical Publication No. 204, ASTM, Philadelphia*, 1959.

_____ and R. Lundgren: "Investigation of the Effect of Transient Loading on the Strength and Deformation Characteristics of Saturated Sands," *Proc. ASTM*, vol. 54, pp. 1288-1306, 1954.

Silver, M. L., C. K. Chan, et al.: "Cyclic Triaxial Strength of Standard Test Sand", *J. Geot. Engg. Div. ASCE*, vol. 102, no. GT 5, pp. 511-523, May 1976.

Singh, B., and S. Prakash: "A Text Book of Soil Mechanics," 4th ed., Nemchand and Bros., Roorkee, India, 1976.

Shockley, W. G., and R. G. Ahlvin: "Non-uniform Conditions in Triaxial Test Specimens," *Proc. Res. Conference on Shear Strength of Cohesive Soils, ASCE*, Boulder, CO, pp. 341-357, 1960.

Stephenson, R. W.: "Ultrasonic Testing for Determining Dynamic Soil Moduli," *Dynamic Geotechnical Testing, ASTM, Special Technical Publication No.* 654, pp. 179-195, 1977.

Stokoe, K. H., and F. E. Richart: In-situ and Laboratory Shear Wave Velocities, *Proc. Seventh Int. Conf. Soil Mech. Found. Engin.*, vol. 1, pp. 403-409, 1973.

_____ and R. D. Woods: In-situ Shear Wave Velocity by Cross-Hole Method, *J. Soil Mech. Found. Div., ASCE*, vol. 98, no. SM 5, pp. 443-460, 1972.

_____ and R. J. Hoar: Variables Affecting In-Situ Seismic Measurements, *Proc. ASCE Specialty Conference on Earthquake Engineering and Soil Dynamics, Pasadena*, vol. 2, pp. 919-938, June, 1978.

SW-AA: "Soil Behavior Under Earthquake Loading Condition," Interim Report No. 1, Subcontract No. 3354, Union Carbide Corp. for U.S. Atomic Energy Commission Contract No. 7405-Eng-26-Dec, 1971.

Taylor, D. W.: "Fundamentals of Soil Mechanics," John Wiley Sons, Inc., New York, 1948.

Thiers, G. R., and H. B. Seed: Cyclic Stress-Strain Characteristics of Clay, *J. Soil Mech. Found. Div., ASCE*, vol. 94, no. SM 6, pp. 555-569, March 1968.

Tschebotarioff, G. P.: Discussion on Strength of Soils Under Dynamic Loads by A. Casagrande and W. L. Shannon, *Trans. ASCE*, p. 825, 1949.

Whitman, R. V.: "Testing of Soils with Transient Loads," *ASTM, Spec. Tech. Pub. No.* 232, p. 242, 1957*a*.

_____ : The Behavior of Soils Under Transient Loadings, *Proc. Fourth Int. Conf. Soil Mech. Found. Engin.*, vol. 1, p. 207-210, 1957*b*.

———— : Shear Strength of Sands During Rapid Loadings, *J. Soil Mech. Found. Div.*, *ASCE*, vol. 94, no. SM 4, pp. 99-132, April 1968.

———— and F. V. Lawrence: Discussion, *J. Soil Mech. Found. Div.*, *ASCE*, vol. 89, no. SM 5, pp. 112-115, 1963.

Woods, R. D.: "Measurement of Dynamic Soil Properties—State of the Art," *Proc. ASCE Specialty Conference on Earthquake Engineering and Soil Dynamics, Pasadena*, June 1978.

Yoshimi, Y., F. E. Richart, S. Prakash, et al.: Soil Dynamics and Its Application to Foundation Engineering, State of the Art Report, *Proc. Ninth International Conference on Soil Mechanics and Foundation Engineering*, Tokyo, pp. 605-50, July 1977.

DYNAMIC EARTH PRESSURE PROBLEM AND RETAINING WALL

5.1 LATERAL EARTH PRESSURE PROBLEM

Earth pressure problems are encountered in retaining walls, bulkheads, sheeting and bracing in cuts, culverts, tunnels, and cofferdams. In many cases, the lateral pressure is statically indeterminate and is not a well-defined and fixed quantity, depending upon the nature of the soils alone; rather, it depends upon the interaction between the structure and the soil and is a function of the deflections and deformations of the structure. The classical earth pressure theories were proposed by Coulomb (1773) and Rankine (1857). Terzaghi's theory (1941) is an improvement over the earlier theories (Terzaghi and Peck, 1967).

However, if a retaining structure does not undergo any deflection, as an abutment of a basement, none of the above theories is applicable. This topic will be discussed first, to be followed by a brief review of Rankine's and Coulomb's theories for the static case. The question of earthquake-type loading on a retaining wall will then be presented in detail.

Earth Pressure at Rest

The stresses acting on an element of soil in a natural soil mass are represented in Fig. 5.1. The soil deposit is assumed to be semi-infinite, isotropic, homogeneous, and elastic. Soil can deform vertically under load, but cannot deform laterally because of its infinite extent. If E and ν are the modulus of elasticity and Poisson's ratio, respectively, of the soil mass, and σ_v and σ_h are vertical and horizontal stress intensities, respectively, at any depth z (Fig. 5.1), then it can be

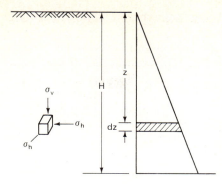

Figure 5.1 "At rest" lateral pressures in a semi-infinite isotropic, homogeneous, and elastic mass.

shown that

$$\sigma_h = K_0 \sigma_v \tag{5.1}$$

in which

$$K_0 = \frac{\nu}{1 - \nu} \tag{5.2}$$

Now

$$\sigma_v = \gamma z$$

and

$$\sigma_h = p_0 = K_0 \gamma z \tag{5.3}$$

where p_0 is designated as *earth pressure at rest*, and K_0 the *coefficient of earth pressure at rest*.

The relationship expressed by Eq. (5.3) is valid for effective stresses. The total lateral pressure below the water table is determined from the effective and neutral components of pressures. The value K_0 is not determined from Poisson's ratio, since soils are not elastic in nature and do not have a well-defined Poisson's ratio. Instead, K_0 depends on the relative density of sands and the processes by which the deposit was formed. The values of the coefficient of earth pressure at rest, in Table 5.1, are based on experience in the field.

Rankine's Earth Pressure Theory

A body of soil is said to be in a state of *plastic equilibrium* if every part of it is in an incipient failure condition. Plastic equilibrium, which can develop in a

Table 5.1 Typical values of K_0

Soil type	K_0	Remarks
Loose sand	0.4	The total lateral pressure
Dense sand	0.6	at any depth is the sum of
Sand, tamped in layers	0.8	lateral pressures due to
Soft clay	0.6	effective and neutral stresses
Hard clay	0.5	

semi-infinite mass of cohesionless soils when acted upon by the force of gravity, was investigated by Rankine (1857).

In Fig. 5.2a, ab is a horizontal surface of a semi-infinite mass of cohesionless soil with a unit weight γ. At depth z below AB, the vertical pressure on ab is

$$P_v = \gamma z \qquad (5.4)$$

After deposition of this mass of soil, the value of the lateral earth pressure p_h corresponds to the at-rest value; that is,

$$p_h = p_0 = K_0 p_v$$

Since this element is symmetrical with respect to a vertical plane, the normal stress on ab is a principal stress. Consequently, the normal stress on the vertical side also is a principal stress. Thus, the principal stresses in the soil mass at

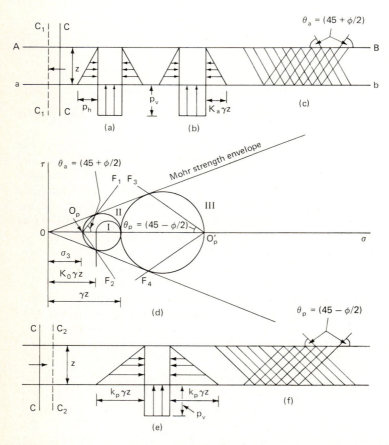

Figure 5.2 (a) At rest condition. (b,c) Rankine's states of plastic equilibrium illustrating active conditions. (d) Mohr stress and strength diagrams (e,f, Illustrating passive conditions).

depth z on plane ab and vertical planes are, respectively,

$$\sigma_1 = \gamma z \qquad \text{and} \qquad \sigma_3 = K_0 \gamma z$$

In Fig. 5.2d, circle I corresponds to the at-rest condition. Now, as the soil mass stretches, plane cc moves to the left to position $c_1 c_1$, lateral pressure (a minor principal stress in this case) decreases, and the diameter of the Mohr circle increases. According to Mohr-Coulomb failure criteria, the greatest diameter that a Mohr circle can have is when the Mohr circle (II) is tangential to the Mohr strength envelope. The origin of planes is O_p, and $O_p F_1$ and $O_p F_2$ are failure planes inclined at $45 + \phi/2$, each to the major principal plane.

A relationship between major and minor principal stresses at incipient failure is given by

$$\frac{\sigma_1}{\sigma_3} = \frac{1 + \sin\phi}{1 - \sin\phi} \tag{5.5a}$$

or

$$\frac{\sigma_1}{\sigma_3} = \tan^2\left(45 + \frac{\phi}{2}\right) \tag{5.5b}$$

or

$$\frac{\sigma_1}{\sigma_3} = N\phi \tag{5.5c}$$

or

$$p_v = \gamma z = p_h N\phi \tag{5.6}$$

or

$$p_h = \frac{\gamma z}{N\phi} = K_a \gamma z \tag{5.7}$$

where K_a, the *coefficient of active earth pressure*,

$$K_a = \frac{1}{N\phi} = \frac{1 - \sin\phi}{1 + \sin\phi} \tag{5.8}$$

It should be noted that once the lateral earth pressure is reduced to the active value, further stretching of the mass has no effect on p_h, but sliding occurs along planes in the direction of $O_p F_1$ and $O_p F_2$, which are horizontally inclined at $45 + \phi/2$. It should be further noted that failure will be incipient on all planes parallel to $O_p F_1$ and $O_p F_2$. The vertical traces of such planes in Fig. 5.2c constitute the *shear pattern*. The corresponding distribution of pressure on the sides and at the base of the soil mass is shown in Fig. 5.2b. The above concepts of the states of plastic equilibrium in an active condition may be extended to a retaining wall problem if the following assumptions are made: (1) the wall face is smooth and vertical and (2) the deformation condition for plastic equilibrium is satisfied.

If the soil mass is compressed and section cc moves to $c_2 c_2$, the Mohr circle corresponding to this state of stress is shown by circle III (Fig. 5.2d). Failure planes, originating from O_p' (the origin of the planes) in this case, are toward $O_p' F_3$ and $O_p' F_4$, each of which is horizontally inclined at $45 - \phi/2$, which is the direction of the minor principal plane in this condition. The shear pattern is sketched in Fig. 5.2f. The soil mass is said to be in the *passive Rankine* state.

The lateral pressure can be determined in this case also by using the equation

$$\frac{\sigma_1}{\sigma_3} = N_\phi \tag{5.5c}$$

Since σ_3 $(= \gamma z)$ is the minor principal stress,

$$\sigma_1 = \gamma z N_\phi = K_p \gamma z \tag{5.9}$$

where the *coefficient of passive earth pressure*

$$K_p = N_\phi = \frac{1 + \sin \phi}{1 - \sin \phi} = \tan^2\left(45 + \frac{\phi}{2}\right) \tag{5.10}$$

It should again be noted that, once the Rankine passive resistance has been mobilized, further compression of the soil causes no increase in soil resistance; instead, slippage occurs along the failure planes indicated in the shear pattern (Fig. 5.2*f*).

Coulomb's Earth Pressure Theory

Unlike Rankine's theory, Coulomb's theory of earth pressure does not assume the wall surface to be smooth. In addition, Coulomb's method can be adapted to any boundary conditions, for example, inclined walls with a break, inclined uniform and nonuniform slopes, and concentrated and distributed surcharge loads. A modified Coulomb method is used to determine the increase in static earth pressure due to a dynamic load (Sec. 5.3).

Assumptions made according to Coulomb's theory are the following:

1. The deformation condition is satisfied.
2. The slope of sliding surface is linear.

When the boundary conditions for Rankine's theory are satisfied, the two theories yield identical results.

According to this theory, the earth pressure is calculated by considering the equilibrium conditions of a sliding trial wedge, abc_1 (Fig. 5.3*a*). The forces acting on wedge abc_1 are the following:

1. W_1, weight of the wedge acting through CG of abc_1
2. Earth pressure P_1, inclined at δ with the normal to the wall where δ is the *angle of wall friction*
3. Reaction R_1 inclined at angle ϕ to the normal to face bc_1

The triangle of forces is shown in Fig. 5.3*b*. P_1 is the value of earth pressure corresponding to assumed failure wedge abc_1. Since this is only a trial wedge, more trials are made by assuming bc_2, bc_3 (not shown) as failure surfaces and constructing force triangles similar to the one in the above figure. The maximum value of P is the *active earth pressure* P_a.

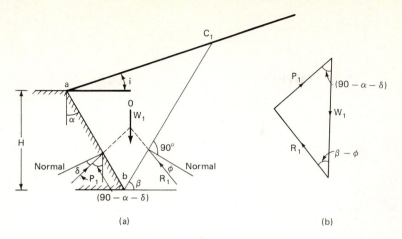

Figure 5.3 (*a*) Forces acting on assumed failure wedge in a noncohesive soil. (*b*) Force triangle.

Coulomb derived the following analytical expression for active earth pressure:

$$P_a = \tfrac{1}{2}\gamma \cdot H^2 \frac{\cos^2(\phi - \alpha)}{\cos^2\alpha \cos(\delta + \alpha)} \frac{1}{\left\{1 + \left[\dfrac{\sin(\phi + \delta)\sin(\phi - i)}{\cos(\alpha - i)\cos(\delta + \alpha)}\right]^{1/2}\right\}^2} \quad (5.11)$$

For determining earth pressure in cohesive soils, the basic principle remains the same, except that for an active case a force of cohesion $C_1 = c \times bc_1$ acts in the direction bc_1 and a force of adhesion $C' = c_a \times ab$ acts in the direction of ba as in Fig. 5.4a. In Fig 5.4b, a force polygon is drawn and P_1 is the earth pressure for assumed failure wedge abc_1.

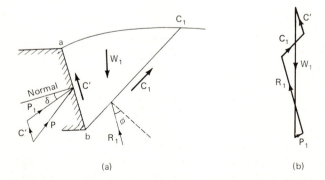

Figure 5.4 Forces on the assumed failure wedge in a cohesive soil. (*b*) Force polygon.

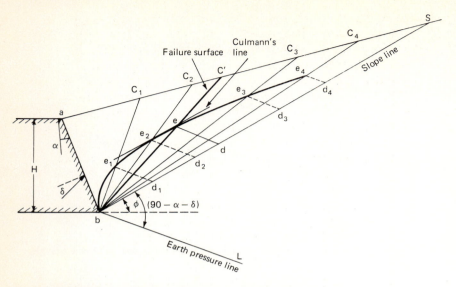

Figure 5.5 Culmann's construction for active earth pressure

Culmann's Graphical Construction

A graphical construction to determine lateral earth pressures for noncohesive soils according to Coulomb's theory was suggested by Culmann (1866). Let us consider a retaining wall of height H, vertically inclined at an angle α. The unit weight of soil is γ and its angle of internal friction is ϕ. The angle of wall friction is δ. The steps in Culmann's construction (Fig. 5.5) are as follows:

1. Draw a dimensional sketch of the wall.
2. Draw a line bS at an angle ϕ with the horizontal through b; bS is known as the *slope line* since it represents the natural slope of the backfill material.
3. Draw bL at an angle $(90-\alpha-\delta)$ below the slope line; bL is known as the *earth pressure line*.
4. Intercept bd_1, equal to the weight of wedge abc_1, to a convenient scale along bs.
5. Draw a line d_1e_1, parallel to the earth pressure line bL, through d_1 and intersecting bc_1 at e_1.
6. Measure d_1e_1 to the same force scale as bd_1; d_1e_1 is the earth pressure for trial wedge abc_1.

A number of trials are made, repeating steps 1 through 6, with bc_2, bc_3, bc_4 as the trial wedges. Then $be_1e_2e_3e_4$ is the trace of earth pressure and is known as *Culmann's line*. Draw a line parallel to bS and tangenial to this curve. The maximum ordinate in the direction of bL is obtained from the point of tangency.† This is the active earth pressure according to Coulomb's theory.

Coulomb's theory does not indicate the distribution of earth pressure on the wall. For backfills inclined horizontally at a uniform slope i, the pressure distribution can be shown to be hydrostatic (Terzaghi, 1943; Prakash, Ranjan, and Saran, 1979). Hence, the total earth pressure acts at a height of $H/3$ above the base of the wall and is inclined at an angle δ with the normal to the wall.

To determine passive pressures, the slope line bS (Fig. 5.5) is drawn below the horizontal line and the rest of Culmann's construction is unaltered.

A brief review of earth pressure on a retaining wall has been presented. The behavior of a retaining wall under an earthquake will now be examined, to be followed by procedures for analysis and design of a retaining wall.

5.2 BEHAVIOR OF RETAINING WALLS DURING EARTHQUAKES

Let us consider a retaining wall $abcd$ of height H (Fig. 5.6a). Let us assume that the retaining wall has undergone enough displacement under static conditions so that the earth pressure on the wall is active earth pressure P_a, and it acts at a height of $H/3$ above the base. A failure wedge bc has also developed. Figures 5.6b and c show ground motion and retaining wall movement, respectively.

Let the ground motion be represented by oa during the time t_1 from left to right (Fig. 5.6b). Because of inertia, the tendency of the wall is to move from right to left during the time interval t_1. Let the wall movement be o_1a_1 towards the left from its equilibrium position, that is, away from the backfill. The failure wedge abc is also moving in the direction of the wall during the time interval t_1.

Now, three situations need to be examined:

1. The rate of movement of the wall and the failure wedge is the same. In this case, there is no further interaction between the wall and the failure wedge. Therefore, the pressures on the wall are unaltered.
2. The wall moves out at a rate which is greater than the rate of movement of the failure wedge. In this case, the interaction between the wall and the failure wedge is reduced and the earth pressure may decrease as compared with the active value under static conditions.
3. The rate of movement of the failure wedge is greater than that of the wall. In this case, the earth pressure on the wall will increase. As a limiting condition, if it is assumed that the retaining wall does not move at all, then the increase in pressure is the maximum, although this is an unrealistic condition that will never be realized in practice for free-standing walls.

---

† *de* in this case.

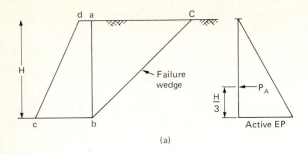

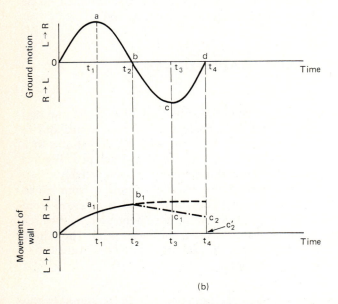

Figure 5.6 Response of retaining wall to ground shaking. (*a*) Retaining wall. (*b*) Ground motion. (*c*) Wall displacement.

It can be seen from the above discussion that wall movement takes place whether pressures on the wall are unaltered, reduced, or increased.

During the time interval, $t_1 t_2$, the wall moves out from a_1 to b_1. The rate of movement of the wall from a_1 to b_1 is probably smaller than that from O_1 to a_1. The ground motion between the time interval, $t_3 t_2$ (Fig. 5.6*b*), is from right to left. The wall will have a tendency to move from left to right. This movement is prevented to a great extent by the presence of the backfill. However, there may be a partial recovery of the displacement of the wall to c_1 from its displaced position, represented by point b_1. Similarly, during the time interval, $t_3 t_4$, the wall movement may be represented by $c_1 c_2$. It will thus be seen that the wall has moved out by $c_2 c_2'$ from its original equilibrium position (under the active pressure P_a), due to one cycle of ground motion *oabcd*. With additional significant pulses of ground shaking during an earthquake, it will thus be seen that the wall keeps on moving away from its static equilibrium position. Hence, the questions to be examined in determining the stability of a retaining wall during an earthquake are the following:

1. How much displacement of the wall occurs?
2. What is the change in earth pressure and where is its point of application?

The second question will be examined first, in detail, because of its simplicity.

5.3 MODIFICATION OF COULOMB'S THEORY

Coulomb's theory has been modified by Mononobe-Okabe, (Mononobe and Matsuo, 1929) by considering an inertia force acting on the failure wedge and determining a new "total" earth pressure.

In Fig. 5.7, a retaining wall of height H and inclined vertically at an angle α retains soil with unit weight γ and an angle of shearing resistance ϕ. The angle of wall friction is δ. The inertia force may act on the assumed failure wedge abc_1 (bc_1 is trial failure surface) both horizontally and vertically. If a_h is the horizontal acceleration and a_v is the vertical acceleration of the wedge of soil, the corresponding inertial forces are $W_1 a_h/g$ horizontally and $W_1 a_v/g$ vertically, where W_1 is the weight of the wedge abc_1. During the worst conditions for wall stability, $W_1 a_h/g$ acts toward the wall and $W_1 a_v/g$ may act vertically, either downward or upward, during an actual earthquake. Therefore, the direction that gives the maximum increase in the earth pressure is adopted in

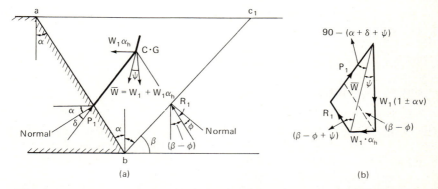

Figure 5.7 Active earth pressure under earthquake loads. (*a*) Forces acting on the failure wedge. (*b*) Forces polygon.

practice. Now,

$$\frac{a_h}{g} = \alpha_h \tag{5.12}$$

and

$$\frac{a_v}{g} = \alpha_v \tag{5.13}$$

in which α_h = horizontal seismic coefficient and α_v = vertical seismic coefficient.

The inertia forces now become $W_1\alpha_h$ and $W_1\alpha_v$ in the horizontal and vertical directions, respectively. The forces acting on the wedge abc_1 may be listed as follows (Fig. 5.7a):

1. Weight of the wedge abc_1, W_1, acting at its CG
2. Earth pressure P_1 inclined at an angle δ to normal to the wall.
3. Soil reaction R_1, inclined at an angle ϕ to normal on the face bc_1.
4. Horizontal inertia force $W_1\alpha_h$, acting at the center of gravity of the wedge abc_1
5. Vertical inertia force $\pm W_1\alpha_v$.

Weight W_1 and the inertia forces $\pm W_1\alpha_v$ and $W_1\alpha_h$ can be combined to give a resultant $\overline{W}_1$, such that

$$\overline{W}_1 = W_1\sqrt{(1 \pm \alpha_v)^2 + \alpha_h^2} \tag{5.14}$$

The resultant $\overline{W}_1$ is vertically inclined at an angle ψ, such that

$$\psi = \tan^{-1}\frac{\alpha_h}{1 \pm \alpha_v} \tag{5.15}$$

The triangle of forces is drawn in Figure 5.7b and the value of P_{total} is determined, in which $P_{\text{total}} = P_a + \Delta P_{\text{dyn}}$.

The maximum value of P is determined by considering other trial surfaces such as bc_2 or bc_3 (not shown), as in Sec. 5.1. This total earth pressure is made up of two components:

1. Coulomb's active earth pressure P_a as determined in Sec. 5.1 for static condition
2. Increase in earth pressure ΔP_{dyn} due to earthquake

The point of application of P_a is $H/3$ above the base of the wall, whereas that of ΔP_{dyn} is recommended at $2H/3$ above the base of the wall (Jacobsen 1951) and at $H/2$ above the base of the wall (IS 1893-1975). However, this topic will be discussed in detail in Sec. 5.6.

Coulomb's analytical expression for total active earth pressure [Eq. (5.11)] is changed by inertia forces to the following:

$$P_{total} = \tfrac{1}{2}\gamma H^2 \frac{\cos^2(\phi - \psi - \alpha)(1 \pm \alpha_v)}{\cos\psi \cos^2\alpha \cos(\delta + \alpha + \psi)}$$

$$\times \frac{1}{\left\{1 + \left[\dfrac{\sin(\phi + \delta)\sin(\phi - i - \psi)}{\cos(\alpha - i)\cos(\delta + \alpha + \psi)}\right]^{1/2}\right\}^2} \qquad (5.16)$$

5.4 MODIFIED CULMANN'S CONSTRUCTION

A graphical construction suggested by Culmann to determine lateral earth pressure in accordance with Coulomb's theory has already been described in Sec. 5.1. A modification of this construction was proposed by Kapila (1962) to account for the inertia of the failure wedge. Let us consider a retaining wall of height H, vertically inclined at an angle α. The unit weight of soil is γ and its angle of internal friction is ϕ. The angle of wall friction is δ. The horizontal and vertical seismic coefficients are $+\alpha_h$ and $+\alpha_v$, respectively.

The modified construction is carried out as follows (Fig. 5.8):

1. Draw a dimensional sketch of the retaining wall.
2. Draw bS' at an angle $\phi - \psi$ with the horizontal. In Culmann's construction, bS is drawn at an angle ϕ with the horizontal.

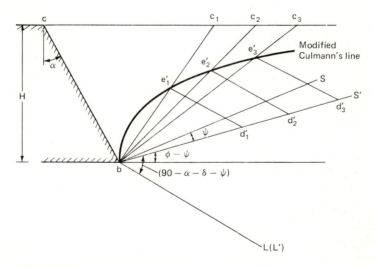

Figure 5.8 Culmann's construction for earthquake loading.

3. Draw bL' at an angle of $90 - \alpha - \delta - \psi$ below bS'. It should be noted that bL' remains unaltered from the static to the dynamic case.
4. Intercept bd_1', equal to $\overline{W}_1$, on a convenient scale. $\overline{W}_1$ is the resultant of $W_1\alpha_h$ and $W_1(1 \pm \alpha_v)$ [Eq. (5.14)].
5. Through d_1' draw $d_1'e_1'$, parallel to bL', intersecting bc_1' in e_1'.
6. Measure $d_1'e_1'$ to the same force scale as bd_1'. Then $d_1'e_1'$ is the total earth pressure for trial wedge bc_1.

A number of trials are made, repeating steps 1 through 6, with bc_2 and bc_3 as the trial wedges. Then $be_1'e_2'e_3'$ is the *modified Culmann's line*.

Draw a line parallel to bS' and tangential to this curve (not shown). The maximum ordinate in the direction of bL' is obtained from the point of tangency. This is the total (static + dynamic) earth pressure according to the modified Coulomb method.

For determining the passive earth pressures due to earthquake action, draw bs' at $\phi - \psi$ below the horizontal. Next, draw bL' at $90 - \alpha - \delta - \psi$ below bS'. The rest of the steps in the above construction remain unaltered.

5.5 ANALYTICAL SOLUTIONS FOR $c - \phi$ SOILS

The modified Coulomb method has been applied to cohesionless soils only. A general solution for determination of total (static plus dynamic) earth pressures for a $c - \phi$ soil has been developed by Prakash and Saran (1966) and Saran and Prakash (1968).

Figure 5.9 shows a wall with face ab in contact with soil and vertically inclined at angle α. The soil retained is horizontal and carries a uniform surcharge q per unit area. The assumed failure surface is vertically inclined at

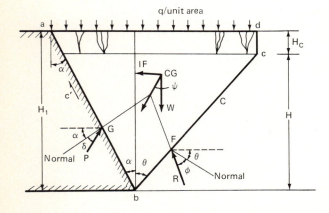

Figure 5.9 Forces acting on a wall retaining c-ϕ soil and subjected to an earthquake type load.

angle θ through b. If the depth of tension crack is H_c, let

$$H_c = n(H_1 - H_c) = nH \tag{5.17}$$

in which H_1 = height of retaining wall and H = height of retaining wall free from cracks.

In this analysis, only the horizontal inertia force has been considered. All of the forces acting on the assumed failure wedge $abcd$ are listed in Table 5.2 along with their horizontal and vertical components.

A summation of the vertical components gives

$$\frac{1}{2}\gamma H^2(\tan\alpha + \tan\theta) + \gamma \cdot nH^2(\tan\alpha + \tan\theta) + \frac{1}{2}\gamma n^2 H^2 \tan\alpha$$
$$- cH - c'H + qH(\tan\alpha + \tan\phi + n\tan\alpha) = P\sin(\alpha + \delta) + F\sin(\theta + \phi) \tag{5.18}$$

A summation of the horizontal components gives

$$- cH\tan\theta + c'H\tan\alpha + (W + Q)\alpha_h = P\cos(\theta + \phi) - F\cos(\theta + \phi) \tag{5.19}$$

Multiply Eq. (5.18) by $\cos(\theta + \phi)$ and Eq. (5.19) by $\sin(\theta + \phi)$, and substitute for W and Q in the above equations from Table 5.2 and letting $c = c'$, we get

$$P\sin(\beta + \delta) = \gamma H^2\left[\left(n + \frac{1}{2}\right)(\tan\alpha + \tan\theta) + n^2\tan\alpha\right]$$
$$\times \left[\cos(\theta + \phi) + \alpha_h\sin(\theta + \phi)\right]$$
$$+ qH\left[(n + 1)\tan\alpha + \tan\theta\right]\left[\cos(\theta + \phi) + \alpha_h\sin(\theta + \phi)\right]$$
$$- cH\left[\cos\beta\sec\alpha + \cos\phi\sec\theta\right] \tag{5.20}$$

in which $\beta = \alpha + \theta + \phi$

Table 5.2 Computation of forces acting on wedge $abcd$ (Fig. 5.9)

Serial no.	Designation	Vertical component		Horizontal component
1	Weight of wedge $abcd$: W	$\frac{1}{2}\gamma H^2(\tan\alpha + \tan\theta)$ $+\gamma nH^2(\tan\alpha + \tan\theta)$ $+\frac{1}{2}\gamma n^2 H^2$	$\downarrow$	---
2	Cohesion: $cH\sec\parallel$	cH	$\uparrow$	$cH\tan\theta \rightarrow$
3	Adhesion: $c'H\sec\alpha$	$c'H$	$\uparrow$	$c'H\tan\alpha \leftarrow$
4	Surcharge: $Q = \alpha$	$q[H(\tan\alpha + \tan\theta) + nH\tan\alpha]$	$\downarrow$	
5	Soil reaction: F	$F\sin(\theta + \phi)$	$\uparrow$	$F\cos(\theta + \phi) \leftarrow$
6	Inertia force: IF	---		$(W + Q)\alpha_h \leftarrow$
7	Earth pressure:	$P\sin(\alpha + \delta)$	$\uparrow$	$P\cos(\alpha + \delta) \rightarrow$

Introducing the following dimensionless parameters

$$(Nac)_{dyn} = \frac{\cos\beta\sec\alpha + \cos\phi\sec\theta}{\sin(\beta + \delta)} \tag{5.21}$$

$$(Naq)_{dyn} = \frac{[(n + 1)\tan\alpha + \tan\theta][\cos(\theta + \phi) + \alpha_h\sin(\theta + \phi)]}{\sin(\beta + \delta)} \tag{5.22}$$

$$(Na\gamma)_{dyn} = \frac{[(n + \frac{1}{2})(\tan\alpha + \tan\theta) + n^2\tan\alpha][\cos(\theta + \phi) + \alpha_h\sin(\theta + \phi)]}{\sin(\beta + \delta)} \tag{5.23}$$

we get

$$P_{dyn} = \gamma H^2(Na\gamma)_{dyn} + qH(Naq)_{dyn} - cH(Nac)_{dyn} \tag{5.24}$$

in which $(Nac)_{dyn}$, $(Naq)_{dyn}$, and $(Na\gamma)_{dyn}$ *are earth pressure coefficients* and depend on α, n, ϕ, δ, and θ.

The values of the earth pressure coefficients in Eqs. (5.21), (5.22), and (5.23) have been determined by optimizing each coefficient. Equation (5.24) gives the upper bound of active earth pressure.

For the static condition, $\alpha_h = 0$. Eqs. (5.21), (5.22), and (5.23) are changed as follows:

$$(Nac)_{stat} = \frac{\cos\beta\sec\alpha + \cos\phi\sec\theta}{\sin(\beta + \delta)} \tag{5.25}$$

$$(Naq)_{stat} = \frac{[(n + 1)\tan\alpha + \tan\theta]\cos(\theta + \phi)}{\sin(\beta + \delta)} \tag{5.26}$$

$$(Na\gamma)_{stat} = \frac{[(n + \frac{1}{2})(\tan\alpha + \tan\theta) + n^2\tan\alpha]\cos(\theta + \phi)}{\sin(\beta + \delta)} \tag{5.27}$$

Equation (5.24) now becomes

$$P_a = \gamma H^2(Na\gamma_{stat} + qH(Naq)_{stat} - cH(Nac)_{stat} \tag{5.28}$$

Maximum values of earth pressure coefficients were also obtained for the static case. It is seen that Nac has the same value in the static as well as in the dynamic case. The ratio of the coefficients from the dynamic to the static case may then be defined as

$$\lambda_1 = \frac{(N_{aqm}\dagger)_{dyn}}{(N_{aqm})_{stat}} \tag{5.29a}$$

$$\lambda_2 = \frac{(N_{a\gamma m})_{dyn}}{(N_{a\gamma m})_{stat}} \tag{5.29b}$$

† Subscript m stands for the maximum value of the coefficient.

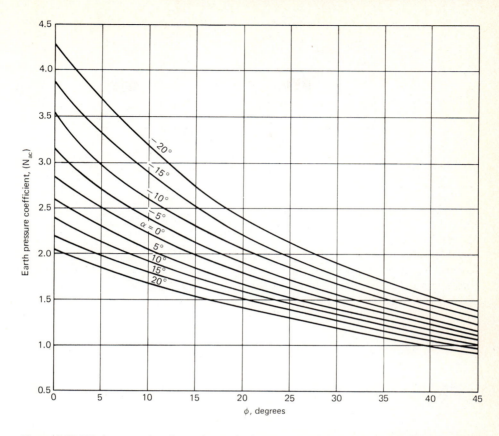

Figure 5.10 $(Nac)_{stat}$ vs. ϕ for all n. [*After Prakash and Saran (1966) and Saran and Prakash (1968)*.]

In Fig. 5.10, Nac has been plotted against ϕ. This plot is independent of n and the inclination of the wall α has been considered from $0°$ to $\pm 20°$ (Prakash and Saran, 1966; Saran and Prakash, 1968). Figures 5.11 and 5.12 show the plot of $(Naq)_{stat}$ versus ϕ for $n = 0$ and $n = 0.2$, respectively. Figures 5.13 and 5.14 show $(Na\gamma)_{stat}$ versus ϕ for $n = 0$ and $n = 0.2$, respectively.

It was found that the values of λ_1 and λ_2 alter slightly with the increase in n. It is therefore recommended that the effect of n on λ_1 and λ_2 not be considered. Secondly, it is found that λ_1 and λ_2 are nearly equal (Prakash and Saran, 1966). Hence, only one value of λ $(= \lambda_1 = \lambda_2)$ has been plotted in Fig. 5.15. The value λ represents the ratio of earth pressure coefficients in the dynamic to the static case and both the coefficients decrease with ϕ; the shape of the curves for different ϕ_h values indicate the rate of decrease of one in relation to the other. Also, λ increases with increasing α_h.

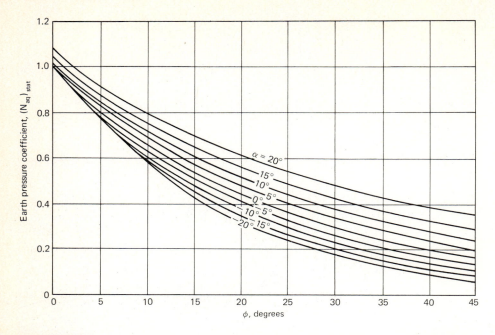

Figure 5.11 $(Naq)_{stat}$ vs. ϕ, $n = 0$. [*After Prakash and Saran (1966) and Saran and Prakash (1968).*]

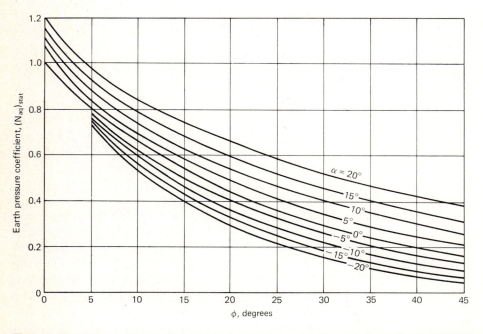

Figure 5.12 $(Naq)_{stat}$ vs. ϕ, $n = 0.2$. [*After Prakash and Saran (1966) and Saran and Prakash (1968).*]

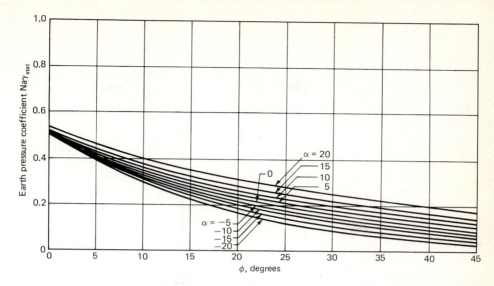

Figure 5.13 $(Na\gamma)_{stat}$ vs. ϕ, $n = 0$. [*After Prakash and Saran (1966) and Saran and Prakash (1968).*]

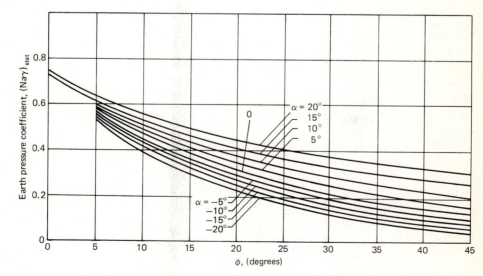

Figure 5.14 $(Na\gamma)_{stat}$ vs. ϕ, $n = 0.2$. [*After Prakash and Saran (1966) and Saran and Prakash (1968).*]

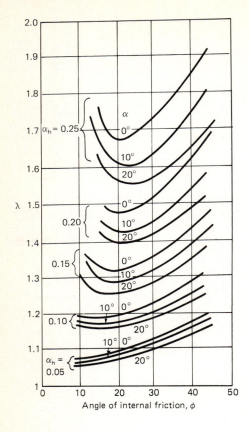

Figure 5.15 λ vs. angle of internal friction ϕ. (*After Prakash and Saran*, 1966.)

5.6 POINT OF APPLICATION

To determine the point of application of the total earth pressure $(P_a)_{\text{dyn}}$, it is necessary to calculate the distribution of earth pressure along the back of the wall. This can be accomplished numerically by computing the total earth pressure to two depths, z and $(z + \Delta z)$, along the wall and assuming a linear distribution over Δz. For the static case and simple boundary conditions, the distribution of earth pressure is hydrostatic.

Prakash and Basavanna (1969) and Saran and Prakash (1970) showed analytically that the distribution of static as well as dynamic active earth pressure behind a rough wall is nonlinear, and developed methods for computing the distribution of earth pressure in two cases. Their solutions, however, need to be reduced to some sort of graphical form to be useful to the practicing engineer. No such analysis is available for dynamic passive earth pressure.

Experimental data indicate that the increase in pressure due to vibrations is much greater near the surface of the ground than at lower depths (Nandkumaran, 1973; Prakash and Nandkumaran, 1979). It is seen that the test data from three different small-scale studies give a better insight into the distribution of static and dynamic earth pressure. The details of this investigation are described in the following section.

5.7 EXPERIMENTAL STUDIES ON SMALL-SCALE WALLS

Many experimental studies have been conducted on small walls to understand the physical behavior of retaining walls during vibrations and to obtain tentative data on the increases in earth pressures and their points of application. The basic principle of earth pressure experiments has been to simulate the strain conditions in backfill, and thus treat the setup as a small prototype.

In the test setup of Mononobe and Matsuo (1950), a box was mounted on a horizontal shake table, filled with dry sand, and subjected to different acceleration levels by exciting the table. The maximum pressures exerted on the wall of the box were measured by means of hydraulic gauges. It was concluded that the maximum pressure increases with base acceleration and the values essentially agreed with those computed by the Mononobe-Okabe formula.

Matsuo (1941) also obtained similar results by conducting tests on a shake table, using sand. However, in these experiments Matsuo found that the dynamic component of pressure acts at two-thirds times the height of the wall.

The same conclusions were derived from tests on dry sand conducted by Jacobsen (1951). In this test setup, a box was mounted on a shake table and the pressures restraining the 3-ft(91.5-cm)-high model wall were measured using dynamometers. The measured earth pressures agreed reasonably with the values computed by the Mononobe-Okabe formula, and the dynamic component of pressures was found to act at the upper third point of the wall. The restraint provided by the dynamometers could affect the results, however.

In the test setup of Matsuo and O'Hara (1960), 40-cm-high walls were excited with vibration for a period of 0.3 s. On fixed walls, it was found that the amplitude of pressure change is large at midheight. In 5-m-high concrete walls, which were excited by a 1-hp oscillator mounted in a trough sunk in the ground 4.5 m away from the wall, pressures were measured on pressure cells. Larger pressures were observed with increasing ground accelerations, with peak pressures at about one-third of the way from the top of the wall.

Ishii, Arai, and Tsuchida (1960) conducted tests using a shake table on which three boxes of different lengths were mounted. The table was excited for a period of about 0.3 s. It was found that the maximum pressure was equal to or lower than the Mononobe-Okabe pressures. Also, the dynamic pressure distribution was parabolic.

Murphy (1960) conducted tests on a solid rubber model of a gravity wall to study the qualitative behavior of backfill during vibrations, and found that the slip surface that developed was flatter than the slip surface under static conditions. The slip surface at Shinizu Harbor, developed in 1930, probably had almost the same inclination.

Tests were performed on three small walls (1-m flexible, 1-m rigid, and 2-m rigid) by Nandkumaran (1973) and reported by Prakash and Nandkumaran (1979).

The 1-m-high walls were mounted on a 5.2 × 2.8 × 1.2-m-high bin placed on a shake table and excited by a pendulum falling freely from a predetermined height. Static earth pressures were measured in both of the walls first. The bin was then excited with different peak accelerations and the dynamic increments of earth pressures were monitored.

Earth pressures, under both static and dynamic conditions, were monitored by eight diaphragm-type earth pressure cells. Deflections and bending moments in a flexible wall were also monitored under static conditions.

Air-dried Ranipur sand, with the following properties, was used:

1. Soil type: SP, poorly graded sands, little or no fines
2. Uniformity coefficient: $C_u = 2.10$
3. Effective size: $D_{10} = 0.13$ mm
4. Specific gravity of solids: $S_s = 2.66$.
5. Relative density at the test condition: 56 percent
6. Angle of internal friction at this relative density: 40°

Typical data from four tests on a 1-m flexible wall and a 1-m rigid wall are listed in Tables 5.3 and 5.4, respectively (Nandkumaran, 1973). In Fig. 5.16, the recorded static and dynamic pressures are plotted along with the K_o (Jaky, 1948) and K_a lines.

Movements during backfilling were not permitted in the rigid wall. Active conditions were then generated by allowing subsequent rotation of the wall. The test bin was then excited and the dynamic increment of pressure with height was recorded. Two types of tests were performed. In one series (tests 1, 2, and 3; Table 5.4), the top of the wall was not allowed to move, while in another (tests 4, 5, and 6), the wall was free to move during the dynamic loading.

While the peak accelerations employed in the 1-m-high walls were large, the acceleration levels in the 2-m-high wall were of the order of 0.3g.

Table 5.3 Particulars of test data on 1-m flexible wall†

Test no.	Total static pressure, g/cm, of wall	Static EP coefficient	Point of application above base, cm	Acceleration in test (peak), g	Total dynamic increment, g/cm, of wall	Point of application above base, cm	Dynamic increment static pressure
1	2	3	4	5	6	7	8
1	2658.0	0.3343	37.60	4.29	1961.0	54.65	0.750
2	2798.7	0.3520	36.00	3.32	1659.5	50.30	0.604
3	2641.3	0.3322	34.25	3.34	1680.0	50.05	0.646
4	2697.0	0.3392	36.00	4.55	2177.0	48.30	0.807

† After Nandkumaran, 1973.

Table 5.4 Particulars of test data on 1-m high rigid wall†

Test no.	Table acceleration, g	Dynamic pressure, g/cm	Point of application above base, cm	Remarks
1	2	3	4	5
1	4.21	2647.0	41.5	No wall movement
2	3.71	2469.5	36.4	No wall movement
3	3.31	1732.5	40.6	No wall movement
4	4.21	2394.0	44.3	Wall moves during shocks
5	3.71	2377.6	37.4	Wall moves during shocks
6	3.31	1486.5	41.2	Wall moves during shocks

† After Nandkumaran, 1973.

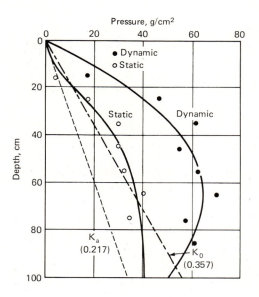

Figure 5.16 Static and dynamic earth pressure distribution behind 1-m-high flexible wall test no. 4. (*After Nandkumaran*, 1973.)

The dynamic earth pressures computed for the peak ground acceleration showed no relationship with the measured earth pressures (Nandkumaran, 1973). However, a plot of peak ground (or table) velocity with the coefficient of dynamic earth pressure $c_p(P_{\text{total}} \div \frac{1}{2}\gamma H^2)$, was found to essentially agree with the theoretical solution, if the ground motion is assumed to have a period of 0.3 s (Fig. 5.17). Table 5.5 lists relevant data on a 2-m-high rigid wall. All of the test results on the 1-m flexible and rigid walls and a 2-m rigid wall were close to the theoretical plot.

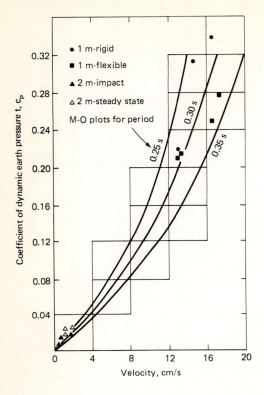

Figure 5.17 Peak ground or table velocity vs. dynamic increment of earth pressure. (*After Prakash and Nandkumaran*, 1979.)

Table 5.5 Peak ground velocities and coefficient of dynamic increment for 2-m-high walls†

Peak ground velocity, cm/s	Coefficient of dynamic increment	Point of application of dynamic increment as % H above base	Remarks
0.56	0.00322	59.4	
0.84	0.00623	61.0	
1.12	0.01052	57.3	Impact load
1.4	0.01710	53.6	
1.68	0.02622	51.4	
0.2	0.002	—	
0.55	0.0065	—	
0.85	0.011	—	Steady state
1.05	0.015	—	

† After Prakash and Nandkumaran, 1979.

The point of dynamic increase in earth pressure was between $0.483H$ and $0.5465H$ in the flexible wall and between $0.364H$ and $0.443H$ from the base in the rigid wall, where H is the height of the wall.

Based upon the above study, the following recommendations are made:

First, the dynamic increment in earth pressure may be computed by the Mononobe-Okabe method. The seismic coefficient α_h can be determined from the following relation:

$$\alpha_h = \frac{V_{max} 2\pi f \cdot 1}{g} \qquad (5.30)$$

in which

V_{max} = peak ground velocity
  f = frequency corresponding to an arbitrarily selected period of ground motion to match the experimental results ($f = 1/0.3$)
  g = acceleration due to gravity

Second, the point of application of dynamic increment can be adopted at $0.55H$ above the base in a flexible wall and at $0.45H$ above the base in a rigid wall.

Analysis of Koyna Wall

Koyna experienced an earthquake on December 11, 1967. The peak ground acceleration was $0.63g$ with a peak ground velocity of 22 cm/s. The spillway basin's gravity wall, which was 70-ft, 4-in high with a 40-ft 2-in-wide base, escaped damage. There was no sign of either overturning or even overstressing of the wall or the foundation soil. Based on an analysis of the wall using the conventional procedures and soil properties used in the original design computations (Krishna, et al., 1969) (namely, the Mononobe-Okabe theory is valid, the inertia force on the wall is given by the product of the weight of the wall and the seismic coefficient, the dynamic increment acts at two-thirds the height of the wall above its base, and the vertical inertia force acts in the worst possible way from the stability standpoint), it was concluded that the wall will overturn at a seismic coefficient of 0.32 and that overstressing of the foundation will occur at a seismic coefficient of 0.26. When the dynamic increment is assumed at midheight, overturning occurs at 0.53 and overstressing at about 0.42. Overstressing does not occur up to $0.5g$ if the dynamic increment acts at $0.45H$ or below. Based on the concept developed above, the equivalent seismic coefficient for computation of total earth pressure is

$$22 \times \left(\frac{2\pi}{0.3}\right) \times \frac{1}{981} = 0.47$$

The wall will be safe then.

Most of the Japanese work reported above was performed at a period of 0.3 s and a good tally was found between observed and measured earth pressures. It is a coincidence that with the peak ground velocity converted to the equivalent ground acceleration with a period of 0.3 s, reasonable tally was found between observed and predicted earth pressures. A peak table velocity of up to about 17 cm/s was used in this investigation.

5.8 DISPLACEMENT ANALYSIS

It was mentioned in Sec. 5.2 that displacements of retaining walls under earthquake-type ground motion are important. No simple and satisfactory methods have been developed so far (1981) to predict displacements of retaining walls during a given ground motion. One highly simplified model for predicting displacements of retaining walls had been proposed by Nandkumaran (1973; 1974). A brief description of this model and salient results are presented in this section.

Mathematical Model

To devise a mathematical model of the retaining wall, foundation, and soil-back-fill system, the deformation of the wall under various types of forces needs to be examined. A rigid wall either moves parallel to itself (translation) or rotates about the heel of the wall at the foundation level, depending on the foundation conditions. However, both forms of movement can also occur simultaneously. In high walls, flexural bending of the wall itself and its base may be important. Therefore, in a true mathematical model, all three types of movement (together with vertical movements, to be more exact) must be considered.

Nandkumaran (1974), however, considered only one degree of freedom in translation. The "wall displacement" has been used as the total displacement from the original equilibrium position of the wall, and the deformation of the soil and the relative displacement between the wall and the soil have not been considered separately.

A one-degree freedom system can be represented as a spring-mass-dash-pot system (Fig. 5.18a). The mass includes the mass of the retaining wall and a part of the backfill that vibrates along with the wall. The spring constant R includes the resistance of soil due to displacement in the backfill and at the base. The dashpot represents the energy absorption characteristics of the system.

Spring constants The resisting forces are provided by the soil behind the wall (Fig. 5.19a) and the soil below the base of the wall (Fig. 5.19b). Therefore, for dynamic analysis, the skeleton curve is as shown in Fig. 5.19c and the final simplified curve used in analysis is shown in Fig. 5.19d. In this figure, the force-displacement relationship is elastoplastic, with higher values of stiffness and the yield level on the compression side.

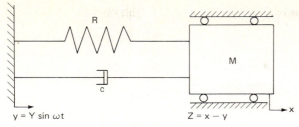

(a) Mathematical model

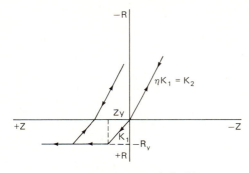

(b) Force displacement relationship

Figure 5.18 Details of mathematical model for dynamic analysis of a retaining wall. (*a*) Mathematical model. (*b*) The force-displacement relationship. (*After Nandkumaran*, 1973.)

Apparent soil mass The soil mass of the backfill participating in the motion was studied on a model test setup (Nandkumaran, 1973) and has been included in the analysis.

Damping values Damping values were arbitrarily selected and varied from 5 to 15 percent of critical damping.

Range of variables Values of variables considered in this analysis are listed in Table 5.6.

Table 5.6 Variables considered in displacement analysis of retaining walls†

Yield displacement Z_y (Fig. 5.18*b*)	0.1, 0.2, 0.3, 0.5, and 1.0 cm
Natural period T_n	1.0, 0.5, 0.3, and 0.2 s
Ground acceleration amplitude a_h	100, 200, and 300 gal
Period of ground motion T_n	0.5, 0.3, 0.2, and 0.1 s
Ratio of stiffnesses η (Fig. 5.18*b*)	2.0 and 3.0
Damping factor (ξ)	5, 10, and 15 %

† After Nandkumaran, 1973; 1974.

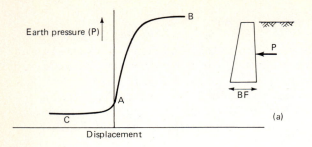

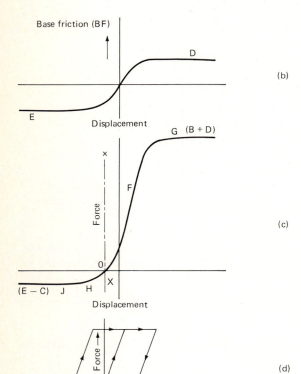

Figure 5.19 Force vs. displacement in a retaining wall. (*After Nandkumaran, 1973.*)

Discussion

The solutions were obtained by the linear acceleration method (Biggs, 1963).

In Fig. 5.20, displacement has been plotted as a function of time. The wall gradually moves away from the backfill and the displacement per cycle after the sixth cycle becomes constant for the case under study. Slip per cycle versus natural period of the wall has been plotted for $Z_y = 0.5$ cm in Fig. 5.21a and for $Z_y = 1.0$ cm in Fig. 5.21b. It will be seen that for a selected acceleration amplitude and the natural period, larger slip occurs when the natural period of the soil-wall system coincides with the period of excitation. Based upon the above results, a tentative procedure for analysis of displacement of a retaining wall may be formulated.

Computation of Displacement of a Retaining Wall

The following information must be known:

1. Section of retaining wall
2. Soil profiles and soil properties
3. Anticipated ground motion

The following information needs to be assumed:

1. Force displacement relationship of the wall in active and passive condition, including base resistance
2. Yield displacement Z_y

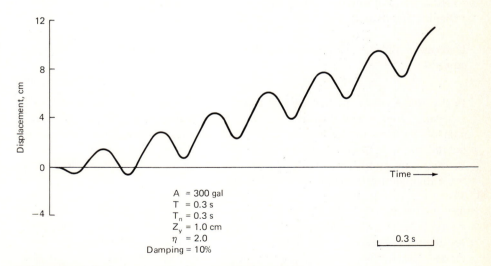

Figure 5.20 Displacement vs. time. (*After Nandkumaran*, 1973.)

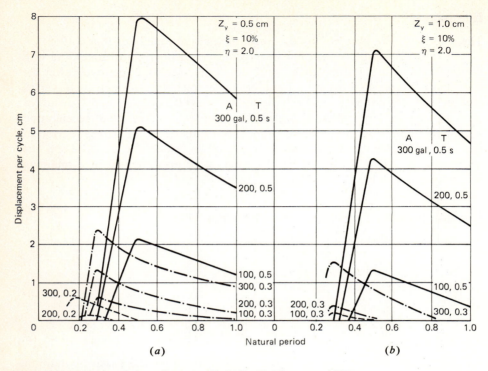

Figure 5.21 Natural period vs. slip per cycle. (*After Nandkumaran*, 1973.)

Guidelines on how to make near-realistic assumptions for the above have been provided by Nandkumaran (1973; 1974) and Prakash et al. (1980).

Displacements may then be computed as follows:

1. Determine the natural period of the wall-Soil system from the following equation:

$$T_n = 2\pi\sqrt{m/k} \tag{5.31}$$

In the above equation, k is the soil stiffness on the tension side as determined in assumptions 1 and 2 above (see Fig. 5.19b), and m may be taken as the sum of the mass of the wall and 0.8 times the mass of the Rankine's wedge behind the wall (Nandkumaran, 1973; 1974).

2. Estimate the number of cycles of uniform ground accelerations equivalent to the anticipated ground motion (see Chap. 8).
3. The slip (plastic displacement) per cycle of ground motion may be determined from Fig. 5.21 for the natural period of the wall, the yield displacement Z_y, and the ground motion characteristics. If the parameters in a given problem are different from those in Fig. 5.21, a linear interpolation may be made. The total slip would be the product of the slip per cycle and the number of cycles.
4. The calculated displacement may be compared with the permissible value.

5.9 INDIAN STANDARD CODE OF PRACTICE

Neither the American Society of Testing and Materials nor the National Bureau of Standards has adopted a standard for (a) computing earth pressures under earthquake-type loading, (b) on the point of application of the dynamic increment, and (c) the displacements of the retaining wall under earthquakes. However, IS 1893–1975 includes useful information on the first two questions. Salient provisions of this standard are as follows:

Active Pressure Due to Earthfill

For general conditions encountered in the design of retaining walls, as illustrated in Fig. 5.7, the active pressure exerted against the wall may be determined from Eq. (5.16).

Point of Application

From the total pressure computed above, subtract the static active pressure obtained by putting $\alpha_h = \alpha_v = \psi = 0$ in Eq. (5.16). The remainder is the dynamic increment. The static component of the total pressure shall be applied at an elevation $h/3$ above the base of the wall. The point of application of the dynamic increment shall be assumed to be at midheight of the wall.

Effect of Saturation on Lateral Earth Pressure

For saturated earthfill, the saturated unit weight of the soil shall be adopted in Eq. (5.16).

For submerged earthfill, the dynamic increment in active earth pressure during earthquakes shall be determined from Eq. (5.16), with the following modifications:

1. The value of δ shall be taken as one-half the value of δ for dry backfill.
2. The value of ψ shall be taken as follows:

$$\psi = \tan^{-1}\frac{\gamma_{\text{sat}}}{\gamma_{\text{sat}-1}}\frac{\alpha_h}{1 \pm \alpha_v}$$

   in which γ_{sat} = saturated unit weight of soil
   α_h = horizontal seismic coefficient
   α_v = vertical seismic coefficient which is $\frac{1}{2}\alpha_h$
3. Buoyant unit weight shall be adopted.
4. From the value of earth pressure found above, subtract the value of earth pressure determined by putting $\alpha_h = \alpha_v = \psi = 0$ by using buoyant unit weight. The remainder shall be dynamic increment.

Hydrodynamic pressure because of water contained in earthfill shall not be considered separately since the effect of acceleration on water has been considered indirectly.

Inertia Forces on the Wall

Concrete or masonry inertia forces due to horizontal and vertical earthquake accelerations are the products of the weight of the wall and the horizontal and vertical seismic coefficients, respectively.†

The above recommendations have been followed in designing a gravity wall in Example 5.3.

5.10 SOLVED EXAMPLES

Example 5.1 A retaining wall is inclined at $10°$ with the vertical. It retains soils with $c = 0.05$ kg/cm^2 and $\phi = 30°$. Determine the total active earth pressure.

If the wall is located in a seismic area where the design seismic coefficient $\alpha_h = 0.1$, determine the change in total earth pressure. Assume soil to be saturated with unit weight of 1.732 g/cm^3 and $\alpha_v = 0$.

GIVEN DATA

Height H_1 of retaining wall	= 6.0 m
Angle of internal friction ϕ	= 30°
Cohesion c	= 0.05 kg/cm^2 = 0.5 T/m^2
Density γ of the backfill	= 1.732 T/m^3
Inclination α of the wall with the vertical	= 10°
Horizontal seismic coefficient α_h	= 0.1
Vertical seismic coefficient α_v	= 0

SOLUTION

Depth H_c of tension cracks $= \dfrac{2c}{\gamma}\sqrt{N\phi}$

$$N\phi = \tan^2\left(45 + \frac{\phi}{2}\right)$$

$$= \tan^2(45 + 15) = 3.0$$

$$H_c = \frac{2 \times 0.5 \times \sqrt{3.0}}{1.732} = 1.0 \text{ m}$$

$$n = \frac{H_c}{H_1 - H_c} = \frac{1}{5} = 0.2$$

† To ensure an adequate safety factor under earthquake conditions, the design shall be such that the safety factor against sliding shall be 1.2 and the resultant of all the forces, including earthquake force, shall fall within the middle three-fourths of the base width provided. In addition, bearing pressure in soil should not exceed the permissible limit.

(a) *Static case* For $\phi = 30°$, $\alpha = 10°$, and $n = 0.2$, the values of earth pressure coefficient $(Nac)_{\text{stat}}$, $(Naq)_{\text{stat}}$, and $(Na\gamma)_{\text{stat}}$ are obtained from Figs. 5.10, 5.12, and 5.14, respectively.

$$Nac_{\text{stat}} = 1.308 \qquad Naq_{\text{stat}} = 0.4 \qquad Na\gamma_{\text{stat}} = 0.27$$

The value of $(P_a)_{\text{stat}}$ is obtained as

$$(P_a)_{\text{stat}} = \left[\gamma H^2 (Na\gamma)_{\text{stat}} + qH(Naq)_{\text{stat}} - CH(Nac)_{\text{stat}}\right] \quad (5.28)$$

In the given problem $q = 0$.

$$(P_a)_{\text{stat}} = 1.732 \times 6^2 \times 0.27 - 0.5 \times 6 \times 1.308$$
$$= 16.835 - 3.924 = 12.91 \text{ T/m}$$

(b) *Earthquake case* The values of earth pressure coefficients are obtained as follows:

$$(Nac)_{\text{dyn}} = (Nac)_{\text{stat}} = 1.308$$
$$(Na\gamma)_{\text{dyn}} = \lambda \cdot (Na\gamma)_{\text{stat}}$$

Value of λ, as obtained from Fig. 5.15 for $\phi = 30°$, $\alpha_h = 0.1$, and $\alpha = 10°$, is 1.209.

$$(Na\gamma)_{\text{dyn}} = 1.209 \times 0.27 = 0.326$$
$$(P_a)_{\text{dyn}} = 1.732 \times 6^2 \times 0.326 - 0.5 \times 6 \times 1.308$$
$$= 20.326 - 3.926 = 16.40 \text{ T/m}$$

The change in earth pressure due to earthquake, that is, dynamic increment

$$(\Delta P_a) = (P_a)_{\text{dyn}} - (P_a)_{\text{stat}}$$
$$= 16.40 - 12.91$$
$$= 3.49 \text{ T/m width of wall}$$

Example 5.2 Compute the static and dynamic active earth pressures on the given retaining walls using Coulomb's theory and Culmann's graphical construction.

Seismic coefficients: $\alpha_h = .1g$ and $\alpha_v = \pm .05g$ (Fig. 5.22).

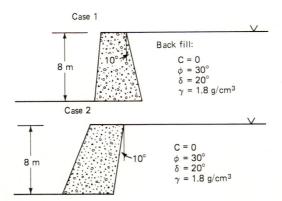

Figure 5.22 Walls of Example 5.2.

SOLUTION

(a) *For Culmann's method*:

(i) Six trial wedges will be used to define Culmann's line, spaced equally.

(ii) Select failure planes to range approximately from $\phi°$ to $(45 + \phi°)$

scales; 1 cm = 0.7 m   and   1 cm = 11,850 kg

(b) A dimensional sketch of the wall is shown in Figure 5.23.

(c) Area-weight calculations for trial wedges:

(i)

$$\Delta abc_1 \cdot \text{area} = \tfrac{1}{2}(\text{base})(\text{height})$$

$$= \tfrac{1}{2}(15.24)(8)$$

$$= 60.96 \text{ m}^2$$

$$\text{vol} = (60.96 \times 1) \text{ m}^3 = 60,960,000 \text{ cm}^3$$

$$\text{weight} = \gamma \cdot \text{vol}$$

$$= 1.8 \text{ g/c}^3 \times 60,960,000 \text{ cm}^3$$

$$= 109,728 \text{ kg (9.26 cm)}$$

(ii) Dynamic case: $\alpha_h = 0.1g$ and $\alpha_v = 0.05g$

$$\overline{W}_1 = \sqrt{[(9.26)(0.1)]^2 + [(9.26)(1.05)]^2} = 9.77 \text{ cm}$$

Dynamic case $\alpha_h := 0.1g$ and $\alpha_v = -0.05g$

$$\overline{W}_1 = \sqrt{[(9.26)(0.1)]^2 + [(9.26)(0.95)]^2} = 8.85 \text{ cm}$$

(iii) The values for all other wedges are presented in tabular form:

$\overline{W}$ (Weight of failure wedges), cm

Wedge	Static	Dynamic $\alpha_h = 0.1g$ $\alpha_v = +0.05g$		Dynamic $\alpha_h = 0.1g$ $\alpha_v = -0.05g$
Δabc_2	7.72	8.14		7.37
Δabc_3	6.18	6.51		5.90
Δabc_4	4.63	4.89		4.42
Δabc_5	3.08	3.25		2.92
Δabc_6	1.55	1.63		1.48

(d) Construction has been shown in Fig. 5.23 for the static case and in Fig. 5.24 for the dynamic case ($\alpha_h = 0.1g$, $\alpha_v = 0.05g$). Total active earth

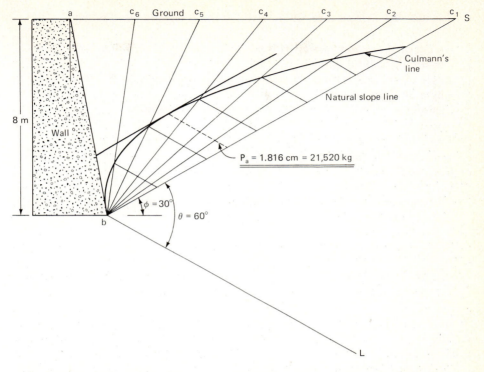

Figure 5.23 Culmann's construction for 8-m wall in case 1 (static) $\alpha = 10°$, Example 5.2.

pressure P_a is 21.52 T/m of wall for the static case, 26.8 T/m of wall for the dynamic case.

(e) The other cases were also solved as above and the following values of earth pressure obtained:

Active Coulomb pressure P_a, T/m of the wall

Case 1			Case 2		
Static	$\alpha_h = 0.1g$	$\alpha_h = 0.1g$	Static	$\alpha_h = 0.1g$	$\alpha_h = 0.1g$
	$\alpha_v = +0.05g$	$\alpha_v = -0.05g$		$\alpha_v = +0.05g$	$\alpha_v = -0.05g$
21.52	26.8	25.040	13.440	18.640	17.200
	$\Delta p_{dyn} = 5.28$	$\Delta p_{dyn} = 3.52$		$\Delta p_{dyn} = 5.200$	$\Delta p_{dyn} = 3.760$

It is seen that maximum pressures occur when $\alpha_v = +0.05g$ in both cases. Also, the total active pressure is considerably smaller in case 2, when the wall is inclined toward the fill.

Example 5.3 Design a retaining wall for the following conditions:

Height of the retaining wall = 8 m
Density of backfill material γ = 1.8 g/cm³
Angle of internal friction for the backfill material ϕ_{back} = 30°
Angle of wall friction δ = 20°
Inclination of the wall face (in contact with the backfill)
    with vertical α = +10°
Angle of internal friction of the soil below the base ϕ_{base} = 33°
Density of soil below the base = 1.95 g/cm³
Cohesion c = 0

The wall is located in a seismic zone for which the design seismic coefficients are:

$$\alpha_h = 0.1 \qquad \alpha_v = 0$$

The fill is not likely to be saturated during its life. The coefficient of friction between the soil and the wall is 0.48 (μ). The following factors of

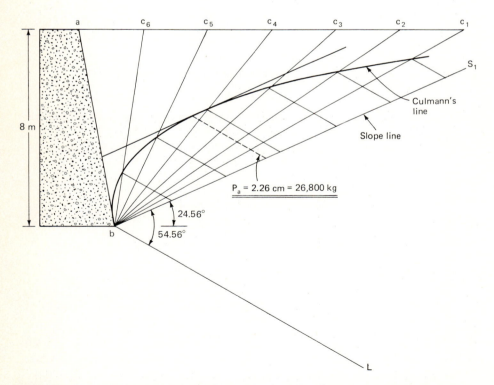

Figure 5.24 Culmann's construction for 8-m wall in case 2 (dynamic) α_h = 0.1, Example 5.2.

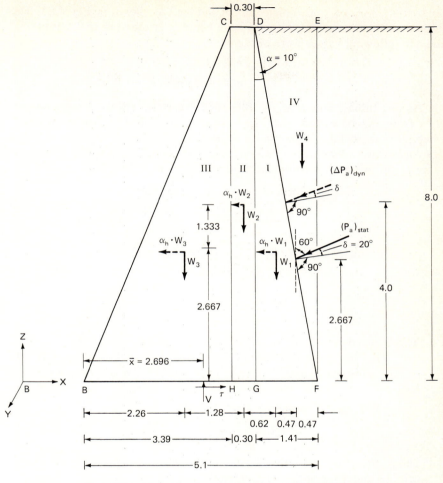

(1) Additional forces due to earthquake are shown by dotted lines.
(2) All dimensions are in meters.

Figure 5.25 Assumed trial dimensions of wall in Example 5.3.

safety will be adopted for design:

(*a*) For overturning: static, 3.0; dynamic, 1.0.
(*b*) For sliding: static, 1.5; dynamic, 1.2.
(*c*) For bearing capacity: static, 3.0; dynamic,† 2.4.

   † An increase of 25 percent in safe allowable pressure will be admissible for earthquake loading conditions for the type of soil under consideration.

SOLUTION   Assume trial dimensions of the wall as shown in Fig. 5.25. The static and dynamic earth pressures have been determined as in Example 5.2 and the following values were obtained:

$$(P_a)_{\text{stat}} = 21.74 \text{ T/m}$$

$$\Delta P_{\text{dyn}} = 4.66 \text{ T/m}$$

As per Indian Standard IS 1893-1975 the static earth pressure acts at $H/3$ from the base and dynamic increment acts at $H/2$ from the base, where H is the height of the wall.

(a) *Static case*   Assume a 1-m width for the wall. The weights of the wall and soil wedge are computed and tabulated in Table 5.7.

(i) Point of application of resultant soil reaction:

$$\bar{X} = \sum \frac{V_i X_i}{\sum V_i} = \frac{235.01 - 50.21}{68.53} = 2.696 \text{ m}$$

$$\text{Eccentricity } e = 2.696 - \frac{5.1}{2} = 0.146 \text{ m}$$

$$\frac{B}{6} = \frac{5.1}{6} = 0.85$$

$$e < \frac{B}{6}$$

Therefore, there will be no tension below the base of the wall.

The design of the retaining wall will be satisfactory if it is safe against overturning and sliding at the base and the soil pressure at the base does not exceed the safe soil pressure.

(ii) Factor of saftey against overturning:

$$\text{FS} = \frac{\text{resisting moments}}{\text{actuating moments}}$$

The resisting and actuating moments have been computed as shown in cols. 13 and 14, respectively, of Table 5.7.

$$\text{FS} = \frac{235.01}{50.21} = 4.68$$

(iii) Factor of safety against sliding at the base:

$$\text{FS} = \frac{\text{resisting force at the base}}{\text{actuating force}}$$

$$= \frac{\mu \sum V}{\text{horizontal component of active earth pressure}}$$

$$= \frac{0.48 \times 68.53}{18.83} = 1.746$$

Hence the wall is safe against sliding at the base.

Table 5.7

m

No.	Item	Dimensions of element, m				Density, T/m³	Weight, W or force, T	Component, T		Coordinates of point of application, m		Moment about B, T − m		Remarks
		a_x	a_y	a_z	Material			V	H	X_i	Z_i	VX_i	HZ_i	
1	2	3	4	5	6	7	8	9	10	11	12	13	14	15
	Weights													
1	W_1	1.41	1.0	8.0	concrete	2.2	12.40	12.40↓	---	4.16	2.667	+51.584†	---	Triangular element
2	W_2	0.30	1.0	8.0	concrete	2.2	5.28	5.28↓	---	3.54	4.000	+18.691	---	Rectangular element
3	W_3	3.39	1.0	8.0	concrete	2.2	29.83	29.83↓	---	2.26	2.667	+67.415	---	Triangular element
4	W_4	1.41	1.0	8.0	soil	1.8	10.15	10.15↓	---	4.63	5.333	+46.994	---	Triangular element
5	Static earth pressure, $(P_a)_{stat}$	---	---	---	---	---	21.74	10.87↓	18.83←	4.63	2.667	+50.328	−50.21†	Vertical Component = $(P_a)_{stat} \cos 60°$; Horizontal Component = $(P_a)_{stat} \sin 60°$
	Total							68.53	18.83			+235.01	−50.21	
6	Dynamic increment, $\Delta(P_a)_{dyn}$	---			---	---	4.66	2.33↓	4.03←	4.395	4.00	+10.24	−16.12	Vertical component = $\Delta(P_a)_{dyn} \cos 60°$; Horizontal component = $\Delta(P_a)_{dyn} \sin 60°$
	Inertia forces													
7	$\alpha_h \cdot W_1$	---	---	---	---	---	1.24	---	1.24←	4.16	2.667	---	−3.307	$\alpha_h = 0.1$
8	$\alpha_h \cdot W_2$	---	---	---	---	---	0.528	---	0.528←	3.54	4.00	---	−2.112	
9	$\alpha_h \cdot W_3$	---	---	---	---	---	2.983	---	2.983←	2.26	2.667	---	−7.95	
	Total							2.33	8.781			+10.24	−29.48	
	Grand total							70.86	27.611			+245.25	−79.69	

† Clockwise (+).

(*iv*) Factor of safety against bearing capacity failure:

$$\text{Total vertical load } V = 68.53 \text{ T}$$

$$\text{Ratio of eccentricity to width} = \frac{e}{B} = \frac{0.146}{5.1}$$

$$= 0.0286$$

For $\phi = 33°$ and $(e/B) = 0.0286$, the values of bearing capacity factors N_γ, N_q, and N_c are obtained from Figs. 6.8, 6.9, and 6.10, respectively:

$$N_\gamma = 27 \qquad N_q = 24 \qquad N_c = 40.0$$

Using Eq. (6.1) and substituting $c = 0$, $D_f = 0$, and the values of bearing capacity factors,

$$Q_d = B \cdot q_d = 5.1 \times \left(\tfrac{1}{2} \times 1.95 \times 5.1 \times 27\right)\text{T}$$

$$= 684.7 \text{ T}$$

The factor of safety against bearing capacity failure

$$= \frac{Q_d}{P(=V)} = \frac{684.7}{68.53} = 9.99$$

The factor of safety against bearing capacity failure being greater than 3, the footing is safe against bearing capacity failure.

(*b*) *Earthquake case* The values of dynamic increment in earth pressure and additional forces due to earthquake are listed in Table 5.7.

(*i*) Point of application of resultant soil reaction:

$$\overline{X} = \frac{245.25 - 79.69}{70.86} = 2.336 \text{ m}$$

which is within the middle three-fourths of the base width as per IS 1893-1975 (Sec. 5.9). Further,

$$\text{Eccentricity } e_{\text{dyn}} = \frac{5.1}{2} - 2.336 = 0.214 < \frac{B}{6}$$

Hence, no tension below the base.

(*ii*) Factor of safety against overturning:

$$\text{FS} = \frac{\text{resisting moments}}{\text{actuating moments}}$$

$$= \frac{245.25}{79.69} = 3.07$$

which is greater than the specified value of the FS.

(*iii*) Factor of safety against sliding:

$$\text{FS} = \frac{0.48 \times 70.86}{27.611} = 1.23$$

which is greater than the permissible FS for the earthquake case.

(*iv*) Factor of safety against bearing capacity failure: Total vertical load $V = 70.86$ T.

$$\frac{e_{dyn}}{B} = \frac{0.214}{5.1} = 0.0419$$

From Fig. 6.8, for $\phi = 33°$ and $\dfrac{e_{dyn}}{B} = 0.0419$, $N_\gamma = 25$.

$$Q_d = Bq_d = 5.1\left(\frac{1}{2} \times 1.95 \times 5.1 \times 25\right)$$

$$= 633.99$$

The FS against bearing capacity failure

$$= \frac{633.99}{70.86} = 8.94$$

which is more than the specified value of the FS.

Example 5.4 Compute the displacement of the wall in Example 5.3 for the following conditions:

  (*i*) period of wall $= 0.30$ s
 (*ii*) $Z_y = 0.5$ cm
(*iii*) $\xi = 10\%$
(*iv*) period of ground motion $= 0.20$
 (*v*) average ground acceleration $= 0.3g$ (300 gals)
(*vi*) Equivalent number of cycles in an earthquake of magnitude 7 will not exceed 10

SOLUTION   From Fig. 5.21*a*,

$$\text{Slip per cycle} = 0.5 \text{ cm}$$

therefore $\qquad\qquad$ Total slip $= 10 \times 0.5 = 5$ cm

If average acceleration of $0.35g$ acts with a period of 0.3 s, then

$$\text{Slip per cycle} = 2.25 \text{ cm}$$

therefore $\qquad\qquad$ Total slip $= 22.5$ cm
If the period of ground motion is 0.5 s, then

$$\text{Slip per cycle} = 0.8 \text{ cm}$$

therefore $\qquad\qquad$ Total slip $= 0.8 \times 10 = 8$ cm

5.11 FINAL COMMENTS

The problems of earth pressure variation due to earthquake motion, point of application of the dynamic increment, and displacement of the wall have been highlighted. An important question in the retaining wall problem is "How much is a particular wall going to deflect from its static equilibrium postion?" The next question is "What is the permissible deflection?"

Considerable literature has appeared on the topic of dynamic increment in earth pressure and its point of application. Excellent summaries of the pertinent literature have been prepared by Seed and Whitman (1970) and Nandkumaran (1974). There is general agreement on the use of the Mononobe theory for computing dynamic increment in earth pressure. But what is the value of seismic coefficient in a given problem? Seed and Whitman (1970) recommended that earth pressure coefficients be adopted as follows:

$$K_{AE} = K_A + \tfrac{3}{4}\alpha_h \qquad (5.32)$$

in which K_{AE} = active earth pressure coefficient under earthquake
K_A = active earth pressure coefficient under static case
α_h = horizontal seismic coefficient

This equation does not provide the answer to the question posed above. Nandkumaran (1973) and Prakash and Nandkumaran (1979) have made a scientific recommendation to estimate the value of seismic coefficient based upon a seismogram for the site and peak ground velocity associated with it. These recommendations have been found to hold for an arbitrarily selected period of 0.3 s. No satisfactory explanation is available for selecting this period. However, the method has been found to work on three small walls and deserves a trial for adoption in practice, without losing sight of engineering judgment.

The question of displacements of walls has been emphasized time and again (Richards and Elms, 1979; Nazarian and Hadjian, 1979). A method for computing displacements of walls based upon the works of Nandkumaran (1973, 1974) and Prakash et al. (1980) has been included only in its simplified form, because many retaining walls do not fail by translation alone. Sophisticated tools like the finite element method are available to solve problems of displacements of walls, but it is recommended that the engineering approach to solving this problem in translation and rotation may yield acceptable results that can be used by practicing engineers without using lengthy computer programs. There is an urgent need to develop such methods.

No information is available on permissible displacements of retaining walls.

There is one more question associated with dynamic earth pressures. In the case of basement walls and abutments of bridges, the static pressures are "at-rest" pressures. During earthquakes, what increases (or changes) in earth pressures on such structures may be expected? Practically no information is available on these changes. However, static at-rest pressures are higher than the active pressures. It is likely that earth pressures during earthquakes may also be higher than the total (static plus dynamic) earth pressures in the active condition. It is tentatively recommended that percentage increases in earth pressures over the static at-rest pressures be assumed equal to the percentage increases in active earth pressures under dynamic conditions. No rational explanation can be offered for the above recommendation at present (1981).

It will thus be seen that there are several questions on the dynamic behavior of retaining walls that have not been adequately investigated and offer fruitful areas for future research. When better answers to the problems posed in this chapter become available, the corresponding recommendations would need revision.

PRACTICE PROBLEMS

5.1 A vertical retaining wall is 8 m high and retains noncohesive soil with $\gamma = 1.7$ g/cm^3, $\phi = 33°$, and $\delta = 22°$. The wall is located in a seismic area where the design seismic coefficients are:

$$\alpha_v = 0.12 \qquad \alpha_h = 0.06$$

Compute the static and dynamic earth pressures on the wall.

5.2 If the wall is Prob. 5.1 is to incline at 10° with the vertical, would you recommend its inclination towards or away from the fill. Justify your answer fully.

5.3 Write a short note on the displacements of retaining walls during earthquakes.

5.4 If you were to write provisions of a U.S. code for determination of seismic earth pressures, how would these provisions be different than those of the corresponding IS code?

5.5 Describe displacement analysis of a retaining wall during an earthquake.

REFERENCES

Biggs, J. M.: "Introduction to Structural Dynamics," McGraw-Hill Book Co., New York, 1963.

Coulomb, C. A.: Essai sur une application des regles des maximis et minimis a quelque problems de statique relalifs a l' architecture, *Mem. Acad. Roy. Pres. Divers-savants*, vol. 7, 1773.

Culmann, K.: "Die Graphische Statik," Mayer and Zeller, Zurich, 1866.

Indian Standard Criteria for Earthquake Resistant Design of Structures," IS 1893–1975, 3d ed.

Ishii, Y., H. Arai, and H. Tsuchida: Lateral Earth Pressure in an Earthquake, *Proc. Second World Conference on Earthquake Engineering*, Tokyo, vol. 1, p. 211, 1960.

Jacobsen, L. S.: "Kentucky Project Report No. 13," Tennessee Valley Authority, ser. 1951, app. D, 1951.

Jaky, J: Pressure in Silos, *Proc. Second Int. Conf. Soil Mech. Found. Engin.* vol. 1, pp. 103–107, 1948.

Kapila, I. P.: Earthquake Resistant Design of Retaining Walls, *Proc. Second Symposium on Earthquake Engineering, University of Roorkee*, pp. 97–108, 1962.

Krishna, J., A. S. Arya, and K. Kumar: "Distribution of the Maximum Intensity of Force in the Koyna Earthquake of December 11, 1967," Earthquake Engineering Studies, University of Roorkee, Roorkee, India, August 1969.

S. Prakash, and P. Nandkumaran: Dynamic Earth Pressure Distribution Behind Flexible Retaining Walls, *Indian Geotech. J.*, vol. 4, no. 3, pp. 207–224, July 1974.

Matsuo, H.: Experimental Study on the Distribution of Earth Pressure Acting on a Vertical Wall during Earthquakes, *J. Japanese Society of Civil Engineers*, vol. 27, no. 2, 1941.

——, and S. Ohara: Lateral Earth Pressures and Stability of Quay Walls during Earthquakes, *Proc. Second World Conference on Earthquake Engineering*, Tokyo, vol. 1, p. 165, 1960.

Mononobe, N.: Earthquake Proof Construction of Masonary Dams, *Proc. World Engineering Congress*, Tokyo, vol. 9, p. 275, 1929.

——, and H. Matsuo: On Determination of Earth Pressure During Earthquakes, *Proc. World Engineering Congress*, Tokyo, 1929.

Murphy, V. A.: The Effect of Ground Characteristics on the Aseismic Design of Structures, *Proc. Second World Conference on Earthquake Engineering*, Tokyo, vol. 1, pp. 231–248, 1960.

Nandkumaran, P.: "Behavior of Retaining Walls Under Dynamic Loads," Ph.D. thesis, Roorkee University, Roorkee, India, 1973.

_____: Behavior of Retaining Walls During Earthquakes, in "Earthquake Engineering," Sarita Prakeshan, Meerut, U.P., India, chap. 17, 1974.

_____ and H. C. Dhiman: A Miniature Earth Pressure Cell for Dynamic Studies, *J. Indian Nat. Soc. Soil Mech. Found. Engin.*, vol. 9, no. 1, pp. 3–12, January 1970.

Nazarian, H. N., and A. H. Hadjian: Earthquake-Induced Lateral Soil Pressures on Structures, *J. Geotech. Engin. Div. ASCE*, vol. 105, no. GT 9, pp. 1049–1066, September 1979.

Niwa, S.: An Experimental Study of Oscillating Earth Pressures Acting on a Quay Wall, *Proc. Second World Conference on Earthquake Engineering, Tokyo*, vol. 1, pp. 281–297, 1960.

Okabe, S.: General Theory on Earth Pressure and Seismic Stability of Retaining Walls and Dams, *J. Jpn. Soc. Civ. Eng.*, vol. 6, 1924.

Prakash, S., and B. M. Basvanna: Earth Pressure Distribution Behind Retaining Walls During Earthquakes, *Proc. Fourth World Conference on Earthquake Engineering, Chile*, vol. 3, pp. 133–148, 1969.

_____, G. Ranjan, and S. Saran: "Analysis and Design of Foundations and Retaining Structures," Sarita Prakashan, Meerut, U.P., India, 1979.

_____ and P. Nandkumaran: Dynamic Earth Pressure Distribution on Rigid Walls, *Proc. Symposium on Earth and Earth Structures Subjected to Earthquakes and Other Dynamic Loads, Roorkee*, vol. 1, pp. 11–16, March 1973.

_____ and _____: Earth Pressures During Earthquakes, *Proc. Second U.S. National Conference on Earthquake Engineering, Stanford*, pp. 613–622, August 1979.

_____, _____, and J. Krishna: "Displacement Analysis of Rigid Retaining Walls in Translation During Earthquakes," Unpublished Report, University Missouri-Rolla, September 1980.

_____ and S. Saran: Static and Dynamic Earth Pressures Behind Retaining Walls, *Proc. Third Symposium on Earthquake Engineering, Roorkee*, vol. 1, pp. 277–288, November 1966.

Rankine, W. J. M.: On the Stability of Loose Earth, *Philos. Trans. R. Soc. London*, V 147 pp. 9–27, 1857.

Richards, R., Jr., and D. G. Elms: Seismic Behavior of Gravity Retaining Walls, *J. Geotech. Engin. Div., ASCE*, vol. 105, no. GT 4, pp. 449–464, 1979.

Saran, S., and A. Prakash: Seismic Pressure Distribution in Earth Retaining Walls, *J. Proc. Fourth European Symposium on Earthquake Engineering, Sofia, Bulgaria*, 1970.

_____ and S. Prakash: Dimensionless Parameters for Static and Dynamic Earth Pressure for Retaining Walls, *Indian Geotech. J.*, vol. 7, no. 3, pp. 295–310, July 1968.

Seed, H. B., and R. V. Whitman: "Design of Earth Retaining Structures for Dynamic Loads," *Proc ASCE Specialty Conference on Lateral Stresses in the Ground and Design of Earth Retaining Structures, Ithaca, N.Y.*, pp. 103–147, 1970.

Terzaghi, K.: A General Wedge Theory of Earth Pressures, *Trans. ASCE*, vol. 106, pp. 68–97, 1941.

_____: "Theoretical Soil Mechanics," John Wiley and Sons Inc., New York, 1943.

_____ and R. B. Peck: "Soil Mechanics in Engineering Practice," 2d ed., John Wiley and Sons, Inc., New York, 1967.

DYNAMIC BEARING CAPACITY

6.1 GENERAL

Dynamic loads on foundations may be caused by the effects of earthquakes or bomb blasts, by operations of machines, and by water wave action. Earthquakes and water wave action induce predominantly horizontal forces in the superstructure, while in the case of bomb blasts the loads may be predominantly vertical. An analysis of the footing may be made considering the dynamic forces to be equivalent to the static forces. For a more realistic picture, a dynamic analysis should be performed. In this chapter, conventional methods of analysis are first presented and then dynamic analyses are introduced. Pile foundations are dealt with in Chap. 7 and machine foundations in Chap. 9.

6.2 FAILURE ZONES BENEATH A SHALLOW CONTINUOUS FOOTING AND ULTIMATE BEARING CAPACITY

We will consider shallow strip footings only (Fig. 6.1), in which the depth of the footing D_f is smaller than or equal to its width B, that is, in which $D_f \leq B$. The assumption of strip footing makes the analysis two-dimensional and relatively simple.

Figure 6.2 shows a surface footing with a rough base in which $D_f = 0$.

In most texts on soil mechanics the failure zones below such a footing are as sketched in this figure (Terzaghi and Peck, 1967; Prakash et al., 1979). Zone I

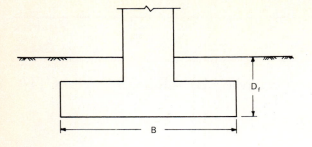

Figure 6.1 A shallow footing of width B and depth $D_f \leq B$.

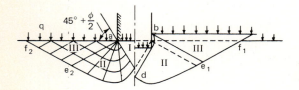

Figure 6.2 Failure zones below a shallow, strip, surface footing in c-ϕ soils.

represents the *elastic wedge* that penetrates the soil along with the footing when the load on the footing increases. Two zones III on either side represent *passive Rankine zones*. The inclination of the passive Rankine zone with the horizontal is $45 - \phi/2$. The two zones II located between zones I and III are *zones of radial shear*. One set of lines of the shear pattern in these zones radiates from the outer edge of the base of the footing. The curved surfaces of sliding de_1 and de_2 are logarithmic spirals.

For cohesive soils, $\phi = 0$, the logarithmic spiral becomes a circle, and zone I in Fig. 6.2 vanishes.

Terzaghi (1943) first published an approximate method for computing the ultimate bearing capacity of soils based on the following assumptions:

1. The base of the footing is rough.
2. The soil above the base of the footing can be replaced with an equivalent surcharge.

Considering the equilibrium of the failure wedges $abde_1 f_1$ and $abde_2 f_2$, Terzaghi derived the following expression for the ultimate unit bearing capacity q_d of shallow strip footings:

$$q_d = cN_c + \gamma D_f N_q + \tfrac{1}{2}\gamma B N_\gamma \tag{6.1}$$

where
$c = $ unit cohesion of soil
$\gamma = $ density of soil
$B = $ width of footing
$D_f = $ depth of footing
$N_c, N_q,$ and $N_\gamma = $ bearing capacity factors

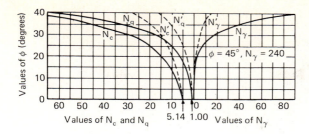

Figure 6.3 Bearing capacity charts. *(After Terzaghi and Peck, 1967. 1967. Reproduced by permission of John Wiley and Sons, New York.)*

Bearing capacity factors depend only on the angle of internal friction of soil and have, therefore, been calculated once and plotted in Fig. 6.3. Total bearing capacity Q_d:

$$Q_d = B(q_d)$$

or

$$Q_d = B\left(cN_c + \gamma D_f N_q + \tfrac{1}{2}\gamma B N_\gamma\right) \tag{6.2}$$

Terzaghi and Peck (1967) recommend that in soft soils, c' and ϕ' should be used and their values determined as follows:

$$c' = \tfrac{2}{3}c \tag{6.3a}$$

and

$$\phi' = \tan^{-1}\left(\tfrac{2}{3}\tan\phi\right) \tag{6.3b}$$

The reduced bearing capacity factors N_c', N_q', and N_γ' for the same value of ϕ are also shown by dashes in Fig. 6.3. Thus, the bearing capacity in such cases is given by

$$Q_d' = B\left(\tfrac{2}{3}cN_c' + \gamma D_f N_q' + \tfrac{1}{2}\gamma B N_q'\right) \tag{6.4}$$

6.3 CRITERIA FOR SATISFACTORY ACTION OF A FOOTING

A footing must satisfy two general requirements:

1. The soil supporting the footing must be safe against shear failure. An adequate factor of safety is provided while assigning allowable loads to a footing.
2. The footing must not settle more than a specified amount.

All footings, although specifically designed for equal settlement, will also undergo some differential settlements, which may equal from two-thirds to three-fourths of the total settlements. According to the Indian Standard Code of Practice (1904–1978), ranges for permissible total and differential settlements of isolated footings and rafts for steel and concrete structures are as given in Table 6.1.

Table 6.1 Maximum and differential settlements of buildings*

Sl No	Type of Structure	Isolated foundation						Raft foundation					
		Sand and hard clay			Plastic clay			Sand and hard clay			Plastic clay		
		Maximum settlement mm	Differential settlement mm	Angular distortion	Maximum settlement mm	Differential settlement mm	Angular distortion	Maximum settlement mm	Differential settlement mm	Angular distortion	Maximum settlement mm	Differential settlement mm	Angular distortion
(1)	(2)	(3)	(4)	(5)	(6)	(7)	(8)	(9)	(10)	(11)	(12)	(13)	(14)
i)	For steel structure	50	0.0033L†	$\frac{1}{300}$	50	0.0033L	$\frac{1}{300}$	75	0.0033L	$\frac{1}{300}$	100	0.0033L	$\frac{1}{300}$
ii)	For reinforced concrete structures	50	0.0015L	$\frac{1}{666}$	75	0.0015L	$\frac{1}{666}$	75	0.002L	$\frac{1}{500}$	100	0.002L	$\frac{1}{500}$

*After IS (1904–1978).

†L is center-to-center distance between columns.

174

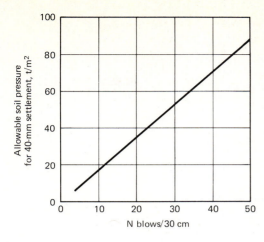

Figure 6.4 Chart for estimating allowable load on footings in sands for 40-mm settlement. *(After Peck, Hansen, and Thornburn, 1974.)*

Settlements of footings in clays are estimated on the basis of principles of consolidation and settlement described by Singh and Prakash (1970). For footings in sands, settlements may be estimated with the help of the chart in Fig. 6.4.

6.4 EARTHQUAKE LOADS ON FOOTINGS

Let us consider the effect of seismic loads on the settlement behavior of a typical building as shown in Fig. 6.5.

Additional forces applied to a spread footing may include:

1. Vertical alternating loads
2. Horizontal alternating loads
3. Alternating moments about one or more axes

If vertical alternating loads predominate, failure may be expected to follow a static pattern, as shown in Fig. 6.2. If horizontal forces are predominant, sliding may occur. Overturning moments probably cause slip surfaces to form alternately on each side of the foundation (Moore and Darragh, 1956).

It is assumed that earthquake moment on a frame induces compression on one side and tension on the other. Thus, the oscillating earthquake force subjects exterior footings to alternating increased compression and its release. If the dynamic force is considered to be an equivalent static force, and if results of a structural analysis of lateral earthquake loads show a 50 percent increase in the vertical loads on the exterior columns, then the exterior footings could be made 50 percent larger to accommodate the combined static and seismic loads and to provide for shear failure considerations. The sizes of the interior footings would not be affected much. Since earthquake loads act for much shorter duration, the

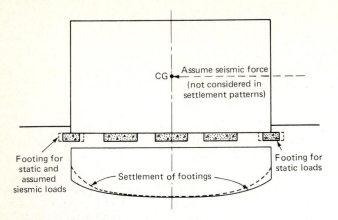

Figure 6.5 Settlement patterns of footings under earthquake-type loading.

settlements of footings under static loads would be reduced, resulting in larger differential settlements.

However, settlements may be important in a study of the performance of footings during earthquakes, particularly when footings rest on sands and sandy soils. In Chap. 4, it was shown that the settlements (deformations) in soil samples depended upon the initial static stress level, the induced earthquake stress level, and the number of cycles of loading. There are not enough data available to warrant any general recommendations; however, in any particular case, the initial static stress level and the induced earthquake stress level can be estimated.

Taylor (1968) prepared a table (Table 6.2) that gives number of acceleration pulses (that is, positive or negative half cycles) of greater magnitude than the given percentage of the maximum acceleration recorded for that earthquake. Data on the Koyna earthquake have been reported by Krishna and Chandrasekaran (1976).

It can be seen from this table that, for earthquakes for which records are available, there are very few pulses that are greater than 75 percent of the maximum acceleration. If pulses greater than 50 percent of the maximum acceleration are considered to be significant, the greatest number is 49. As these are half cycles, this is equivalent to about 25 full cycles. Also, according to Seed (1960), the horizontal acceleration may approach its peak intensity as many as 15 to 20 times in a period of about half a minute. Including aftershocks, the total number of large vibrating pulses may thus be as great as 50 or 60. Therefore, the number of cycles of dynamic loading that may be considered in an analysis of footings is 50. It is therefore recommended that a plate-load test be performed to assess settlements under static and dynamic stresses, as well as settlements under the actual footing under the same stress levels. These may be computed on the

Table 6.2 Data from accelerograms†

Description of earthquake	Maximum acceleration, g	Duration, s	No. of pulses greater than given percentage of maximum acceleration		
			75%	50%	25%
El Centro (Dec. 30, 1934)—NS	0.27	25	1	3	37
El Centro (Dec. 30, 1934)—EW	0.18	25	3	18	79
El Centro (May 18, 1940)—NS	0.32	30	6	24	69
El Centro (May 18, 1940)—EW	0.23	30	5	24	69
Santa Barbara (June 30, 1941)—N45E	0.22	18	3	7	17
Santa Barbara (June 30, 1941)—S45E	0.24	18	2	3	8
Olympia, WA (Apr. 13, 1949)—S80W	0.32	26	1	10	90
Olympia, WA (Apr. 13, 1949)—S10E	0.18	26	8	49	140
Koyna, India (Dec. 11, 1967)‡					
H-component	0.65	10.7	2.5	7	26

†After Taylor (1968).
‡After Krishna and Chandrasekaran (1976).

basis of the following relationships: For sands,

$$S_f = S_p \left[\frac{B_f(B_p + 30.48)}{B_p(B_f + 30.48)} \right]^2 \tag{6.5}$$

for clays,

$$S_f = S_p \frac{B_f}{B_p} \tag{6.6}$$

in which S_f = settlement of foundation, also designated as S_0
             S_p = settlement of plate
             B_f = foundation width, cm
             B_p = plate width, cm

A suggested arrangement of a plate-load test is as follows: Mount a Lazan-type oscillator on a rigid steel plate. Preferably, the weights of the oscillator and the plate should be such that the stress induced on the base of the plate is at least 70 g/cm^2, according to IS 1888–1971. The position of eccentrics is adjusted so that the desired amount of dynamic stress intensity is attained at a predetermined frequency of excitation. Static loading is then applied to the test plate by gravity loading and the deformation is observed on dial gauges until its rate becomes negligible. About an hour may suffice for this state to be attained in the case of sands, while about 24 h may be required for clays. The load increment may be applied in one step, up to the design load intensity for static loads. After all settlement has occurred under static loads, the oscillator is operated for 50 cycles only and settlement of the plate is determined. This is plate settlement S_p.

A dynamic test is performed in addition to a static-plate-load test in a new pit. The settlement of the foundation S_f is then computed for the dynamic case. If it is within permissible limits, the design is acceptable; if it is not within these limits, the design needs modification.

Hardly any data that could serve as preliminary estimates are available on this subject. Sridharan (1962), Eastwood (1953), Converse (1953), and Nagraj (1961) report data on settlement of footings for different combinations of static and dynamic loads. The plate-load test suggested above could be adopted and run with the routine plate-load test (Prakash, 1974).

The frequency of vibrations of the oscillator should be far removed from the natural frequency of the vibrator-soil system. The natural frequency may be estimated from principles discussed in Chap. 9.

6.5 EFFECT OF HORIZONTAL LOAD AND MOMENT

Let us consider a water tower foundation (Fig. 6.6). Seismic force can then be considered to be acting at the center of gravity of the tower full of water. Loads on the foundation will predominantly consist of a moment and a horizontal thrust, in addition to a vertical static load. Pressure distribution below the foundation will not be uniform.

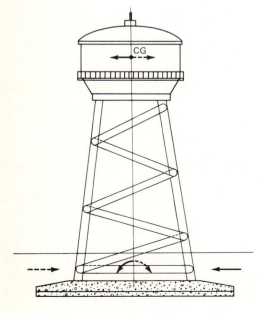

Figure 6.6 A water tower on isolated footing under the action of horizontal loads and moments.

One of the following three cases may arise, depending on whether the effects of moment are predominant as compared with the horizontal thrust, or reverse is the case, or the effects of both types of load are predominant.

1. If the effect of moment only is predominant, the footing is then an eccentrically loaded footing.
2. If the effect of thrust only is important, the footing is then under the action of an inclined central load. This may not hold for most practical cases.
3. If the effects of both moment and thrust are important, the footing is then subjected to an eccentric inclined load.

A brief analysis of the footing for each of the three cases follows.

Eccentric Load on Footing

The moment M on the footing is replaced by an eccentric vertical load so that eccentricity e equals M/Q, where Q is the central vertical load due to static dead and live loads.

Figure 6.7 shows a footing under the action of a load Q acting with eccentricity e. It is known from principles of elementary strength of materials that if $e < B/6$, the footing is in compression throughout. As e exceeds $B/6$, there is loss of contact of the footing with the soil for $(3e - B/2)$ portion of the width.

For $e < \dfrac{B}{6}$,
$$q_{max} = \frac{Q}{A}\left(1 + 6\frac{e}{B}\right) \tag{6.7}$$

For $e > \dfrac{B}{6}$,
$$q_{max} = \frac{Q}{A}\left(\frac{4B}{3B - 6e}\right) \tag{6.8}$$

and

$$q_{min} = 0 \text{ at a distance of } 3\left(\frac{B}{2} - e\right) \text{ from the edge of the footing}$$

The concept of *effective width* B' was introduced by Meyerhof (1953), on the basis of small-size-model footing tests, for computing the ultimate bearing capacity of the eccentrically loaded footing, where

$$B' = (B - 2e) \tag{6.9}$$

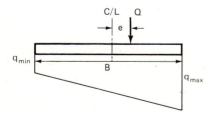

Figure 6.7 A footing under the eccentric load Q, $\dfrac{e}{b} < \dfrac{1}{6}$

Example 6.1 Compute the ultimate load-carrying capacity of a 2-m-square footing resting on the following soil:

$$\phi = 36°$$

$$\gamma = 1800 \text{ kg/m}^3$$

Assume

$$\gamma D_f = 1000 \text{ kg/m}^2 \quad \text{and} \quad \frac{e}{B} = 0.2$$

Therefore,

$$e = 0.4 \text{ m}$$

SOLUTION Effective width $B' = B - 2e = 2 - 0.8 = 1.2$ m. The bearing capacity factors from Fig. 6.3 are:

$$N_q = 35$$

$$N_\gamma = 45$$

Therefore, the load taken by the footing is computed from Eq. (6.2),† by replacing B with area $A = 1.2 \times 2.0$ m²:

$$Q_d = (1.2 \times 2)\left[(1000 \times 35) + \left(\tfrac{1}{2} \times 1800 \times 1.2 \times 45\right)\right]$$

$$= 2.4(35,000 + 48,600)$$

$$= 200,000 \text{ kg} = 200 \text{ t}$$

This method suffers from the fact that only the ultimate bearing capacity is analyzed. A footing subjected to moment will always undergo some tilt. A new method for analyzing the bearing capacity and the tilt of such footings has been proposed by Prakash and Saran (1971, 1973).

New method of designing eccentrically loaded footings An analytical solution for determining the ultimate bearing capacity of a strip footing under eccentric vertical load has been developed, assuming a one-sided failure (Saran, 1969; Prakash and Saran, 1971). In the field, it had been observed that failure of footings occurred by rotation. The failure of the Transcona Grain Elevator is a classic example of such a failure (Prakash, et al., 1979). The results of bearing capacity computation have been expressed in the form of bearing capacity factors N_γ, N_q, and N_c with the difference that these factors are functions of the angle of internal friction of soil ϕ and the eccentricity of the footing, expressed in terms of the ratio of eccentricity e to width B of the footing. The loss of contact of the footing width with increases in eccentricity was accounted for while evaluating the bearing capacity factors. Thus, the bearing capacity is

† Neglecting shape factors.

expressed by Eq. (6.10):

$$q_d = \tfrac{1}{2}\gamma B N_\gamma + \gamma D_f N_q + c N_c \qquad (6.10)$$

The bearing capacity factors N_γ, N_q, and N_c have been plotted in Figs. 6.8, 6.9, and 6.10, respectively.

For designing footings under eccentric vertical loads, the following need to be examined:

1. bearing capacity
2. settlement of the point under the load
3. tilt of the footing

In order to estimate the settlements and tilts of eccentrically loaded footings, two-dimensional and three-dimensional model tests were conducted on dense and loose, dry sands. Two-dimensional tests were conducted on 5-cm- and 10-cm-wide footings. Three-dimensional tests were conducted on 7.5-cm-, 10-cm-, and 15-cm-square footings and 10-cm-wide rectangular footings with L/B ratios of 2, 3, and 4. These footings were tested at the surface as well as at depths equal to the widths of the footings. Footings were subjected to one-way eccentricity in the transverse direction of the footing. Surface footings were tested for the eccentricities so that e/B ratios were 0, 0.1, 0.2, 0.3, and 0.4. Footings tested at depths equal to widths of the footings ($D_f/B = 1$) were subjected to the eccentricities so that e/B ratios had the values 0, 0.1, and 0.2. Each test was repeated three times to insure the reproducibility of test results (Prakash and Saran, 1973, 1977).

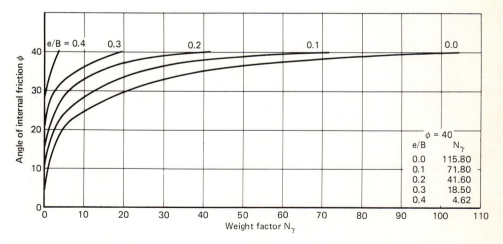

Figure 6.8 Bearing capacity factor N_γ vs. ϕ and e/B of 0.1, 0.2, 0.3, 0.4. *(After Prakash and Saran 1971.)*

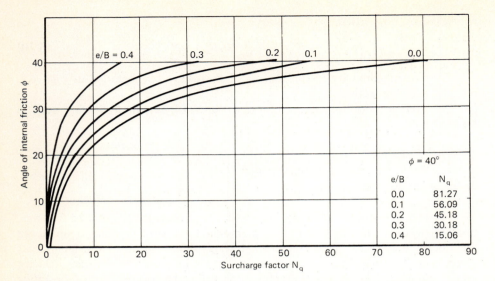

Figure 6.9 Bearing capacity factor N_q vs. ϕ and e/B of 0.1, 0.2, 0.3, 0.4. *(After Prakash and Saran 1971.)*

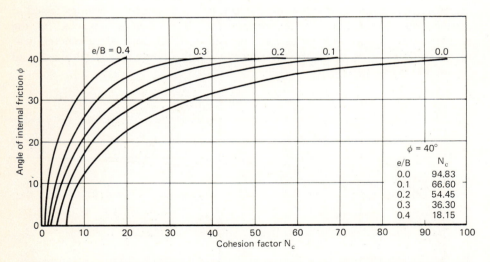

Figure 6.10 Bearing capacity factor N_c vs. ϕ and e/B of 0.1, 0.2, 0.3, 0.4. *(After Prakash and Saran 1971.)*

Results of the two-dimensional model tests conducted on dense sand were used to verify the analytical solutions, and excellent agreement was observed between the two. Failure took place by local shear in the two-dimensional tests on loose sand. Equation (6.10) holds good if the bearing capacity factors are substituted for the reduced value of ϕ given in Eq. (6.3b).

The cohesion c may also be replaced by the c' as in Eq. (6.3a). Shape factors were evaluated by comparing the ultimate bearing capacities of model footings of different shapes (Prakash and Saran, 1971, 1973, and 1977; Saran, 1969). Shape factors $\Delta\gamma$ and Δ_q were obtained for bearing capacity factors N_γ and N_q, respectively, as given in the following equations:

$$\Delta\gamma = 1.0 + \left(\frac{2e}{B} - 0.68\right)\left(\frac{B}{L}\right) - \left(\frac{3e}{2B} - 0.43\right)\left(\frac{B}{L}\right)^2 \qquad (6.11)$$

in which L = length of the footing, and

$$\Delta_q = 1.0 \text{ for all shapes of footings} \qquad (6.12)$$

For shape factor Δ_c to be applied to N_c, the following values are proposed based upon the analysis of test data by Meyerhof (1953) for eccentrically loaded footings:

$$\Delta_c = 1.2 \text{ for square footings } (L/B = 1)$$

$$= 1.0 \text{ for strip footing } (L/B \geq 8) \qquad (6.13)$$

To obtain the value of Δ_c for rectangular footings, a linear interpolation may be made.

Settlement of a centrally loaded footing is estimated on the basis of a load test (IS 1893-1971).† A design method for determining the settlement and tilt of an eccentrically loaded footing from a standard load test has been proposed.

An eccentrically loaded footing settles as shown in Fig. 6.11. S_e and S_m represent the settlement of the point under the load and the settlement of the edge of the footing, respectively. Maximum settlement occurs at the edge of the footing. If t is the tilt of the footing, then S_m is given by (Fig. 6.11):

$$S_m = S_e + \left(\frac{B}{2} - e\right)\sin t \qquad (6.14)$$

In the model tests reported above, S_e and t were measured. S_m was then computed with the help of Eq. (6.14). The settlements (S_0) of such footings, under central vertical load were also determined. Plots of S_e/S_0 and e/B and of S_m/S_0 and e/B for *equal factor of safety* indicated that the average relationships can be represented by the following simple expressions:

$$\frac{S_e}{S_0} = 1.0 - 1.63\frac{e}{B} - 2.63\left(\frac{e}{B}\right)^2 + 5.83\left(\frac{e}{B}\right)^3 \qquad (6.15)$$

$$\frac{S_m}{S_0} = 1.0 + 2.31\frac{e}{B} - 22.61\left(\frac{e}{B}\right)^2 + 31.54\left(\frac{e}{B}\right)^3 \qquad (6.16)$$

† Or ASTM Designation No. 1194-72.

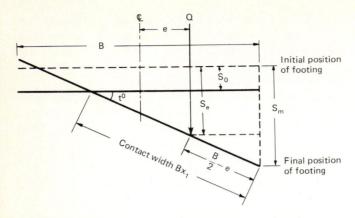

Figure 6.11 Settlement and tilt of an eccentrically loaded footing.

The above correlations are unique and were found to be independent of sand density and of the size and shape of the footings (Saran, 1969; Prakash and Saran, 1977).

These correlations hold good for e/B up to 0.4 since the model tests were conducted only up to this eccentricity. In practice, however, foundations are designed with much smaller eccentricity.

It is evident from Eqs. (6.15) and (6.16) that the values of S_e and S_m can be obtained if S_0 is known. In the case of sand, S_0 (or S_f) can be determined from Eq. (6.5) by conducting a standard plate-load test.

For clay, settlement may vary in direct proportion to the width of the footing.

Substituting the values of S_e and S_m in Eq. (6.14), the values of tilt t can be obtained.

Thus, settlements and tilts of footings subjected to moments can be predicted from plate-load tests under central loads. The ultimate bearing capacity can be determined by using bearing capacity factors.

Proposed design procedure To design eccentrically loaded footings, the following data must be known:

1. Vertical load and moment or vertical load and its eccentricity from the center
2. Characteristics of soil: ϕ, c, and/or standard penetration (N) value
3. Plate-load test data: load-versus-settlement curve obtained from standard plate-load test
4. Permissible values of the settlement, S_m and tilt, t
5. Factor of safety to be used against shear considerations

Using the above data, the following procedure is suggested:

1. *Trial dimensions of footing*: Assume trial dimensions of the footing and its depth below ground level.
2. e/B: Compute the value of eccentricity e from the load data. Then determine e/B.
3. *Computing settlements*
   (a) Determine value of S_e/S_0 and S_m/S_0 for the computed value of e/B from Eqs. (6.15) and (6.16).
   (b) Compute S_0 from the known permissible value of the settlement S_m.
   (c) Using Eq. (6.5) or other computations, compute the value of S_p.
4. *Plate-load test data*
   (a) From the given load-versus-settlement curve, obtain the value of the bearing pressure q_b that corresponds to the settlement S_p.
   (b) Determine the value of the ultimate bearing capacity by using either the intersection-tangent method or other computations.
5. *Failure criteria of plate*
   (a) Compute the ultimate bearing capacity of the plate using general shear failure and local shear failure considerations separately. Appropriate shape factors for the plate may be determined from Eqs. (6.11) to (6.13) for $e/B = 0$.
   (b) Compare the computed values of the ultimate bearing capacity of the plate with the observed value obtained in step 4b. If the observed value is close to one of the computed values, then the failure of the actual footing will be considered according to that value; otherwise, a factor will be determined which, when multiplied by the general shear value, gives the observed value.
6. *Factor of safety of the footing*
   (a) Compute the ultimate bearing capacity q_{d0} of the actual footing for $e/B = 0$ using the failure criteria established in step 5b.
   (b) The factor of safety F_s, is then given by:

$$F_s = \frac{q_{d0}}{q_b} \tag{6.17}$$

   Since Eq. (6.5) is obtained for equal pressure under the footing and the plate, the actual footing should not be subjected to greater unit stress than that obtained from the load-versus-settlement curve for the settlement S_p in 4a.
   (c) If F_s is greater than the permissible value of the factor of safety, it is allright or else the design may be revised with new dimensions.
7. *Allowable load*
   (a) Compute the ultimate bearing capacity q_d of the actual footing for the computed value of e/B and use the failure criterion established in step 5b.

(b) Obtain the allowable bearing capacity q_a by dividing the ultimate bearing capacity q_d by the factor of safety determined in step 6b.

(c) Compute the allowable load by multiplying q_a by the footing area.

(d) Compare the allowable load with the given vertical load. The footing design is satisfactory if the allowable load is greater than the design load. Otherwise, revise the design with larger footing dimensions.

8. *Tilt*: Compute the value of the tilt from Eq. (6.14) and compare it with the permissible tilt.

The footing design is satisfactory if the computed tilt is smaller than the permissible value. Otherwise, the design needs to be revised with larger footing dimensions. The procedure developed above is, at best, to be regarded as a tentative method for such a design. In predominantly noncohesive soils, the governing factor is the settlement and not the bearing capacity. Therefore, the data on which the above procedure is based need to be reworked to evolve a simpler and possibly more rational procedure, particularly for noncohesive soils.

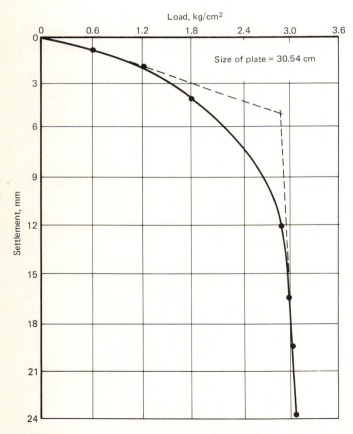

Figure 6.12 Pressure settlement of a plate 30.54 cm square in Example 6.2.

Example 6.2 Design a footing that is subjected to a total vertical load of 70 t and a moment of 23.8 t·m. The soil characteristics are as follows:

$$c = 0.025 \text{ kg/cm}^2 \qquad \phi = 35° \qquad \gamma = 1.75 \text{ g/cm}^3$$

A unit-load-versus-settlement curve (Fig. 6.12) was obtained by conducting a standard plate-load test at the site. Permissible values of the settlement, S_m, and tilt, t of the footing are given as 20 mm and 1°, respectively.

SOLUTION

1. *Trial dimensions of footing*   Let us assume trial dimensions of the footing as 2 × 2 m square at a depth of 1.0 m below ground level.

2. e/b From the load data:

$$e = \frac{23.8}{70} = 0.34 \text{ m}$$

Hence,

$$e/B = \frac{0.34}{2} = 0.17$$

3. *Computing settlements*
   (*a*) Substituting the value of e/B as 0.17 in Eqs. (6.15) and (6.16), we get

$$\frac{S_e}{S_0} = 0.683$$

and

$$\frac{S_m}{S_0} = 0.884$$

   (*b*) As the value of permissible settlement is 20 mm,

$$S_m = 20 \text{ mm}$$

Hence

$$S_0 = \frac{20}{0.884} = 22.7 \text{ mm}†$$

   (*c*) From Eq. (6.5) for $B_f = 200$ cm and $B_p = 30.54$ cm,

$$\frac{S_0}{S_p} = 3.02$$

Therefore,

$$S_p = \frac{22.7}{3.02} = 7.5 \text{ mm}$$

---

† Settlement of a centrally loaded footing with an equal factor of safety may be more than the settlement of the edge of the eccentrically loaded footing.

4. *Plate-load test data*
   (a) From the plate-load test result (Fig. 6.12), the bearing pressure q_b corresponding to the settlement, 7.5 mm, is 2.4 kg/cm^2.
   (b) When the intersection-tangent method is used, the ultimate bearing capacity of the plate is 2.90 kg/cm^2.
5. *Failure criteria of the plate*
   Figure 6.12 shows that the failure of the soil is like a general shear failure; thus the failure of the actual footing (2 m × 2 m wide) will be considered in general shear only.

6. Factor of safety
   (a) The ultimate bearing capacity q_{d0} of the footing for $e/B = 0$. By reading the values of N_γ, N_q, and N_c factors from Figs. 6.8 to 6.10, respectively, for $e/B = 0$ and $\phi = 35°$, we get:

$$N_\gamma = 40 \qquad N_q = 39 \qquad N_c = 58$$

From Eqs. (6.11) to (6.13), shape factors $\Delta\gamma$, Δ_q, and Δ_c come out as 0.75, 1.0, and 1.2, respectively, for $e/B = 0$ and $B/L = 1$. Then using shape factors with Eq. (6.10):

$$q_{d0} = \left(0.75 \times \tfrac{1}{2} \times 1.75 \times 200 \times 40 + 1.75 \times 100 \times 39\right.$$
$$\left. + 1.2 \times 25 \times 58\right)\tfrac{1}{1000}$$
$$= 13.80 \text{ kg/cm}^2$$

(b)
$$F_s = \frac{q_{d0}}{q_b} = \frac{13.80}{2.4} = 5.75$$

   (c) The factor of safety, 5.75, is more than the given factor of safety, 3.0; therefore, the design will be done for this factor of safety. It should be noted that since the soil has a high value for the angle of internal friction, the factor of safety against failure is rather high.

7. *Allowable load*
   (a) The ultimate bearing capacity q_d of the footing: By reading the values of N_γ, N_q, and N_c factors from Figs. 6.8, 6.9, and 6.10, respectively, for $e/B = 0.17$ and $\phi = 35°$, we get:

$$N_\gamma = 20.2 \qquad N_q = 31.0 \qquad N_c = 39.0$$

From Eqs. (6.11) to (6.13), shape factors $\Delta\gamma$, Δq, and Δ_c come out as 0.835, 1.0, and 1.2, respectively, for $e/B = 0.17$ and $B/L = 1$. Then, using shape factors with Eq. (6.10):

$$q_d = \left(0.835 \times \tfrac{1}{2} \times 1.75 \times 200 \times 20 + 1.75 \times 100 \times 31 + 1.2\right.$$
$$\left. \times 25 \times 39\right)\tfrac{1}{1000}$$
$$= 9.5 \text{ kg/cm}^2$$

(b) $q_a = \dfrac{q_d}{\text{Factor of safety}} = \dfrac{9.5}{5.75} = 1.65 \text{ kg/cm}^2$

(c) Allowable load $Q_a = 1.65 \times 200 \times 200 = 66$ t which may be accepted

(d) Allowable load Q_a is close to the given vertical load on the footing, 70 t. Hence, the design is safe.

8. *Tilt* From Eq. (6.14):

$$\sin t = \frac{S_m - S_e}{B/2 - e} = \frac{(0.884 - 0.6683) \times 22.7}{\dfrac{2000}{2} - 34}$$

or

$$t = 0.42°$$

The 0.42° tilt of the footing is less than the permissible value of 1 degree. Thus, the design is also safe with respect to tilt considerations.

Therefore, the 2.0-m × 2.0-m wide footing at 1 m below ground level has suitable bearing capacity as well as undergoing settlement and tilt within permissible limits.

Inclined Load on a Footing

According to the conventional method of analysis of a footing subjected to an inclined load R (Teng, 1965), this load is resolved into a vertical component Q_v and a horizontal component Q_H. The footing is designed for a vertical central load, just as though the horizontal load were not acting. Next, the stability of the footing against a horizontal load is analyzed by evaluating the total horizontal resistance and the horizontal force. The total horizontal resistance consists of passive soil resistance P_p and frictional resistance F at the base of the footing (Fig. 6.13).

Total passive resistance $P_p = \frac{1}{2} k_p \gamma H^2$
Total active pressure $P_a = \frac{1}{2} k_a \gamma h^2$
Total resistance at the base $F = c \times \text{area} + \mu Q_v$

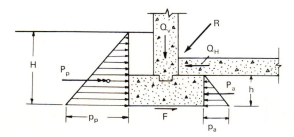

Figure 6.13 Forces acting on a footing subjected to inclined loads.

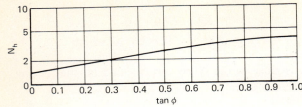

Figure 6.14 Bearing capacity factor N_h vs. ϕ. *(After Janbu, 1957.)*

in which μ is the coefficient of friction between footing and soil.

$$\text{Factor of safety against sliding} = \frac{P_p + F - P_a}{Q_H} \qquad (6.18)$$

Considerable movement of the foundation is required to fully mobilize the passive resistance. Thus, only one-third to one-half of the passive resistance is used in Eq. (6.18).

Meyerhof (1953) and Janbu (1957) have extended the analysis of bearing capacities for inclined loads.

According to Janbu:

$$\frac{Q + N_h Q_h}{A} = N_c c + \gamma D_f N_q + \frac{1}{2}\gamma B N_\gamma \qquad (6.19)$$

Values of N_h can be read from Fig. 6.14.

Meyerhof (1953) derived reduction factors for N_γ and N_c (Table 6.3). The vertical load is then computed by multiplying the appropriate bearing capacity factor by the reduction factor.

Eccentric Inclined Load on a Footing

When the load is both eccentric and inclined, the reduction factor is combined with the reduced width (Prakash et al., 1979).

Table 6.3 Reduction factors for vertical bearing capacities of shallow footings with horizontal bases subjected to inclined loads

Bearing capacity factor	D_f/B	Inclination of load with vertical				
		0°	10°	20°	30°	45°
N_γ	0	1.0	0.5	0.2	0	—
	1	1.0	0.6	0.4	0.25	0.15
N_c	0–1	1.0	0.8	0.6	0.4	0.25

Horizontal displacements of the footing may occur under inclined loads; no information is available on the magnitude of these displacements. For more detailed treatments the reader is referred to Prakash et al., 1979.

Table 6.4 Basic horizontal seismic coefficients for some important towns in India

Town	Zone	Basic horizontal seismic coefficient α_0	Town	Zone	Basic horizontal seismic coefficient α_0
Agra	III	0.04	Jorhat	V	0.08
Ahmadabad	III	0.04	Kanpur	III	0.04
Ajmer	I	0.01	Kathmandu	V	0.08
Allahabad	II	0.02	Kohima	V	0.08
Almora	IV	0.05	Kurnool	I	0.01
Ambala	IV	0.05	Lucknow	III	0.04
Amritsar	IV	0.05	Ludhiana	IV	0.05
Asansol	III	0.04	Madras	II	0.02
Aurangabad	I	0.01	Madurai	II	0.02
Bahraich	IV	0.05	Mandi	V	0.08
Bangalore	I	0.01	Mangalore	III	0.04
Barauni	IV	0.05	Monghyr	IV	0.05
Barcilly	III	0.04	Moradabad	IV	0.05
Bhatinda	III	0.04	Mysore	I	0.01
Bhilai	I	0.01	Nagpur	II	0.02
Bhopal	II	0.02	Nainital	IV	0.05
Bhubaneswar	III	0.04	Nasik	III	0.04
Bhuj	V	0.08	Nellore	II	0.02
Bikaner	III	0.04	Panjim	III	0.04
Bokaro	III	0.04	Patiala	III	0.04
Bombay	III	0.04	Patna	IV	0.05
Burdwan	III	0.04	Pilibhit	IV	0.05
Calcutta	III	0.04	Pondicherry	II	0.02
Calicut	III	0.04	Pune	III	0.04
Chandigarh	IV	0.05	Raipur	I	0.01
Chitradurga	I	0.01	Rajkot	III	0.04
Coimbatore	III	0.04	Ranchi	II	0.02
Cuttack	III	0.04	Roorkee	IV	0.05
Darbhanga	V	0.08	Rourkela	I	0.08
Darjiling	IV	0.05	Sadiya	V	0.08
Dehra Dun	IV	0.05	Simla	IV	0.05
Delhi	IV	0.05	Sironj	I	0.01
Durgapur	III	0.04	Srinagar	V	0.08
Gangtok	IV	0.05	Surat	III	0.04
Gauhati	V	0.08	Tezpur	V	0.08
Gaya	III	0.04	Thanjavur	II	0.02
Gorakhpur	IV	0.05	Tiruchirapalli	II	0.02
Hyderabad	I	0.01	Trivandrum	III	0.04
Imphal	V	0.08	Udaipur	II	0.02
Jabalpur	III	0.04	Vadodara	III	0.04
Jaipur	II	0.02	Varansai	III	0.04
Jamshedpur	II	0.02	Vijayawada	III	0.04
Jhansi	I	0.01	Visakhapatnam	II	0.02
Jodhpur	I	0.01			

Table 6.5 Permissible increase in allowable bearing pressure or resistance of soils*

SL. no. (1)	Type of soil mainly constituting the foundation (2)	Permissible increase in allowable bearing pressure, %					
		Piles passing through any soil but resting on soil type I (3)	Piles not covered under col. 3 (4)	Raft foundations (5)	Combined or isolated RCC footing with tie beams (6)	Isolated RCC footing without tie beams or unreinforced strip foundations (7)	Well foundations (caissons) (8)
i)	Type I rock or hard soils: Well-graded gravels and sand-gravel mixtures with or without clay binder, and clayey sands poorly graded or sand clay mixtures (GB, GW, SB, SW, and SC)† having N‡ above 30, where N is the standard penetration value.	50	—	50	50	50	50
ii)	Type II medium soils: All soils with N between 10 and 30 and poorly graded sands or gravelly sands with little or no fines (SP†) with $N > 15$	50	25	50	25	25	25
iii)	Type III soft soils: All soils other than SP† with $N < 10$	50	25	50	25	—	25

Note 1: If any increase in bearing pressure has already been permitted for forces other than seismic forces the total increase in allowable bearing pressure when seismic force is also included shall not exceed the limits specified above.

Note 2: Submerged loose sands and soils falling under classification SP with standard penetration values less than the values specified in *Note* 4 below, the vibrations caused by earthquake may cause liquefaction or excessive total and differential settlements. In important projects this aspect of the problem need be investigated and appropriate methods of compaction or stabilization adopted to achieve suitable N. Alternatively, deep pile foundation may be provided and taken to depths well into the layers which are not likely to liquefy.

Note 3: The piles should be designed for lateral loads neglecting lateral resistance of soil layers liable to liquefy.

Note 4: Desirable field values of N are as follows:

Zones III, IV, and V	15
Zones I and II	10

*After IS 1873-1975.

†See IS 1498-1970, Classification and identification of soils for general engineering purposes (first revision).

‡See IS 2131-1963, Method of standard penetration test for soils.

193

6.6 PROVISION OF RELEVANT STANDARDS

In practice, for an earthquake-resistant design, spread footings of columns must be interconnected at right angles with tie beams in two directions. The bending moments and shear forces in these beams may be computed as follows (Taylor, 1968):

1. Determine the moment at the foot of each column assuming that the column base is fixed.
2. Next, assuming that the footing has no resistance to rotation, distribute the column moments found above in proportion to the stiffness of the foundation beams and columns joined at each footing.

The horizontal reinforcement in the grade beams must be 0.8 percent of the cross-sectional area of the beams, or sufficient to carry in tension a force equal to the force of an earthquake on the heavier of the two reinforced columns. The stirrups may be 6 mm in diameter, 23 cm center to center (Prakash and Sharma, 1969).

If the soil beneath the footings is homogeneous and footings experience equal vertical settlements, the shears and moments in the frames are not materially altered as if the footings are resting on a rigid medium. However, if the footings are resting on a dissimilar medium, which results in differential settlements or rotations of the footings, then the loads in the frames may be appreciably altered. In fact, due to the erratic nature of soils and the dependence of foundation settlements on sizes of footings, load intensities, nature of soils, and several other factors not precisely defined, the effects of differential settlements and rotations of footings are likely to be felt by the structure. No simple analysis is available to compute the effects of differential distortions of footings on superstructures.

The grade beams recommended above are believed to increase the rigidity of the entire foundation; this may help reduce the differential distortions between individual footings.

The Indian Standard (IS 1893-1975) considers that the whole country is divided into five zones, with each zone being assigned a design seismic coefficient α_0 which varies from 0.01 to 0.08. The horizontal acceleration is the seismic coefficient multiplied by the acceleration caused by gravity g. Basic horizontal seismic coefficients for some important towns in India are listed in Table 6.4. The Standard further recommends that, when earthquake forces are included, the permissible increases in the allowable bearing pressures of soils be as given in Table 6.5, depending upon the type of foundation.

The Applied Technology Council (1978) has prepared the Tentative Provisions for the Development of Seismic Regulations for Buildings. These provisions are quoted here for guidance only and are not necessarily to be rigorously adopted. The relevant provisions pertaining to shallow footings are:

1. *Seismic performance* is a measure of the protection provided for the public and building occupants against potential hazards resulting from the effects of earthquake motions on buildings. There are four "seismic performance categories" assigned to buildings: A, B, C, and D. Seismic performance category D is assigned to provide the highest level of design performance criteria.
2. *Design ground motions* are defined in terms of *effective peak acceleration A_a* or *effective peak velocity-related acceleration A_v*. Maps have been prepared in which the United States has been divided into seven zones. Coefficient A_a or A_v may then be read from Table 6.6.
3. Individual spread footings in buildings of seismic performance category C should be interconnected by ties. Such a construction should be capable of carrying, in tension or compression, a force equal to $A_v/4$ of the largest footing or column load, unless it can be demonstrated that equivalent restraint can be provided by other approved means.

With the present state of knowledge, it is uncertain as to whether or not these provisions are overly conservative. There is a great need to adopt these provisions and see their impact on costs and performance during earthquakes.

There are six methods of handling the problem of dynamic bearing capacity under transient loading (Basavanna et al., 1974).

1. Pseudostatic method
2. Method based on single-degree freedom system
3. Method based on wave propagation
4. Method based on equilibrium of failure wedge
5. Nondimensional analysis
6. Numerical technique

The first method has been discussed in detail. It is proposed to describe two solutions based upon equilibrium of failure wedges. Basavanna et al. (1974) have prepared an excellent review of the other methods.

Table 6.6 Coefficients A_a and A_v

Map area number	Coefficient A_a	Coefficient A_v
7	0.4	0.4
6	0.3	0.3
5	0.2	0.2
4	0.15	0.15
3	0.10	0.10
2	0.05	0.05
1	0.05	0.05

6.7 DYNAMIC ANALYSES FOR VERTICAL LOADS

Triandafilidis (1965) studied the responses of footings in cohesive soils subjected to vertical dynamic load pulses of defined shape. The analysis is based on the following assumptions:

1. The footing is continuous and supported on the surface.
2. The soil mass participating in the foundation motion is rigid and exhibits the rigid plastic stress-strain characteristics shown in Fig. 6.15a.
3. The forcing function is assumed to be an exponentially decaying pulse.
4. The influences of the strain rate on the shear strength of the soil and the dead weight of the foundation have not been considered.

Disturbing Force

The only disturbing force is an externally applied dynamic pulse. The moment of this pulse about the center of rotation O (Fig. 6.15b) is

$$M_{dp} = \tfrac{1}{2} p_t \times B^2 \tag{6.20}$$

in which p_t = externally applied time-dependent pulse and B = width of foundation.

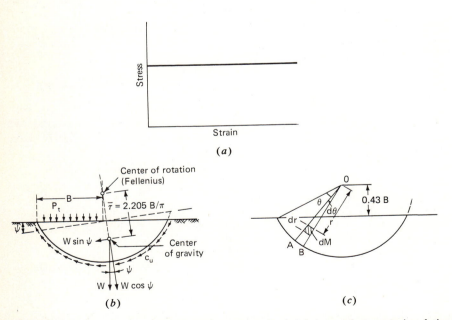

Figure 6.15 Analysis of a footing for dynamic vertical load. (*a*) Assumed stress-strain relationship. (*b*) Forces acting on failure wedge displaced by amount ψ from its original position. (*c*) Computation of polar mass moment of inertia of the soil wedge. *(After Triandafilidis, 1965.)*

Restoring Forces

The restoring forces consist of the shearing resistance along the rupture surface, the inertia of the soil mass participating in motion, and the resistance caused by displacement of the center of gravity of the soil mass (Fig. 6.15b). The moments of these restoring forces about the center of rotation can then be computed:

Soil resistance The static bearing capacity of a continuous footing along the failure surface (Fellenius, 1927) is

$$p_s = 5.54 c_u \qquad (6.21a)$$

in which c_u is undrained shear strength of the soil.

Fellenius demonstrated that when there is a purely cohesive material and the footing rests on the ground, then the critical center of rotation for a circular failure surface will be located vertically above the inner edge of the foundation at a distance of $0.43B$ above the ground surface, in which case Eq. (6.21a) holds.

Resisting moment due to shear strength M_{rs} around the axis of rotation O is

$$M_{rs} = \tfrac{1}{2} p_s B^2 \qquad (6.21b)$$

Soil inertia An applied pulse imparts an acceleration to the soil mass. The resisting motion M_{ri} around the axis of rotation may be expressed as

$$M_{ri} = I_0 \ddot{\psi} \qquad (6.22)$$

in which I_0 = polar mass moment of inertia of the semicircular mass, and $\ddot{\psi}$ = angular acceleration of the rotating body.

I_0 may be expressed from Fig. 6.15c, as

$$I_0 = \int r^2 \, dM - \text{polar moment of inertia of the triangle } OAB \text{ about the axis of}$$

rotation in which $dM = (r \cdot d\theta \cdot dr) \dfrac{\gamma}{g}$

Integrating within appropriate limits, we obtain

$$I_0 = \frac{0.31}{1.36} \gamma \pi B^2 \frac{B^2}{g} \qquad (6.23a)$$

or

$$I_0 = \frac{1}{1.36} \frac{W B^2}{g} \qquad (6.23b)$$

in which $W = 0.31 \gamma \pi B^2$ = weight of the circular wedge mass participating in motion (Fig. 6.15b).

Resistance due to displacement of the center of gravity The displaced position of the soil mass generates a restoring moment M_{rw}, which may be expressed as

$$M_{rw} = W \bar{r} \sin \psi \qquad (6.24a)$$

For small rotations, assuming $\sin \psi \approx \psi$, the above equation may be written as

$$M_{rw} = W\bar{r}\psi \qquad (6.24b)$$

in which $\bar{r} = 2.205\,B/\pi$.

Equation of Motion

By equating the moments of the driving forces to those of the restoring forces, the following equation of motion is obtained:

$$M_{dp} + M_{rs} + M_{ri} + M_{rw} = 0 \qquad (6.25)$$

Substituting for moments and rearranging, we get

$$\ddot{\psi} + \frac{3g}{\pi B}\psi = \frac{0.68g}{W}(p_t - p_s) \qquad (6.26)$$

Letting $3g/\pi B = k^2$, we get

$$\ddot{\psi} + k^2\psi = \frac{0.68g}{W}(p_t - p_s) \qquad (6.27)$$

If the pulse p_t is in the following form:

$$p_t = p_0 e^{-\beta t}$$

or

$$p_t = \lambda p_s e^{-\beta t} \qquad (6.28)$$

in which

$p_0 = \lambda p_s$ instantaneous peak intensity

β = a coefficient indicating the decay rate of the pulse

λ = overload factor

Substituting p_t from Eq. (6.28) into Eq. (6.27), we get

$$\ddot{\psi} + k^2\psi = \frac{0.68 g p_s(\lambda e^{-\beta t} - 1)}{W} \qquad (6.29)$$

or

$$\ddot{\psi} + k^2\psi = A e^{-\beta t} - B \qquad (6.30)$$

in which

$$A = \frac{0.68 g p_s \lambda}{W}$$

$$B = \frac{0.68 g p_s}{W}$$

Equation (6.30) is similar to the equation of motion [Eq. (2.37a)] with the damping term absent. Thus, the expression for natural frequency may be written:

$$\omega_n = k = \sqrt{\frac{3g}{\pi B}} \tag{6.31}$$

and

$$T = \frac{2\pi}{\omega_n}$$

or

$$T = 2\pi\sqrt{\frac{\pi B}{3g}} \tag{6.32}$$

Now the equation of motion [Eq. (6.30)] can be solved for a given type of pulse and initial conditions in the following form:

$$\psi = c_1 \cos kt + c_2 \sin kt + \frac{A}{k^2 + \beta^2} e^{-\beta_t} + \frac{B}{k^2} \tag{6.33}$$

Equation (6.32) helps in determining the natural period of vibration of the footing. From the solution in Eq. (6.33) the entire history of motion may be traced.

In practice, an engineer is usually interested in the peak values of angular rotation, which may be solved by differentiating ψ and determining the instant $t = t_c$ when $\dot{\psi} = 0$. This was done numerically by Triandafilidis (1965) and, by substituting this t_c in Eq. (6.33), the maximum angular rotation was obtained in the following form

$$\psi_{\text{max}} = NB \tag{6.34}$$

in which N = dynamic load factor s^2

and has been evaluated for footings measuring 2 ft (0.6 m), 5 ft (1.5 m) wide. The other values of different variables are:

$$\beta = 0.0, 0.5, 1.0, 2.0, 5.0, 10.0, 50.0\,\text{s}^{-1}$$
$$\lambda = 1.10, 1.25, 1.50, 1.75, 2.0, 3.0, 4.0, 5.0$$

Earlier, Triandafilidis (1961) had carried out a similar investigation in which the effect of surcharge had also been included for discontinuous functions.

6.8 DYNAMIC ANALYSIS FOR HORIZONTAL LOADS

Based on more or less similar concepts, Chummar (1965) extended the analysis by Triandafilidis (1961) for footings in $c - \phi$ soil, under earthquake-type loading that was essentially a horizontal thrust at floor levels. The assumption in this analysis may be stated as:

1. The long surface footing carries a vertical load, and the failure of this footing occurs with the application of a horizontal dynamic load acting at a certain height above the base of the footing.

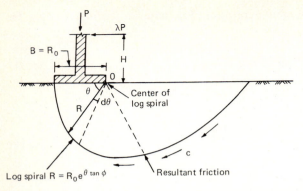

Figure 6.16 Failure surface in a footing resting on c-ϕ soil. *(After Prakash and Chummar, 1967.)*

2. The resulting motion in the footing is of a rotatory nature.
3. The failure surface is a logarithmic spiral with its center on the base corner of the footing, which is also the center of rotation (Fig. 6.16).
4. The rotating soil mass is considered to be a rigid body rotating about a fixed axis.
5. The soil exhibits rigid plastic, stress-strain characteristics.

Static Bearing Capacity

The static bearing capacity of the footing is calculated by assuming that the footing fails when acted upon by a vertical static load, which causes rotation of the logarithmic spiral failure surface. The ultimate static bearing capacity q_d is given by

$$q_d = cN_c + \tfrac{1}{2}\gamma B N_\gamma \tag{6.35}$$

in which $c=$ cohesion

$B=$ the footing width and equals R_0, the initial radius of the spiral

$\gamma=$ unit weight of the soil

$N_c, N_\gamma =$ bearing capacity factors for the assumed type of failure

Considering moment of the forces about O, the center of rotation:
Moment due to cohesion c,

$$M_{RC} = \frac{cR_0^2}{2\tan\phi}(e^{2\pi\tan\phi} - 1) \tag{6.36}$$

Moment due to weight W of soil wedge,

$$M_{RW} = \frac{R_0^3\tan\phi(e^{3\pi\tan\phi} + 1)}{9\tan^2\phi + 1}\gamma \tag{6.37}$$

in which ϕ is the angle of internal friction. The ultimate load q_d has a moment about O equal to

$$q_d \frac{R_0^2}{2}$$

in which

$$q_d = \frac{c}{\tan\phi}(e^{2\pi\tan\phi} - 1)$$

$$+ \frac{2\gamma R_0 \tan\phi(e^{3\pi\tan\phi} + 1)}{9\tan^2\phi + 1} \tag{6.38}$$

Combining Eqs. 6.35 and 6.38, we get

$$N_\gamma = \frac{4\tan\phi(e^{3\pi\tan\phi} + 1)}{9\tan^2\phi + 1} \tag{6.39}$$

and

$$N_c = \frac{e^{2\pi\tan\phi} - 1}{\tan\phi} \tag{6.40}$$

It could be seen that for a purely cohesive soil the spiral becomes a semicircle and

$$N_C = 2\pi$$

Dynamic Equilibrium

The condition of dynamic equilibrium is established by formulating an equation that will describe the motion of the footing after it has been acted upon by the dynamic pulse. The footing carries a vertical load P at its center. The failure of the footing results from a dynamic load that acts horizontally at a height H above the base of the footing. The driving forces are the externally applied loads:

$D_1 = $ the static load coming on the footing

$D_2 = $ the time-dependent dynamic pulse acting on the superstructure

The resisting forces are

$R_1 = $ soil resistance due to friction

$R_2 = $ soil resistance due to cohesion

$R_3 = $ resisting forces caused by the eccentricity of center of gravity of the rotating soil mass from the center of rotation

$R_4 = $ resistance to the displacement of the center of gravity of the moving soil mass

$R_5 = $ inertia force of the failure wedge

Each of these forces is considered separately.

The force D_1 due to the static central load

$$P = \tfrac{1}{2}B\left(cN_c + \tfrac{1}{2}\gamma BN_\gamma\right) \tag{6.41}$$

A factor of safety of 2 has been considered. The moment of this force about the center of rotation is

$$M_{D_1} = P\frac{B}{2} \tag{6.42}$$

As a general case, the dynamic pulse D_2 is represented by a time function p_t. The pulse is acting horizontally at a height H above the base of the footing. The moment about the center of rotation is

$$M_{D_2} = P_t H$$

$$= M_t \tag{6.43}$$

The frictional resisting force R_1 passes through the center of rotation. Consequently, this force has no moment about the center of rotation. Therefore,

$$M_{R_1} = 0 \tag{6.44}$$

The cohesive resisting force acts along the length of the failure surface and its moment M_{R_2} about this center of rotation is

$$M_{R_2} = \xi c R_0^2 \tag{6.45}$$

where

$$\xi = \frac{e^{2\pi\tan\phi} - 1}{2\tan\phi}$$

a dimensionless quantity, and $= N_c/2$ also [Eq. (6.40)]. When $\phi = 0$, ξ could be seen to be equal to π.

The resisting force R_3 is due to the eccentricity of the weight W or the soil mass within the failure surface. The resisting moment of R_3 is equal to $W\bar{x}$, where $\bar{x}$ is the distance between the center of gravity of the soil mass and the center of rotation (Fig. 6.16).

$$M_{R_3} = \int_0^\pi \gamma \tfrac{2}{3} R \cos\theta \tfrac{1}{2} R \, d\theta R$$

$$= -\frac{\gamma R_0^3 \tan\phi (e^{3\pi\tan\phi} + 1)}{9\tan^2\phi + 1} \tag{6.46}$$

The negative sign indicates that $\bar{x}$ is negative and the moment is clockwise in direction.

Denoting

$$\tan\phi(e^{3\pi\tan\phi} + 1)/9\tan^2\phi + 1,$$

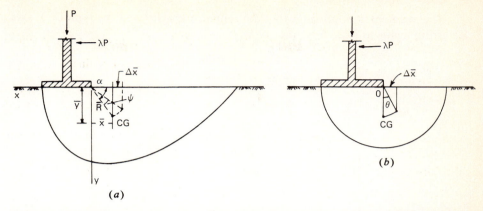

Figure 6.17 Determination of CG and its displacement in the log spiral for (*a*) noncohesive soil, (*b*) cohesive soil. *(After Prakash and Chummar, 1967.)*

a dimensionless quantity, by ε,

$$M_{R_3} = \varepsilon \gamma R_0^3 \qquad (6.47)$$

If $\phi = 0$, $M_{R_3} = 0$.

The force R_4 comes into play due to displacement of the center of gravity of the soil mass in the failure wedge from its initial position. If the rotation of the footing at any instant is ψ, the center of gravity is horizontally displaced $\Delta \bar{x}$, as given by Fig. 6.17*a*.

$$\Delta \bar{x} = \bar{R} \cos(\alpha - \psi) - \bar{x}$$

Assuming that ψ is small,

$$\Delta \bar{x} = \bar{R} \psi \sin \alpha$$

Then the moment of this force about the center of rotation is

$$M_{R_4} = W \Delta \bar{x}$$

$$= W \bar{R} \psi \sin \alpha = W \psi \sqrt{\bar{x}^2 + \bar{y}^2} \, \sin \alpha$$

Referring to Figs. 6.16 and 6.17*a*:

$$\bar{x} = \frac{\displaystyle\int_0^\pi \frac{2}{3} R \cos \theta \frac{1}{2} R d\theta R \gamma}{\displaystyle\int_0^\pi \frac{1}{2} R d\theta R \gamma}$$

$$= \frac{-4 R_0 \tan^2 \phi (e^{3\pi \tan \phi} + 1)}{(9 \tan^2 \phi + 1)(e^{2\pi \tan \phi} - 1)} \qquad (6.48)$$

The negative sign indicates that the center of gravity is to the right of Y axis. Referring again to Figs. 6.16 and 6.17a:

$$\bar{y} = \frac{\int_0^\pi \frac{2}{3} R \sin \frac{1}{2} Rd\theta R\gamma}{\int_0^\pi \frac{1}{2} Rd\theta R\gamma}$$

$$= \frac{4}{3} \frac{R_0 \tan\phi (e^{3\pi \tan\phi} + 1)}{(9 \tan^2\phi + 1)(e^{2\pi \tan\phi} - 1)} \tag{6.49}$$

$$\bar{R} = \frac{4R_0 \tan\phi (e^{3\pi \tan\phi} + 1)}{3(\sqrt{9 \tan^2\phi + 1})(e^{2\pi \tan\phi} - 1)} \tag{6.50}$$

$$W = \int_0^\pi \frac{1}{2} R^2 d\theta \gamma$$

$$= \frac{\gamma R_0^2 (e^{2\pi \tan\phi} - 1)}{4 \tan\phi} \tag{6.51}$$

Thus

$$M_{R_4} = \beta R_0^3 \psi \sin\alpha \tag{6.52}$$

in which

$$\beta = \frac{e^{3\pi \tan\phi} + 1}{3\sqrt{9 \tan^2\phi + 1}}$$

a dimensionless quantity.

For a purely cohesive soil, $\beta = \frac{2}{3}$.

The moment about the center of rotation due to inertia force of the failure wedge is given by $M_{R_5} = I(d^2\psi/dt^2)$, where I is the mass moment of inertia of the moving rigid soil mass about the axis of rotation:

$$I = \frac{\gamma}{g} \int_0^\pi \int_0^{R_0} R^3 d\psi \, dR$$

$$= \frac{\gamma R_0^4}{g \times 16 \tan\phi} (e^{4\pi \tan\phi} - 1) \tag{6.53}$$

$$M_{R_5} = \frac{\mu \gamma R_0^4}{g} \frac{d^2\psi}{dt^2} \tag{6.54}$$

in which

$$\mu = \frac{(e^{4\pi \tan\phi} - 1)}{16 \tan\phi}$$

a dimensionless quantity.

For a semicircular failure surface $\mu = \pi/4$.

General Equation of Motion

By equating the moments about the center of rotation of the driving and resisting forces, the equation of motion is obtained as

$$M_{D_1} + M_{D_2} = M_{R_1} + M_{R_2} + M_{R_3} + M_{R_4} + M_{R_5} \tag{6.55}$$

Evaluating the terms and simplifying, we get

$$\frac{d^2\ddot{\psi}}{dt^2} + k^2\psi = A\left(M_t + \frac{PB}{2} - E\right) \tag{6.56}$$

in which

$$k = \sqrt{\frac{q\beta \sin \alpha}{R_0 \mu}} \tag{6.57a}$$

is the natural circular frequency of the system and

$$A = \frac{g}{\gamma R_0 4\mu} \tag{6.57b}$$

$$E = \xi c R_0^2 + \varepsilon\gamma R_0^3 \tag{6.57c}$$

Solution of the Equation of Motion

The differential equation of motion developed is solved for one case of dynamic pulse. The assumed pulse is shown in Fig. 6.18; P_{max} is the maximum value of a horizontal force acting at height H above the base of the footing, and t_d is the time during which it attains this value. The moment of this pulse about the center of rotation can also be represented by a similar figure since M_t equals $P_t H$.

When $t < t_d$ the moment is given by

$$M_t = \frac{M_{max} t}{t_d} \tag{6.58}$$

and for $t > t_d$

$$M_t = 0 \tag{6.59}$$

M_{max} is thus a known quantity.

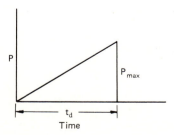

Figure 6.18 Dynamic pulse.

There will thus be two different equations of motion, one for $t \leq t_d$ and the other for $t > t_d$.

Solution for $t \leq t_d$ The equation of motion for $t \leq t_d$ is

$$\frac{d^2\psi}{dt^2} + k^2\psi = A\left(M_{max}\frac{t}{t_d} + \frac{PB}{2} - E\right) \tag{6.60}$$

The solution of this standard form of differential equation is

$$\psi = C_1 \cos kt + C_2 \sin kt$$
$$+ \frac{A}{k^2}\left(M_{max}\frac{t}{t_d} + \frac{PB}{2} - E\right) \tag{6.61}$$

The constants C_1 and C_2 are evaluated from the initial condition; that is,

1. When $t = 0$, $\psi = 0$;
2. When $t = 0$, $\dfrac{d\psi}{dt} = 0$;

which give

$$C_1 = \frac{A}{k^2}\left(E - \frac{PB}{2}\right)$$

and

$$C_2 = -\frac{AM_{max}}{k^3 t_d}$$

Hence

$$\psi = \frac{A}{k^2}\left(E - \frac{PB}{2}\right)\cos kt - \frac{A}{k^3}\frac{M_{max}}{t_d}\sin kt$$
$$+ \frac{A}{k^2}\left(\frac{M_{max}t}{t_d} + \frac{PB}{2} - E\right) \tag{6.62}$$

Solution for $t \geq t_d$ The equation of motion now becomes

$$\frac{d^2\psi}{dt^2} + k^2\psi = A\left(\frac{PB}{2} - E\right) \tag{6.63}$$

The solution of this differential equation is

$$\psi = C_3 \cos kt + C_4 \sin kt + \frac{A}{k^2}\left(\frac{PB}{2} - E\right) \tag{6.64}$$

The constants C_3 and C_4 are evaluated as follows:
From Eq. (6.62),

$$\psi(\text{when } t = t_d) = \frac{A}{k^2}\left(E - \frac{PB}{2}\right)\cos kt_d$$
$$- \frac{A}{k^3}\frac{M_{max}}{t_d}\sin kt_d + \frac{A}{k^2}\left(M_{max} + \frac{PB}{2} - E\right) \tag{6.65}$$

From Eq. (6.64),

$$\psi(\text{when } t = t_d) = C_3 \cos kt_d + C_4 \sin kt_d$$
$$+ \frac{A}{k^2}\left(\frac{PB}{2} - E\right) \tag{6.66}$$

Equating these two values of ψ gives

$$C_3 \cos kt_d + C_4 \sin kt_d = \frac{A}{k^2}\left(E - \frac{PB}{2}\right)\cos kt_d$$
$$- \frac{A}{k^3}\frac{M_{max}}{t_d}\sin kt_d + \frac{A}{k^2}M_{max}$$
$$= G \quad \text{(say)} \tag{6.67}$$

From Eq. (6.62),

$$\frac{d\psi}{dt}(\text{when } t = t_d) = -\frac{A}{k}\left(E - \frac{PB}{2}\right)\sin kt_d$$
$$- \frac{A}{k^2}\frac{M_{max}}{t_d}\cos kt_d + \frac{A}{k^2}\frac{M_{max}}{t_d} = H \quad \text{(say)} \tag{6.68}$$

From Eq. (6.64),

$$\frac{d\psi}{dt}(\text{when } t = t_d) = -C_3 k \sin kt_d + C_4 k \cos kt_d \tag{6.69}$$

By equating the values of $\dfrac{d\theta}{dt}$

$$- C_3 k \sin kt_d + C_4 k \cos kt_d = H \quad \text{(say)} \tag{6.70}$$

Solving the simultaneous Eqs. (6.67) and (6.70), we get

$$C_3 = \frac{Gk \cos kt_d - H \sin kt_d}{k}$$

$$C_4 = \frac{Gk \sin kt_d + H \cos kt_d}{k}$$

The equation of motion thus gives the following two solutions for ψ:
For $t \le t_d$,

$$\psi = \frac{A}{k^2}\left(E - \frac{PB}{2}\right)\cos kt - \frac{A}{k^3}\frac{M_{max}}{t_d}\sin kt$$
$$+ \frac{A}{k^2}\left(\frac{M_{max}t}{t_d} + \frac{PB}{2} - E\right) \tag{6.71}$$

For $t \ge t_d$,

$$\psi = \frac{Gk \cos kt_d - H \sin kt_d}{k}\cos kt$$
$$+ \frac{Gk \sin kt_d + H \cos kt_d}{k}\sin kt$$
$$+ \frac{A}{k^2}\left(\frac{PB}{2} - E\right) \tag{6.72}$$

Numerical Evaluation of the Solution

The solution was numerically evaluated to study the effects of different variables, such as soil properties, footing sizes, and durations of pulses, on the
response of the footing (Prakash and Chummar, 1967). The values of different
variables are listed in Table 6.7.

The vertical static load considered is only half the ultimate value. The
footing fails under a horizontal dynamic load only. Since elastic deformations
are not considered, the equations of motion developed are valid only after
failure surfaces are developed. While evaluating the equation of motion numerically, one can see that the value of the rotation angle ψ is negative for values of
driving moments that are less than resisting moments. This only means that the
failure surface has not developed. The maximum intensity of the dynamic
horizontal load is given as $P_{max} = P\lambda$, where P is the static load and λ is the
"overload ratio." The value of λ is increased gradually and it is checked whether
ψ at $t > t_d$ (that is, when maximum dynamic pulse has acted) is positive or not.
The value of λ that makes ψ change from negative to positive is the *critical
overload ratio* λ_{cr}.

To facilitate understanding of the type of motion of the footing taking place,
the curves of angle of rotation ψ versus time t are plotted in Figs. 6.19 to 6.24 for
typical cases.

Table 6.7 Range of variables

c, g/cm^2	ϕ, deg	t_d, s	B, m	H, m	Factor of safety
0	15	0.05,0.1, 0.15,0.2, 0.25	1, 2, 3	4, 8, 12	2 for all cases
250	0, 5, 10, 15	0.05,0.1, 0.15,0.2, 0.25	1, 2, 3	4, 8, 12	2 for all cases
500	0, 5, 10, 15	0.05,0.1, 0.15,0.2, 0.25	1, 2, 3	4, 8, 12	2 for all cases
1,000	0, 5, 10, 15	0.05,0.1 0.15,0.2, 0.25	1, 2, 3	4, 8, 12	2 for all cases
2,000	0, 5, 10, 15	0.05,0.1, 0.15,0.2, 0.25	1, 2, 3	4, 8, 12	2 for all cases
4,000	0, 5, 10, 15	0.05,0.1, 0.15,0.2, 0.25	1, 2, 3	4, 8, 12	2 for all cases

Discussion

From plots of ψ versus t, Figs. 6.19 and 6.20, it may be seen that the maximum value of ψ occurs at almost the same instant t_{cr} for different types of soils. The value t_{cr}, however, depends upon t_d, the duration of the pulse. Since ψ decreases beyond t_{cr}, the structure will collapse only if $\psi_{\max}$ is greater than a limiting value.

Maximum rotation of the footing $\psi_{\max}$ decreases with the angle of internal friction of soil ϕ and increases with cohesion c (Figs. 6.21 and 6.22). This may be explained from the fact that the mass of the failure wedge increases with ϕ and resistance of the soil to dynamic pulses increases while c does not influence the mass of the wedge. A considerable portion of the dynamic resistance is contributed by inertia of the mass of the soil wedge.

This indicates that footings on frictional soils are capable of resisting dynamic loads more effectively than those on cohesive soils. However, the effects of compaction of sands due to vibrations and liquefaction of fine saturated sands are excluded from this discussion.

Figure 6.23 shows that wider footings undergo smaller maximum deformations.

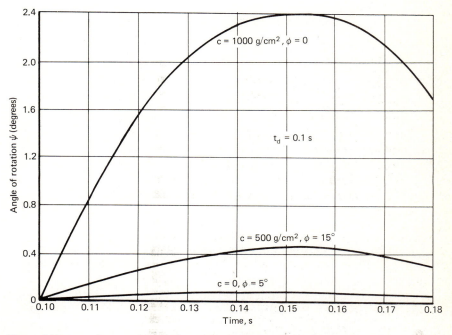

Figure 6.19 ψ vs. t for $t_d = 0.1$ s. *(After Prakash and Chummar, 1967.)*

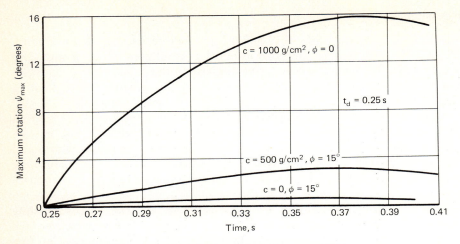

Figure 6.20 ψ vs. t for $t_d = 0.25$ s. *(After Prakash and Chummar, 1967.)*

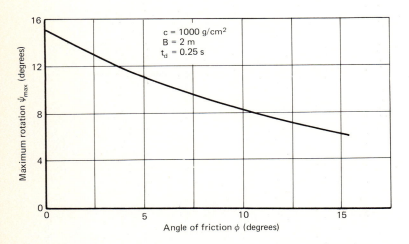

Figure 6.21 Angle of internal friction ϕ vs. ψ_{max}. *(After Prakash and Chummar, 1967.)*

Figure 6.24 shows that the duration t_d of the dynamic pulse has a marked effect on ψ_{max}. Doubling of the value of t_d more than doubles the value ψ_{max}, while the maximum intensity of the pulse has not been changed.

As mentioned earlier, the ultimate horizontal dynamic load that the footing may take is equal to $\lambda_{cr} P$, where P is the static load and λ_{cr} is the critical overload ratio. It is noted that the values of λ_{cr} are independent of the variables considered and equal 0.38.

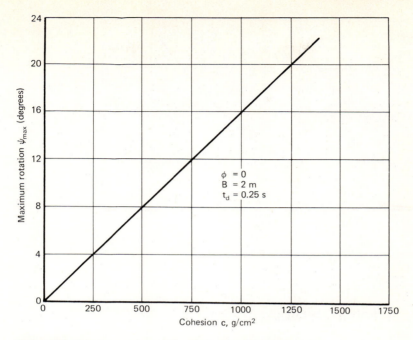

Figure 6.22 Cohesion vs. ψ_{max}. *(After Prakash and Chummar, 1967.)*

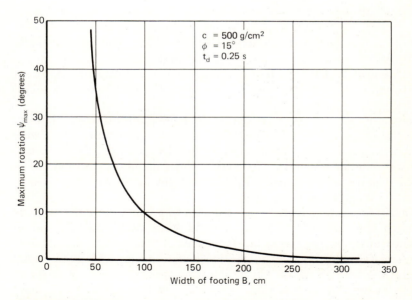

Figure 6.23 Width of footing vs. ψ_{max}. *(After Prakash and Chummar, 1967.)*

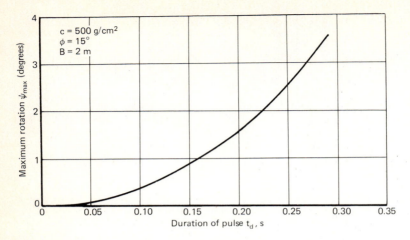

Figure 6.24 t_d vs. ψ_{max}. *(After Prakash and Chummar, 1967.)*

6.9 EXPERIMENTAL WORK

In most of the experimental work on dynamic bearing capacity of footings under nonvibratory loads, the loads used are vertical, since these investigations have been conducted in connection with the design of footings against nuclear blast. The problem of footing behavior under earthquakes has not been adequately investigated.

Selig and McKee (1961) tested small footings under static and dynamic loads. The dynamic load used was an impulsive load obtained by dropping a weight from a known height. The tests were performed on Ottawa sand, which has minimum and maximum densities of 1.54 g/cm³ (96.3 lb/ft³) and 1.8 g/cm³ (112.7 lb/ft³).

Three-dimensional tests were conducted in a box approximately 120 cm square and 100 cm deep. The footings were made of aluminum. They were circular and rectangular, with bearing areas of from 25 cm² (4 in²) to 393.75 cm² (63 in²). To simulate the roughness of actual footings, the bottoms of the blocks were knurled. The maximum density of the sand in the dense state was close to 1.8 g/cm³ (112.3 lb/ft³).

Two-dimensional experiments were conducted in a container with two glass sides measuring approximately 57.5 cm long and 44 cm high, spaced about 10 cm apart. The density of the sand in the dense state in the two-dimensional tests was 1.74 g/cm³ (109 lb/ft³), and in the loose state it was 1.58 g/cm³ (98.5 lb/ft³). A grid was used on the sand surface by one of the glass sides so that any movement of the sand could be readily observed. The footings were 5 cm and 7.5 cm wide and 10 cm long to fit between the glass plates. Figure 6.25 shows

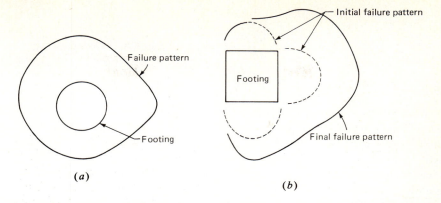

Figure 6.25 Failure pattern in static footing model tests. (*a*) Symmetrical failure pattern for 9-in circular surface footing. (*b*) Double failure patterns for 4-in-square surface footing. (*After Selig and McKee, 1961.*)

intersections of the failure planes with the surface of the sand.† When the peaks of the load-displacement curves were reached, differential displacements in the sand surface began to indicate the failure zone with increased displacements; the position of failure surface did not change. In addition, in about 10 percent of the tests, a second failure surface was observed immediately after the first, as shown in Figure 6.25*b*. The load displacement did not change abruptly when the second surface developed. Similar test data on footings of different sizes have subsequently been reported by Ghumman (1965) and by Prakash and Ghumman (1978). Most of the failure patterns were intermediate between the idealized failure patterns corresponding to symmetrical and to one-sided failures.

In two-dimensional tests on dense sand, both symmetrical and one-sided failures were observed. Well-defined failure patterns were observed in both cases. In loose sand, however, no well-defined shear planes developed. Instead, the distortion of the sand extended continuously outward from the bottom of the footing.

Dynamic Tests

The failure patterns in dynamic loading were of an entirely different nature in the three-dimensional tests. There was a depression close to the footing. In contrast to the static pattern, the dynamic pattern did not exhibit a single clearly defined shear surface. Part of the sand mound (Fig. 6.26) surrounding the footing after impulsive loading was created by sand being thrown out from around the edge of the footing.

† In static tests.

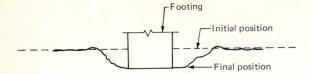

Figure 6.26 Settlement pattern of footing in impact test. *(After Selig and McKee, 1961.)*

Fifty-seven tests were performed by dropping weights on square footings placed on the surface of dense sands. In Fig. 6.27, footing settlement associated with the dynamic load has been plotted against the drop height. The test results indicated linear variation of settlement-versus-drop height.

Since no well-defined failure surfaces developed in the dynamic cases, failure under dynamic loading was assumed to have occurred when the footing settlement had reached or exceeded the settlement at failure for the same footing loaded statically. In all except two tests, the settlement in dynamic tests was greater than that in static tests, and this criterion was therefore satisfactory.

In two-dimensional tests on dense sand, when a weight of 13.2 kg was dropped from a height of 50 cm, 7.5-cm-wide footing settled by 1.17 cm. The deformation pattern was similar to that in local shear in static tests. However, when the same weight was dropped twice, the settlement increased to 5.39 cm and a well-defined failure pattern developed. This is considered to be the result of the changed boundary conditions due to the first drop (Selig and McKee, 1961).

This study shows clearly the modes of deformation of footing subjected to impulsive loading.

In a continuation of the above study, Shenkman and McKee (1961) described an apparatus by which dynamic loads could be applied through the pneumatic-hydraulic device. High-speed motion pictures were obtained for the two-dimensional footings, and force-time and displacement-time histories were obtained for the three-dimensional footings in the preliminary tests performed.

Cunny and Sloan (1961) performed tests on 11.25-cm- and 22.5-cm-square footings on dense, dry sand and backswamp clay. The machine was capable of

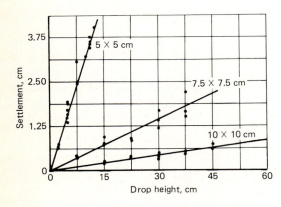

Figure 6.27 Settlement of footings with height of drop of the weight. *(After Selig and McKee, 1961.)*

developing up to 22,722 kg (50,000 lb) dynamic or static loads that could be applied either in tension or compression. The load rise time could be generally controlled from about 3 to 150 ms. The full dynamic load could be maintained for times varying from 0 to 1 s, and the load decay varied from about 20 ms to 10 s. The footings were placed in a soil cart which measured about 100 cm by 340 cm and 90 cm deep and was mounted on heavy-duty truck casters.

The sand density was 1.65 g/cm^3 (103.4 lb/ft^3), which corresponded to 96 percent relative density. In the direct shear tests, the angle of internal friction for a normal load of 3 kg/cm^2 was about 32°. The top 30 cm of the sand specimen was marked at about 7.5-cm vertical intervals with black onyx powder to aid in visually locating failure planes below the footings after the test.

The moisture content of the clay tested was 1.7 percent wet of the optimum moisture content, and the average density was slightly more than the standard proctor dry density of 1.536 g/cm^3 (96 lb/ft^3). The value of c was 1.2 kg/cm^2 and $\phi = 4°$.

Both static and dynamic tests were performed. The static bearing capacity of a footing was determined first. For dynamic tests on sands, the programmed dynamic loads ranged from 115 to 165 percent of the computed ultimate static bearing capacities. The rise times were intended to be the fastest possible, the dwell times ranged between 0 and 500 ms, and the decay times ranged between 100 and 350 ms.

The programmed dynamic loads on footings in clay ranged from 97 to 130 percent of the computed ultimate static bearing capacity.

Typical results of dynamic tests are shown in Table 6.8.

In these tests, it was found that there is no tendency for the footings to tilt. The increase in bearing capacity of sands in dynamic tests is in accordance with the concepts of strength at fast rates of loading. The behavior of clay, however,

Table 6.8 Results of small-scale static and dynamic tests on sand and clay*

Dynamic test	Machine load, lb	Static capacity, %	Load overshoot, lb	Rise time, ms	Dwell time, ms	Decay time, ms	Footing deformation potentiometers		
							No. 1, in	No. 2, in	No. 3, in
Sand									
No. 1	800	104	0	18	122	110	0.28	0.05	0.11
No. 2	2,800	154	340	8	420	255	—	—	—
No. 3	2,175	120	100	90	280	290	0.83	0.93	0.95
No. 4	3,250	125	250	11	0	350	0.40	0.42	0.40
Clay									
No. 1	2,275	93	575	9	170	350	0.50	0.50	0.48
No. 2	2,820	117	280	9	0	380	0.66	0.72	0.70
No. 3	2,970	121	490	10	0	365	1.70	1.68	1.70
No. 4	2,950	97	630	9	0	360	0.58	0.55	0.55

*After Cunny and Sloan, 1961.

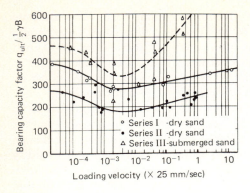

Figure 6.28 Bearing capacity factor $N_\gamma (= q_{ult}/\frac{1}{2}\gamma B)$ vs. loading velocity in dynamic tests on sands. *(After Vesic, Banks, and Woods, 1965.)*

is rather erratic, but this could be due to experimental errors. More data is needed to clarify this point. Vesic, Banks, and Woodward (1965) performed tests on 10.2-cm-diameter model footings placed on dense sand in a tank, 127 cm $\times$ 127 cm $\times$ 178 cm deep. Both dry and submerged sand tests were performed. The rate of loading of the footings was varied from about 2.5×10^{-4} mm/s to over 250 mm/s. Continuous records of load and settlements were obtained. It was found that the bearing capacity of both dry and submerged sands decreased as the rate of loading increased from slow to moderately rapid values of about 0.05 mm/s (Fig. 6.28). However, as loading was increased to very rapid rates, there was a steady increase in the bearing capacity. In tests with dry sand, the increase was not appreciable. In the saturated state, the increase was very pronounced and the final values were several times higher than their corresponding values in static tests.

It was shown in Chap. 4 that the shear strength of sands increases as loading rates are increased. Hence, the decreases in bearing capacity up to a certain rate of loading are contradictory to most data on shear strengths of soils. However, the increases in bearing capacity with faster rates of loading are not appreciable in dry sand. Increases in the angle of internal friction in dry sands due to faster loading rates are not appreciable, either. The undrained strength of saturated dense sand increases about 15 to 20 percent over its static drained strength. Hence, the increase in bearing capacity of submerged sand due to negative pore pressures is in accordance with accepted strength concepts.

6.11 FINAL COMMENTS

It will be seen that solutions to the problems have been generally attempted for earthquake loading and blast loading. Analytical solutions have been obtained for highly simplified loading conditions and idealized soils. Experimental verifications of these analytical solutions have not been seriously attempted, and they are not easy to obtain.

The Indian Standard specifies increases in allowable bearing capacity under earthquake loading. ATC tentative recommendations require that tie beams be designed for $Av/4$, both in tension and compression, for performance category c. The financial impact of this provision and the resulting safety are still undetermined.

Fundamentally speaking, a definition for dynamic bearing capacity has not yet evolved!

Another important question is that of footing-soil interaction. Footings are always connected with the columns and the superstructure. Therefore, the predicted settlements and tilts are going to be different than those estimated for isolated footings.

Veletsos (1977, 1978) has highlighted the interaction problem and has offered an approach for solving it by considering the foundation and superstructure as a unit under earthquake loading. Since there needs to be a simple solution to the interaction problem, this approach may be used in practice.

At the present state of practice for earthquake loading, it is recommended that

1. bearing capacity may only be determined by the Meyerhof (1953) method for eccentric vertical loads
2. bearing capacity, settlements, and tilts may be determined by methods proposed by Prakash and Saran (1971, 1977)
3. interconnecting beams be provided to tie the foundations as tentatively recommended by the Applied Technology Council (1978).

REFERENCES

Applied Technology Council: "Tentative Provisions for the Development of Seismic Regulations for Buildings," Publication No. ATC-3-08, June, 1978.

ASTM (D1194-72) Standard Method for Bearing Capacity of Soil for Static Load on Spread Footings (Reapproved 1977).

Basavanna, B. M., V. H. Joshi, and S. Prakash: "Dynamic Bearing Capacity of Soils under Transient Loading," *Bull. Ind. Soc. Earthq. Tech.*, vol. 2, no. 3, pp. 67–84, September, 1974.

Chummar, A. V.: "Dynamic Bearing Capacity of Footings," Master of Engineering Dissertation, University of Roorkee, Roorkee, India, 1965.

Converse, F. J.: "Compaction of Sand at Resonant Frequency," Symp. on Dynamic Testing of Soils, ASTM, Spec. Tech. Pub. No. 150, pp. 124–137, 1953.

Cunny, R. W., and R. C. Sloan: "Dynamic Loading Machine and Results of Preliminary Small-Scale Footing Tests," Symp. on Soil Dynamics, ASTM Spec. Tech. Pub. No. 305, pp. 65–77, 1961.

Eastwood, E.: Vibrations in Foundations, *Struc. Eng.*, vol. 3, pp. 82–93, March, 1953.

Fellenius, W.: "Erdstatische Berechnungen," 4th ed., W. Ernst Und Sohn, Berlin, 1948.

Ghumman, M. S.: "Effect of Shape of Footings on Bearing Capacity," Master of Engineering Dissertation, University of Roorkee, Roorkee, India, 1965.

Indian Standard Method of Load Test on Soils, IS 1888-1971, 1st rev., Indian Standards Institution, New Delhi.

Indian Standard Criteria for Earthquake Resistant Design of Structures, IS 1893-1975, 3d rev., Indian Standards Institution, New Delhi.

Indian Standard Code of Practice for Structural Safety of Buildings: Foundation, IS 1906-1978, 2d rev., Indian Standards Institution, New Delhi.

Indian Standard Method of Standard Penetration Soils, IS 2131-1963, Indian Standards Institution, New Delhi.

Indian Standard Method for Determination of Allowable Bearing Pressure for Soils for Shallow Foundations, IS 6403-1971, Indian Standards Institution, New Delhi.

Janbu, N.: Earth Pressures and Bearing Capacity Calculations by Generalized Procedure of Slices, *Proc. Fourth Int. Conf. Soil Mech. Found. Engin.*, London, vol. 2, pp. 207–213, 1957.

Krishna, J., and A. R. Chandrasekaran: "Elements of Earthquake Engineering," Sarita Prakashan, Meerut, U.P., India, 1976.

Meyerhof, G. G.: The Bearing Capacity of Footings Under Eccentric and Inclined Loads, *Proc. Third Int. Conf. Soil Mech. Found. Engin.*, Zurich, vol. I, pp. 440–45, 1953.

Moore, W. W., and R. D. Darragh: Some Considerations in the Design of Footings for Earthquakes, *Proc. First World Conf. Earthquake Engin.*, Berkeley, CA, paper no. 28, 1956.

Nagraj, C. N.: "Effect of Vibration on Settlement," Symp. on Foundation Engineering, Bangalore, May, 1961.

Peck, R. B., W. E. Hansen, and T. H. Thornburn: "Foundation Engineering," 2d ed., John Wiley and Sons, Inc., New York, 1974.

Prakash, S.: Aseismic Design of Foundations, in "Earthquake Engineering," Sarita Prakashan Meerut, pp. 333–345, 1974.

_____ and A. V. Chummar: Response of Footings to Lateral Loads, *Proc. Int. Symp. on Wave Propagation and Dynamic Properties of Earth Materials*, Albuquerque, New Mexico, pp. 679–691, 1967.

_____ and M. S. Ghumman: Effect of Shape on Bearing Capacity of Model Footings in Sand, *J. Inst. Engin.*, C13, vol. 59, pt. 1, p. 185, November, 1978.

_____, G. Ranjan, and S. Saran: "Analysis and Design of Foundations and Retaining Structures," Sarita Prakashan Meerut, U.P., India, 1979.

_____ and S. Saran: Bearing Capacity of Eccentrically Loaded Footings, *J. Soil Mech. Found. Div. ASCE*, vol. 97, no. SM 1, pp. 95–111, 1971.

_____ and _____: A New Method of Designing Eccentrically Loaded Rigid Footings, *J. Indian Geotech. Soc.*, vol. 3, no. 1, pp. 1–11, 1973.

_____ and _____: Settlement and Tilt of Eccentrically Loaded Footings, *J. Struct. Engin.*, Roorkee, vol. 4, no. 4, pp. 166–176, January, 1977.

_____ and H. D. Sharma: "Analysis of Pile Foundations against Earthquakes," *Indian Concrete Journal*, pp. 205–220, June, 1969.

Saran, S.: "Bearing Capacity of Footings Subjected to Moments," Ph.D. Thesis, University of Roorkee, Roorkee, India, 1969.

Seed, H. B.: Soil Strength During Earthquakes, *Proc. Second World Conf. Earthquake Engin.*, Tokyo, vol. 1, pp. 183–199, 1960.

Selig, E. T., and K. E. McKee: Static and Dynamic Behavior of Small Footings, *J. Soil Mech. Found. Div., ASCE*, vol. 87, no. SM 6, pp. 29–47, December, 1961.

Shenkman, S., and K. E. McKee: "Bearing Capacities of Dynamically Loaded Footings," Symp. on Soil Dynamics, ASTM Spec. Tech. Pub. No. 305, pp. 78–90, 1961.

Singh, B., and S. Prakash: "Soil Mechanics and Foundation Engineering," 4th ed., Nemchand and Bros., Roorkee, India, 1970.

Sridharan, A.: "Settlement Studies of a Model Footing Under Dynamic Load," *Proc. Second Symp. on Earthquake Engin.*, Roorkee, p. 377, November, 1962.

Taylor, P. W.: "Design of Spread Footings for Earthquake Loadings," *Proc. Fifth Australia-New Zealand Conference on Soil Mechanics and Foundation Engineering*, pp. 221–229, 1968.

Teng, W. C.: "Foundation Design," Prentice-Hall of India, New Delhi, 1965.

Terzaghi, K.: "Theoretical Soil Mechanics," John Wiley and Sons, Inc., New York, 1943.

_____ and R. B. Peck: "Soil Mechanics in Engineering Practice," John Wiley and Sons, Inc., New York, 1967.

Triandafilidis, G. E.: "Analytical Study of Dynamic Bearing Capacity of Foundations," Ph.D. Thesis, University of Illinois, Urbana, Illinois, 1961.

_____: The Dynamic Response of Continuous Footings Supported on Cohesive Soils, *Proc. Sixth Int. Conf. Soil Mech. Found. Engin.*, Montreal, vol. 2, pp. 205–208, 1965.

Veletsos, A. S.: Dynamics Structure-Foundation Systems, in W. J. Hall (ed.): "Structural and Geotechnical Mechanics: A Volume Honoring N. M. Newmark," Prentice-Hall, Inc., Englewood Cliffs, NJ, pp. 333–361, 1977.

_____: Soil Structure Interaction for Buildings During Earthquakes, *Proc. Second Int. Conf. Microzonation*, San Francisco, vol. 1, pp. 111–134, 1978.

Vesic, A. S., D. C. Banks, and J. M. Woodward: "An Experimental Study of Dynamic Bearing Capacity of Footings on Sand," *Proc. Fifth Int. Conf. Soil Mech. Found. Engin.*, Paris, vol. 2, pp. 209–213, 1965.

SEVEN

PILE FOUNDATIONS

7.1 GENERAL

When the subsoil immediately beneath a structure on shallow footings is too weak to support the structure, the depth of the foundation is increased until more suitable soil is encountered. In such cases, the load of the structure may be transferred onto the subsoil through pile foundations.

Depending upon their use, piles are usually divided into several categories, including bearing piles, friction piles, laterally loaded piles, tension piles, and compaction piles. Piles are of timber, steel, and reinforced concrete. So long as they are capable of sustaining stresses in tension, compression, and bending, the analysis is not materially altered.

Commercially available piles include vibro, Franki, pressure, Rodio, Raymond, Hindustan Ziessal, Armco, monotube, and cobipiles. For their properties and sizes, the reader is referred to the manufacturers' catalogs.

In this chapter, pile hammers, including the vibratory pile driver, will be briefly discussed; this will be followed by an estimation of the allowable load on a single pile. A detailed discussion of pseudostatic and dynamic analysis of piles under lateral loads will then be presented for piles in sands and clays. A procedure for the design of piles to withstand earthquakes will be included, and provisions of relevant codes on the analysis and design of piles under seismic conditions will also be described.

7.2 PILE HAMMERS

Piles are driven by blows from a hammer, which is referred to as a *pile driver*. The direction of fall of the hammer is guided either vertically or at an inclination, as the case may be. If the hammer is raised through a rope and is allowed to fall freely on top of the pile, it is called a *drop hammer*. If the hammer is lifted by steam pressure and is allowed to fall under gravity, it is called a *single-acting steam hammer*. If steam pressure is used to add to the downward energy it is a *double-acting steam hammer*. A *diesel hammer* is a self-contained unit that includes a fuel tank and injectors and is lighter and more easily transported than a steam hammer. A diesel hammer operates more slowly than a double-acting steam hammer. The rate of energy of a hammer blow is specified by the manufacturer. The rated energy of a Vulcan (016) hammer, for example, is 48,750 ft·lb. For driving large-diameter piles to great depths, as for offshore drilling platforms, a hammer with rated capacity of up to 180,000 ft·lb has been manufactured (Peck et al., 1974).

The principle of vibrations has been extensively employed by Soviet engineers for driving piles. A vibrating hammer, consisting of an oscillator driven by an electric motor, is mounted on top of the pile. The operation of the oscillator, termed a *vibratory driver*, is illustrated in Fig. 7.1a. A mechanical

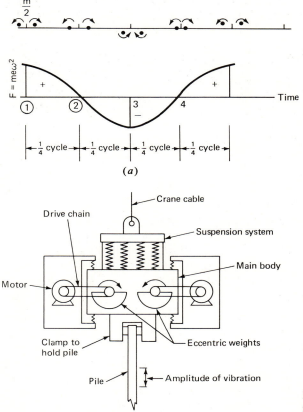

Figure 7.1 (*a*) Principle of a mechanical oscillator. (*b*) Vibro-driver.

vibrator consists of shafts in pairs geared together and driven by a motor. Eccentric masses $m/2$ each are mounted on the shafts at equal eccentricity e from the center of the shaft. At instant 1, the centrifugal forces of both the eccentric masses are additive and the horizontal force is zero. At instant 2, after a quarter cycle of motion, the horizontal forces caused by the two eccentric masses cancel each other, and there is no component of force in the vertical direction. In passing from position 1 to position 2, the horizontal forces balance at every instant, and the vertical forces are additive.

The maximum vertical force is

$$P_{max} = me\omega^2 \tag{7.1}$$

and it varies sinusoidally with time as

$$P_t = me\omega^2 \sin \omega t \tag{7.2}$$

in which
$m/2$ = each eccentric mass
e = eccentricity
ω = circular frequency of rotation

Figure 7.1b shows details of a vibrodriver (Dalmatov, 1962). Levkin (1960) described the particulars of the vibratory drivers that were used in the U.S.S.R. during the 1950s. The information is summarized in Table 7.1

VP-1 operates at only one frequency and has the following structural parts (Fig. 7.2):

1. the body of the vibratory machine, consisting of a steel box with outside guide rollers and loops at the upper corners for raising the vibrator
2. four working shafts (to which eccentric masses are attached) connected to the body of the vibrator by bearings
3. a conical base for attaching the pile to the vibrator
4. an electric motor, which is geared with the working shaft of the vibratory hammer

The conical base is attached to the bottom of the vibrator by bolts. This cone is then attached to the head of the pile, which sinks as a result of the vibratory force.

The VP-160 is a low-frequency, eight-shaft vibrator that may be used in pairs. The construction of the vibratory driver permits separate control of the vibration frequency, the magnitude of the exciting force, and the load moment. This vibratory driver is adapted for synchronous operation and has been used for the sinking of an RCC shell, 18 m long and 1.6 m in diameter, with a wall thickness of 10 cm.

MKT-hydraulic vibratory driver/extractor details are listed in Table 7.2.

Table 7.1 Particulars of vibratory drivers in use in the U.S.S.R.*

S. no.	Type	Dimensions in plan, mm	Height with base, mm	Weight, t	Static moment of eccentrics kg·cm	Frequency r/min	Maximum exciting force, t	Amp. of driver in neutral gear, cm	Power of motor, kW	Capacity of pile for which used, t
1	VP-1	1,300 × 1,240	1,650	4.5	10,000	420	19.0	2	60	up to 100
2	VP-2	950 × 950	1,270		4,000	445	8.4	2	22	up to 50
3	VP-3†	1,560 × 1,500	2,000	7.5	26,300	408	44.2	3	100	up to 200
4	VP-160	1,500 × 1,180	3,100	10.4	39,000	800/400	100		155	
						900/450	130			
						1,010/505	160			
5	VP-250‡						250			

* After Levkin (1960).

† Also used for sinking pile shells weighing up to 15 t. A case of sinking a 15.5-m-long concrete shell with an outer diameter of 90 cm and wall thickness of 6 cm in silty sand is cited.

‡ Used for sinking RCC shells up to 6 m diameter with wall thickness of 15–30 cm (app) in sand with fine gravel up to a depth of 40 m.

Figure 7.2 Pile driver VP-1. *(After Levkin, 1960.)*

Mr. Albert G. Bodine, Jr., of California designed a Bodine sonic hammer,† which drives a pile at its fundamental frequency and is claimed to be a vibration-free hammer. It is purported to drive piles very efficiently. In one case, 36 concrete piles were driven in 11 h. Its performance was compared with that of a steam hammer. The steam hammer sank a pile 20.1 m (67 ft) in 90 min while the vibratory unit, working about 9 m away, sank a similar pile 21.3 m (71 ft) in 42 s. The other pile moved only about 7.5 cm (3 in) during this period. The soil at the site was very-fine-to-coarse sand with some gravel and traces of silt. In yet another case, the vibratory unit installed and extracted a 22.5-m (75-ft) pile seven times while the steam hammer drove its pile only 3.6 m (12 ft) into the ground. The advantage of the sonic driver over the others is claimed to be due to its high-frequency operation, up to 100 Hz, as opposed to frequencies ranging from 8 to 22 Hz for the Russian and French machines.

In general, the loss of energy in the vibratory hammer is considerably less than that in a conventional hammer, because, in the latter, much of the energy of the impact is dissipated in compressing the cushion blocks, driving head, or

---

† At the present (1981) it is not used in the United States.

Table 7.2 Hydraulic vibratory driver/extractor*

Mfr. Model	Driving force at SSF,† t	Hydraulic motor output hp at SSF	Steady-state frequency at rated press-flow	Vibrating weight, lb	Eccentric moment, in·lb	Driving amplitude, in	Rated flow at SSF, gal/min	Rated pressure at SSF, lb/in²	Hydraulic motor efficiency, %	Engine operating, r/min	Net weight exciter, lb
MKT V-20	100.6	295	1,650	9,000	2,600	0.58	110	5,000	92	2,000	10,650
MKT V-16	78.3	161	1,750	7,600	1,800	0.47	75	4,000	92	1,900	9,250
MKT V-5	30.0	59	1,450	4,000	1,000	0.50	50	2,700	75	2,000	5,100

* Courtesy of MKT Geotechnical Systems.
† SSF = steady-state frequency.

both, in overcoming the inertia of the pile itself, and in skin friction that may possibly develop between widely spaced blows.

A serious disadvantage of the vibratory hammer is that during the driving operation the load-carrying capacity of a pile cannot be estimated.

Vibratory pile drivers are now gaining popularity throughout the world.

7.3 ALLOWABLE LOADS ON PILES

Allowable loads on piles may be estimated by the following methods:

Pile-Driving Formulas

The basic principle of all pile-driving formulas is that energy of the hammer is used up in driving the pile and in losses. It is assumed that the resistance of piles to further penetration under the working load has a direct relation to their resistance to the impact of the hammer when they are being driven. Thus, the dynamic formulas take into consideration the weight and drop of the hammer, the weight of the pile, and the penetration of the pile under each blow. The loss of energy is due to the elastic compression of the pile, the helmet, the packing, and the soil around the pile, and to the inertia of the pile. The physical characteristics of the soil do not appear in most dynamic formulas (Tomlinson, 1969). Also, empirical relations are often used for estimating losses, which are assumed to be proportional to the dynamic resistance.

Details of pile-driving formulas and their critical evaluation have been given by Chellis (1961) and Bowles (1977).

Wave Equation

It is well understood that pile driving is not a simple case of impact, which may be solved directly by Newton's laws. Instead, pile driving is a case of longitudinal wave propagation in a rod. If a rod that is fixed at the bottom and free at the top is hit by a hammer blow, a compression wave propagates through it with a velocity v_r,

$$v_r = \sqrt{\frac{E}{\rho}} \tag{3.5}$$

in which E = Young's modulus of pile material and ρ = its mass density.

The wave-equation analysis predicts the soil load resistance, the stresses in the pile during driving, and the ultimate load capacity of the pile at the time of driving versus driving resistance in bpi (or blow/cm).

The analysis is based on the one-dimensional wave equation and is carried out by considering the hammer ram striking an elastic cushion, generally the hammer cushion, which rests on the drivehead atop the pile. In Fig. 7.3a, the hammer-cushion-pile configuration is shown with an optional cushion inserted between the drivehead (pile cap) and the pile. In Fig. 7.3*b*, an idealized lumped-mass model is illustrated wherein the ram and pile cap are considered to be masses, and the hammer cushion and optional pile cushion are considered to be springs. The pile is divided into a series of lumped masses connected by springs. Attached to the masses are elastic-plastic springs and dashpots that simulate the resistance of the soil. The time-displacement behavior of the idealized system is analyzed by starting when the hammer ram strikes the pile cushion at an initial specified velocity (Davisson, 1975).

Ordinarily, an ultimate resistance R_u for the pile is assumed and the analysis is performed to determine the net set of the pile tip; the reciprocal of set is the driving resistance, which is usually expressed in blows per inch (bpi). By repeated application of the process, a sufficient number of R_u-bpi points can be generated to produce a curve. At the same time, peak force in any spring in the system can be obtained and translated to stress in the pile cross section.

An example of the data obtained from a wave-equation analysis is presented in Fig. 7.3*c*. In this case, an 18 in OD × 0.375 in (45 cm OD × 0.94 cm) 75 ft (22.5 m) long pile was considered embedded 35 ft (10.5 m). It was assumed that 50 percent of the ultimate load capacity occurred at the tip, and the remaining 50 percent occurred uniformly over the embedded portion of the pile. The pile was driven with a no. 1 Vulcan hammer for which an efficiency of 70 percent is considered appropriate. The hammer cushion was a standard aluminum-micarta stack.

The solid line in Fig. 7.3*c* is the ultimate resistance R_u at the time of driving plotted versus bpi. The dashed line is the stress in the pile head plotted versus bpi. For example, at 10 bpi the ultimate resistance of the pile is 150 T and the peak stress in the pile head is approximately 21,000 lb/in². If the pile is driven to 10 bpi and a static load test performed to failure, three cases can be defined. In the first case, if the ultimate load capacity is approximately 150 T, the point will plot on the computed curve. In such a case, capacity by dynamic formula equals static capacity.

The remaining two cases in Fig. 7.3*c* are functions of soil changes that take place after driving. In many soil conditions, setup or freeze occurs after the completion of pile driving, and the static capacity plots higher than the predicted capacity. In the example shown, a point is indicated at 200 T; thus, approximately 50 T of freeze or increase in pile capacity occurs after driving. The third case occurs when the load test capacity falls below the predicted capacity; in Fig. 7.3*c* a point is shown at 125 T indicating that a relaxation of 25 T occurred after driving. Note that the load capacity computed by the wave-equation analysis is used as a reference to define the amount of freeze or relaxation that occurs. For further application of the wave-equation method to the solution of the problem of pile driving, reference may be made to Davisson (1975), Bowles (1977), and Federal Highway Administration Publication No. IP 76-13.1 to -13.4. It has been reported by Chellis (1962) that results from Hiley's formula agree fairly well with those obtained by wave equation except that the former tends to underestimate the capacities of long, heavy piles and mandrels.

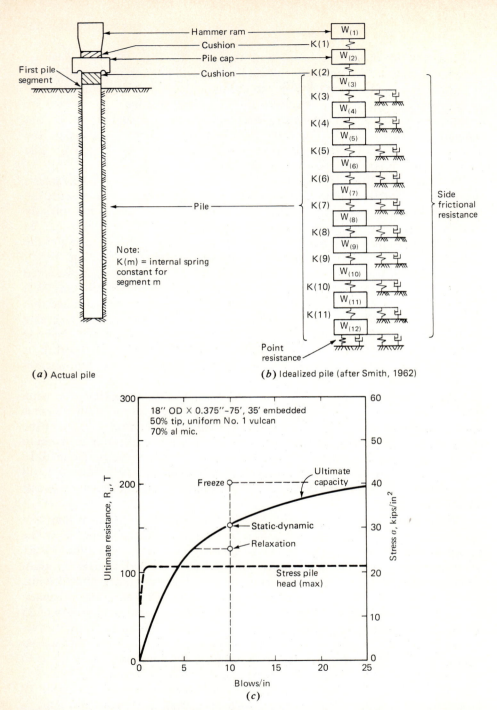

(a) Actual pile

(b) Idealized pile *(after Smith, 1962)*

Note:
K(m) = internal spring
constant for
segment m

18″ OD × 0.375″–75′, 35′ embedded
50% tip, uniform No. 1 vulcan
70% al mic.

(c)

Figure 7.3 Method of representing pile for purposes of calculation in wave equation. (*a*) Actual pile. (*b*) Idealized pile. *(After Smith, 1962.)* (*c*) Ultimate resistance vs. blows per inch by wave equation. *(After Davisson, 1975.)*

Static Formulas

According to static formulas, the total load-carrying capacity of a pile is the sum of end-bearing and frictional resistance along the shaft (Tomlinson, 1969; Peck et al., 1974; Prakash et al., 1979). Values of skin friction for different soils have been observed and a table of recommended values is given by Chellis (1962).

The end bearing is computed by using formulas of ultimate bearing capacity for shallow footings developed by Terzaghi [Eq. (6.1)]. Because piles are definitely deep footings, an estimate based on Terzaghi's approximate bearing capacity formulas is far from realistic.

Cone-Penetration Tests

In penetration tests, a cone is driven by either a static or a dynamic load. The cone is attached to the end of a pipe. By alternately driving the cone and the rod, end-bearing and friction values per unit area can be estimated (Meyerhof, 1956; Menzenback, 1961; Veen and Boersma, 1957; Sharma, 1964). Meyerhof (1976) presented an excellent and detailed report on the subject.

For further discussion on use of cone-penetration test data for determination of allowable load on a pile, reference may be made to Tomlinson (1969) and Prakash et al. (1979).

Load Test

A load test on a working pile is essential for a large job and is the best method available for ascertaining the allowable load on a pile. A load test on a working pile is termed a *routine test* according to the Indian Standard Code of Practice as opposed to an *initial test* on a test pile. In a routine test, the pile is loaded to $1\frac{1}{2}$ times the estimated safe load-carrying capacity of the pile. The load is applied on the cap, usually by means of a hydraulic jack, and total settlement is recorded. Rebound of the pile head is recorded if a cyclic load test is performed. Then the net settlement, which is the difference of total settlement and the rebound of the pile, is computed. The test load is applied in equal installments of about one-fifth the estimated safe load. The load is kept constant until the rate of movement of the pile top is not more than 0.02 mm/h. ASTM Designation 1143-74 gives a detailed description of the equipment used and the manner in which a load test in axial compression is carried out on a pile. However, the method of interpretation is not included.

The safe load, as per the Indian Standard (IS 2911-1964), is assessed as the least of the following:

1. two-thirds of the final load at which the total settlement attains a value of 12 mm unless more settlement is permissible for a particular structure
2. two-thirds of the final load at which the net settlement increases to 6 mm unless more settlement is permissible

Other criteria for interpretation of a load settlement graph are described by Chellis (1961, 1962).

Because piles are installed in groups, the methods of estimating the capacity of groups of piles from the capacity of a single pile in different types of soil are described by Peck et al. (1974), Winterkorn and Fang (1976), Prakash et al. (1979).

7.4 EFFECT OF VIBRATIONS ON PILES

A sand mass that is subjected to vibrations tends to increase in density with a corresponding decrease in voids. In a mass of saturated sand below ground-water level, such increases in density are accompanied by the expulsion of water from the soil mass. The movement of soil grains is associated with the decrease of effective stresses. If the soil is under a certain initial shear stress, the effect of vibrations is felt to a different degree (see Chap. 8).

A pile driven in the soil introduces additional shear stresses in the soil mass. If it is exposed to vibrations, excessive settlements are likely to occur. In order to study the effect of vibrations on piles, Swiger (1948) performed tests on piles driven in sand. A static load was first applied on a pile, which was then vibrated while under a constant load. The vibrator consisted of a plate 30 cm in diameter and 2.5 cm thick that was mounted with an eccentricity of 1 in. The speed of the vibrator could be varied from about 400 r/min to 3000 r/min. The pile was vibrated at its natural frequency, determined experimentally to be 500 r/min. The static load on the pile was 61 kips and 121 kips respectively. The rate of settlement with the higher static load was several times that with the smaller load.

Experiments were conducted by Agarwal (1967) and Prakash and Agarwal (1971) on vertical model piles embedded in sand at 33 percent relative density. The piles were loaded with a predetermined fraction of upward static pullout resistance, and the tank containing piles was subjected to vertical vibrations at 2.3 Hz and 5.2 Hz. It was found that the number of cycles of motion needed to pull out the pile a predetermined distance of 2 cm decreased with an increase in the static stress level and the acceleration of motion.

A systematic study on penetration of piles under vertical vibrations has been conducted by Ghumman (1981). A model pile 6 cm in diameter and 160 cm long was subjected to a predetermined static load. The vertical vibrations were then imparted by a fully counterbalanced mechanical oscillator, which could be excited to different frequencies (Fig. 7.4).

Significant variables have been isolated, and the penetration of a pile and its static bearing capacity can be determined analytically with the help of expressions that have been developed.

These experiments highlight the importance of vibrations in inducing the settlement of piles.

Earthquakes introduce lateral forces on piles. The energy supplied to a structure may be absorbed in the elastic and plastic deformations of the

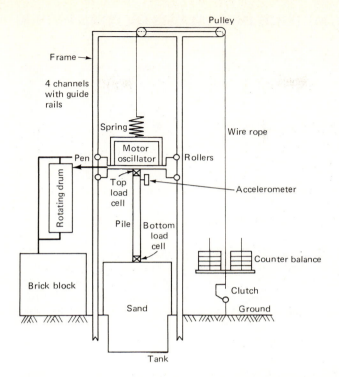

Figure 7.4 A setup for study of penetration of piles under axial vibrations. *(After Ghumman, 1981.)*

superstructure and the substructure. Eccentric loads may be introduced on the piles, similar to the case of footings.

Lateral forces on the superstructure are assumed to be transferred to the ground through the pile cap as lateral loads and moments, and the stability of the piles is checked against these loads. Vertical loads are always present. These may cause buckling of the piles, particularly if free-standing lengths are large, or they may increase the deflections. Therefore, buckling of the piles and the beam-column action become important. As in the case of shallow footings, the pile caps of individual columns are interconnected by grade beams (see Sec. 6.6).

Piles may be used to support the foundations of machines in soils of inadequate strength. The introduction of piles alters the elastic coefficients of the soil system of the foundation. Both the natural frequency and the amplitudes of motion are affected.

In all vibration problems, resonance needs to be avoided. Hence, the natural frequency of the soil-pile system needs to be evaluated.

In the following sections, the actions of piles under lateral loads are examined first. Next, the natural frequency of the pile-soil system, dynamic analysis, and the design of piles against earthquakes are discussed.

7.5 CONVENTIONAL METHOD OF ANALYSIS OF PILES UNDER LATERAL LOADS

According to conventional analyses, the bending resistance of piles is disregarded. Two cases may arise.

Piles Subjected to Moment (Case A)

This analysis is based on the following assumptions:

1. The pile cap is rigid.
2. The load on each pile due to moment is proportional to its distance from the center of gravity of the pile group.
3. The settlement of a pile is proportional to the load acting on this pile.

Figure 7.5a shows a pile group subjected to a total vertical load ΣV at the center of gravity of the group and a moment ΣM. Reactions in each pile caused by vertical load and moment are shown in Fig. 7.5b and c, respectively. In Fig. 7.5d, the loads are the sums of those in Fig. 7.5b and c. The same loads would be produced if ΣV were to have an eccentricity e where

$$e = \frac{\Sigma M}{\Sigma V} \tag{7.3}$$

From static equilibrium, Σ (moments) = 0.
Therefore,

$$\Sigma M = P_1 d_1 + P_2 d_2 + P_3 d_3 + P_4 d_4 \tag{7.4}$$

Because the linear distribution of the load has been assumed, we obtain

$$\frac{P_1}{d_1} = \frac{P_2}{d_2} = \frac{P_3}{d_3} = \frac{P_4}{d_4} \tag{7.5}$$

or

$$P_2 = P_1 \frac{d_2}{d_1} \qquad P_3 = P_1 \frac{d_3}{d_1} \qquad P_4 = P_1 \frac{d_4}{d_1} \tag{7.5a}$$

Substituting P_2, P_3, and P_4 in terms of P_1 from Eq. (7.5a) in Eq. (7.4), we obtain

$$\Sigma M = P_1 \left(\frac{d_1^2}{d_1} + \frac{d_2^2}{d_1} + \frac{d_3^2}{d_1} + \frac{d_4^2}{d_1} \right) \tag{7.5b}$$

or

$$P_1 = \frac{\Sigma M d_1}{\Sigma d^2} \tag{7.5c}$$

or

$$P_n = \frac{\Sigma M}{\Sigma d^2} d_n \tag{7.5d}$$

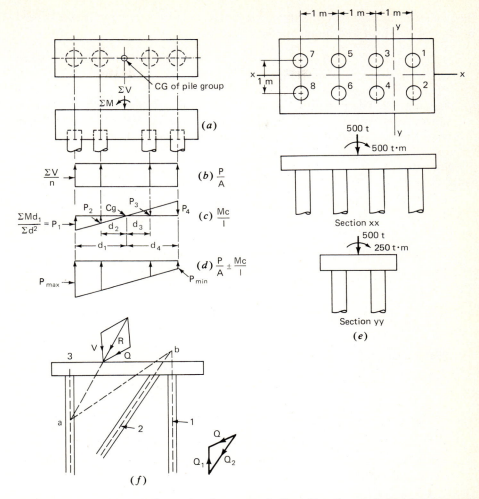

Figure 7.5 Computation of pile reactions in a group of piles subjected to vertical load and moment. (*a*) Section through group. (*b*) Load distribution due to vertical loads. (*c*) Load distribution due to moment. (*d*) Resultant load in each pile. (*e*) Solution of pile loads—Example 7.1. (*f*) Resolution of pile loads in a group with battered piles.

In Eq. (7.5*d*), *n* stands for the number of pile in which total resistance has to be evaluated, and if there is a moment $\Sigma M'$ in the other plane, it can be shown that

$$P'_m = \frac{\Sigma M'}{\Sigma d'^2} d'_m \qquad (7.5e)$$

in which m = the number of pile in the other plane and d'_m = the distance of the pile from the center of gravity of the group. Total reaction in any pile caused by the vertical load and moments then becomes

$$P = \frac{\Sigma V}{n} \pm \frac{\Sigma M}{\Sigma d^2} d_n \pm \frac{\Sigma M'}{\Sigma d'^2} d'_m \qquad (7.6)$$

Example 7.1 The pile group shown in Fig. 7.5e is subjected about the axes shown to a vertical load of 500 t and a moment of 500 t·m and 250 t·m respectively. Compute the maximum and minimum loads in the piles.

SOLUTION

$$n = 8$$

$$\Sigma d_n^2 = 2(0.5^2 + 1.5^2)2 = 10 \text{ m}^2$$

$$\Sigma d'^2_m = 8(0.5)^2 = 4 \text{ m}^2$$

Pile 1 is subjected to the maximum reaction; therefore,

$$P_1 = \frac{500}{8} + \frac{500 \times 1.5}{10} + \frac{250 \times 0.5}{4}$$

$$= 62.5 + 75 + 31.25 \text{ t}$$

$$= 168.75 \text{ t}$$

Pile 8 is subjected to the smallest reaction; therefore,

$$P_8 = \frac{500}{8} - \frac{500 \times 1.5}{10} - \frac{250 \times 0.5}{2}$$

$$= 43.75 \text{ t uplift}$$

It is assumed that the piles resist all moments by tension and compression and are not subjected to any bending. The lateral movement of the pile group is neglected.

Piles Subjected to Lateral Loads (Case B)

Because the piles are assumed to withstand either tension or compression only, some of the piles must be vertically inclined so that the lateral load is properly carried by the pile group. According to Culmann's† graphical method, piles are grouped according to their slopes. It is also assumed that the piles in each group are subjected to equal axial loads. The following steps are followed to analyze the pile groups:

1. Draw a dimensional sketch of the pile foundation (Fig. 7.5f).
2. Locate the center line of each group of parallel piles.

† Referred to by Teng (1962).

3. Draw the resultant R of all external forces applied on the pile foundation. R intersects the center line of the piles in group 3 at point a (Fig. 7.5f).
4. Join ab where b is the point of intersection of the centerlines of groups 1 and 2.
5. Resolve R into Q and V, Q being parallel to ab and V being vertical.
6. Group 3 is subjected to total axial force V.
7. Resolve load Q into axial loads along the centerlines of group 2 and group 1; Q_1 and Q_2 act along the centerlines of groups 2 and 1, respectively.

If the piles are driven in more than three directions, the pile reactions are compounded further.

The analyses described above ignore the capacity of soil to withstand horizontal loads and the capacity of piles to withstand bending. Hence, these are not realistic analyses.

An analysis of a pile subjected to a lateral load, which accounts for the soil-pile interaction, is discussed in the following section.

7.6 ACTION OF A VERTICAL PILE UNDER LATERAL LOADS

The two usual approaches to the problem of laterally loaded piles involve limit analysis or elastic methods (Reese and Matlock, 1956).

In the limit analysis, it is assumed that maximum soil resistance acts against the pile, as shown in Fig. 7.6. In this analysis, it is assumed that the strength of the soil is constant with depth and that the pile deflects sufficiently to develop

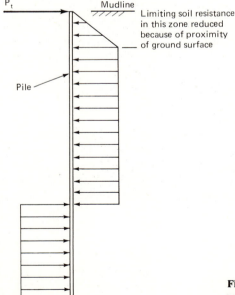

Pile

P_t

Mudline

Limiting soil resistance in this zone reduced because of proximity of ground surface

Figure 7.6 Example of force diagram for limit analysis. *(After Reese and Matlock, 1956.)*

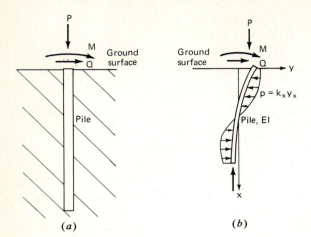

Figure 7.7 (*a*) Pile loads. (*b*) Soil resistance and deflected shape.

full resistance along the length considered. Soil strength may be mobilized with large deformation of the pile. Hence, with small loads, some sort of elastic analysis is desirable.

Figure 7.7 shows the deflected shape of the pile as well as the soil reactions when the deflections are small. A laterally loaded pile has often been treated as a beam on an elastic foundation (Fig. 7.8). For a true elastic medium, the soil reaction p and the deflection y at a given point are affected by reactions and deflections at all other points on the beam. According to a simpler assumption introduced by Winkler (1867), the elastic soil medium is replaced by a series of infinitely close, independent, elastic springs. The stiffness of these springs may

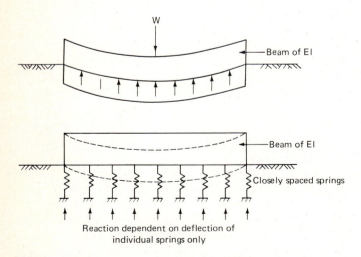

Figure 7.8 Winkler's idealization of a beam on elastic foundation.

then be written as

$$k = \frac{p, \text{kg/cm}}{y, \text{cm}} \qquad (7.7)$$

The stiffness k is also termed the *modulus of the subgrade reaction*. In the pile problem, the pile is vertical and the soil reactions are horizontal. For this case, the k is termed the *modulus of the horizontal subgrade reaction*. Palmer and Thompson (1948) expressed the modulus as a function of depth (Fig. 7.9):

$$k_x = k_h \left(\frac{x}{L_s}\right)^n \qquad (7.8)$$

in which k_h = value of k at the tip of the pile

         x = any length along the pile

         n = a coefficient equal to, greater than, or smaller than 1.

Terzaghi (1955) recommended that n be taken as approximately unity for sands and zero for precompressed clays, although there are indications that value of n of 1.5 may be more appropriate for sands (Davisson and Prakash, 1963). For clays, it is likely that a value of n greater than zero is more realistic than a value of zero. For a rigid pile (defined below), a tentative value of 0.15 has been recommended (Davisson and Prakash, 1963).

For $n = 1$,

$$k_x = \frac{k_h}{L_s} x = n_h x \qquad (7.9)$$

in which n_h = constant of modulus of horizontal subgrade reaction.

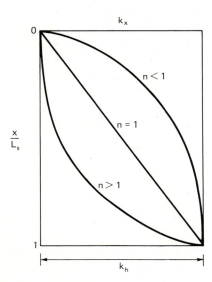

Figure 7.9 Soil modulus as a function of depth. *(After Palmer and Thompson, 1948.)*

The increase in k with depth in noncohesive soils and normally loaded clays and silts is due to two reasons: These soils frequently exhibit an increase in strength with depth as a result of overburden pressures and natural deposition and consolidation processes; and pile deflections decrease with depth for any given loading, and the corresponding equivalent elastic moduli of soil reaction tend to increase with decreasing deflection.

Prakash and Agarwal (1967) reported test data on model piles subjected to horizontal load at 5 cm above the sand surface. The pile lengths were 10, 20, 30, 40, 50, and 60 cm. The deflections of piles at ground level, are shown in Fig. 7.10. It is seen that as the pile length increases, the ground deflection of a pile of constant cross section decreases at the same load. This decrease in deflection occurs first at a very rapid rate. Subsequently, this rate decreases, and, beyond a characteristic length of the pile, the deflections are not materially affected. This length L_α is defined as the *infinite length of the pile*. This length would obviously be a function of pile stiffness EI and soil stiffness k. The greater the pile stiffness, the greater L_α, and the greater the soil stiffness, the smaller L_α.

The concept of an "infinitely long pile" can also be derived from consideration of Fig. 7.7b. Because soil reactions are introduced only upon deflection of the pile, it is obvious that, for a given load and pile section, there is a characteristic pile length beyond which the deflections of the pile are negligible. This length corresponds to L_α.

It is easy to imagine that for the deflection of the pile y_x under a given load and at any depth, x is composed of the rigid-body movement and that which is due to curvature of the pile. The latter decreases as the pile stiffness EI increases, while other things remain the same. If the pile becomes rigid enough so that its deflections, due to curvature, may be neglected as compared with its rigid-body movements, it is called a *rigid pile* or a *pole*. Analytical expressions

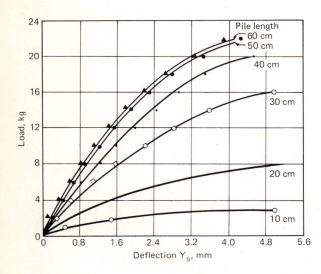

Figure 7.10 Lateral load vs. deflection with different pile embedment. *(After Prakash and Agarwal, 1967.)*

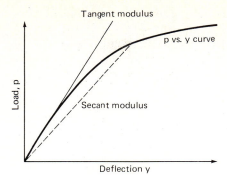

Figure 7.11 Typical soil reaction deflection curve.

will be developed subsequently in the chapter for classifying piles as infinitely long or rigid.

Stress, strain, and load-deformation relations in soils are invariably nonlinear (Fig. 7.11). For loads of less than one-third to one-half their ultimate values, the load-deflection curve can be adequately expressed by a tangent modulus. For larger loads, a secant modulus is more appropriate. The secant modulus is dependent upon load level. Therefore, application of the theory of linear elasticity to the solution of pile problems is not strictly justified; however, to account for the nonlinearity between the load and pile deflection (or soil resistance and pile deflection), two approaches may be adopted:

1. One may employ repeated application of the elastic theory. Soil resistance moduli are adjusted upon completion of each trial run until satisfactory compatibility is obtained between the predicted soil behavior and the load-deflection relationships required by an elastic pile (Matlock and Reese, 1962).
2. The relationship between the secant modulus and the tangent modulus can be defined in terms of strain level, as was the case of the relationship between shear moduli at different strains in Chap. 4. However, the strain levels in soils along the length of the pile have not been defined, and a considerable amount of research is needed to solve this problem. Guidelines on n_h or k_x values to be adopted for a practice problem are discussed in a subsequent section. In any case, the final computed values of deflections and bending moments are not very sensitive to changes in soil modulus values.

7.7 SOLUTION FOR PILES IN NONCOHESIVE SOILS

A typical foundation pile of length L_s and flexural stiffness EI is shown in Fig. 7.12. The depth x is measured downward from the ground line. The boundary conditions at the top consist of an imposed moment M_g and a shear Q_g, and each is shown acting in a positive sense. The soil modulus variation for which

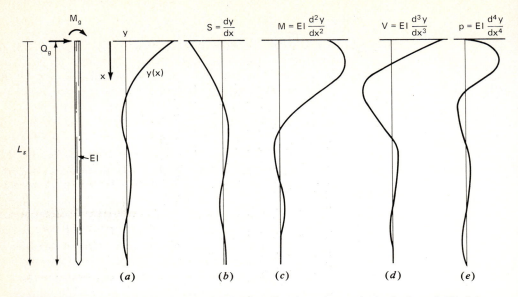

Figure 7.12 A pile of length L_s fully embedded in soil and acted upon by loads Q_g and M_g. (*a*) Deflection y. (*b*) Slope dy/dx. (*c*) Moment $EI\,d^2y/dx^2$. (*d*) Shear $EI\,d^3y/dx^3$. (*e*) Soil reaction $EI\,d^4y/dx^4$.

the solution is available is defined by

$$k_x = n_h x \tag{7.9a}$$

Figure 7.12*a* shows the $y(x)$ curve of the pile. Once this curve is known, its derivatives yield slope, moment, shear, and soil reaction, which are shown in Fig. 7.12*b*, *c*, *d*, and *e*, respectively. The factors on which the deflection of the pile $y(x)$ depends are:

Q_g, M_g, EI of pile, k_x of soil, L_s, x and L_α, the characteristic length of the infinitely long pile.

Instead of L_α, a quantity T, termed the *relative stiffness factor*, may be used. T has units of length and is related with L_α through the following relationship:

$$T = \frac{L_\alpha}{\lambda} \tag{7.10}$$

in which λ is a positive integer. Now $y(x)$ may be expressed as

$$y(x) = Y(x, T, L_s, k, EI, Q_g, M_g) \tag{7.11}$$

If the deflections are small and if an elastic behavior is assumed, the principle of superposition may be applied. Therefore, the effects of an imposed lateral load Q_g and imposed moment M_g may be considered separately, as shown in Fig. 7.13*a*. Sign convention is also shown in this figure.

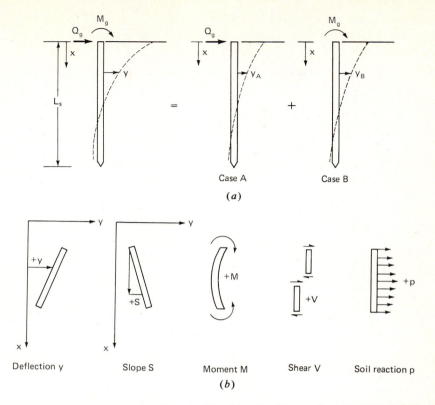

Figure 7.13 (*a*) Application of the principle of superposition to the laterally-loaded-pile problem. (*b*) Sign convention. *(After Matlock and Reese, 1962.)*

If y_A represents the deflection caused by the lateral load Q_g and y_B the deflection caused by M_g, the total deflection is

$$y = y_A + y_B \qquad (7.12)$$

Furthermore, it is the ratios y_A/Q_g and y_B/M_g that are important in the elastic solution. Thus the solutions for Cases A and B may be expressed as

$$\frac{y_A}{Q_g} = f_A(x, T, L_s, k, EI) \qquad (7.13a)$$

and

$$\frac{y_B}{M_g} = f_B(x, T, L_s, k, EI) \qquad (7.13b)$$

in which f_A and f_B are two different functions of the same terms. In each case, there are six terms and two dimensions (force and length) involved. There are, therefore, four independent, nondimensional groups that can be formed. The

arrangements chosen are (Matlock and Reese, 1962):
Case A:

$$\frac{y_A EI}{Q_g T^3}, \frac{x}{T}, \frac{L_s}{T}, \frac{kT^4}{EI} \tag{7.14a}$$

Case B:

$$\frac{y_B EI}{M_g T^2}, \frac{x}{T}, \frac{L_s}{T}, \frac{kT^4}{EI} \tag{7.14b}$$

Each of the nondimensional terms formulated above can be assigned the following names and symbols:

$$\frac{x}{T} = Z \qquad \text{(depth coefficient)} \tag{7.15}$$

$$\frac{L_s}{T} = Z_{\text{max}} \quad \text{(maximum depth coefficient)} \tag{7.16}$$

$$\frac{kT^4}{EI} = \phi(z) \quad \text{(soil modulus function)} \tag{7.17}$$

$$\frac{y_A EI}{Q_g T^3} = A_y \qquad \text{(deflection coefficient for Case A)} \tag{7.18}$$

$$\frac{y_B EI}{M_g T^2} = B_y \qquad \text{(deflection coefficient for Case B)} \tag{7.19}$$

Thus, from Eqs. (7.18) and (7.19),

$$y_x = y_A + y_B = A_y \frac{Q_g T^3}{EI} + B_y \frac{M_g T^2}{EI} \tag{7.20}$$

Proceeding in a similar manner, the solutions for other quantities may be expressed as follows:
Slope:

$$S_x = S_A + S_B = A_s \frac{Q_g T^2}{EI} + B_s \frac{M_g T}{EI} \tag{7.21}$$

Moment:

$$M_x = M_A + M_B = A_m Q_g T + B_m M_g \tag{7.22}$$

Shear:

$$V_x = V_A + V_B = A_V(Q_g) + B_V \frac{M_g}{T} \tag{7.23}$$

Soil reaction:

$$p_x = p_A + p_B = A_p \frac{Q_g}{T} + B_p \frac{M_g}{T^2} \tag{7.24}$$

From the theory of a beam on an elastic foundation, the equation of the deflected beam is

$$EI\frac{d^4y}{dx^4} = p \tag{7.25}$$

From Winkler's hypothesis, $p = -ky$. Soil reaction is always in a direction opposite to deflection; hence the negative sign is used. The basic equation for a beam on an elastic foundation, or for a laterally loaded pile, may then be written as

$$\frac{d^4y}{dx^4} + \frac{k}{EI}y = 0 \tag{7.26}$$

Because the applied lateral load Q_g and an applied moment M_g have been considered separately, according to the principle of superposition, Eq. (7.26) becomes
Case A:

$$\frac{d^4y_A}{dx^4} + \frac{k}{EI}y_A = 0 \tag{7.27a}$$

Case B:

$$\frac{d^4y_B}{dx^4} + \frac{k}{EI}y_B = 0 \tag{7.27b}$$

Substituting for y_A, $\frac{k}{EI}$, and $\frac{x}{T}$ in nondimensional forms from Eqs. (7.18), (7.17), and (7.15), respectively, in Eq. (7.27a and b), we obtain
Case A:

$$\frac{d^4A_y}{dz^4} + \phi(z)A_y = 0 \tag{7.28}$$

Case B:

$$\frac{d^4B_y}{dz^4} + \phi(z)B_y = 0 \tag{7.29}$$

To obtain a particular set of nondimensional A and B coefficients, it is necessary to specify $\phi(z)$ and to define T.

For sands and other soils whose soil modulus may be assumed to increase linearly with depth, $\phi(z)$ may be equated to z. Hence, in Eq. (7.17), by substituting for k from Eq. (7.9), we get

$$\frac{n_h x T^4}{EI} = \frac{x}{T} \tag{7.30}$$

or

$$T = \sqrt[5]{\frac{EI}{n_h}} \tag{7.31}$$

Reese and Matlock (1956), who defined $\phi(z)$ and T, as above, obtained the solution of Eqs. (7.28) and (7.29) by using the finite-difference method for the coefficients A and B. Deflection (y), slope (s), moment (M), shear (V), and soil reaction (p) coefficients for Q_g and M_g are shown in Tables 7.3 and 7.4 respectively (Matlock and Reese, 1961).

Based on the boundary conditions Q_g and M_g and the resulting A and B coefficients, relations can be derived so that problems involving other boundary conditions (such as a partially or completely restrained top) may be solved (Reese and Matlock, 1956; Matlock and Reese, 1961).

Matlock and Reese (1962) showed that by considering the soil modulus variation of the form given in Eq. (7.8) for $n = \frac{1}{2}$, 1, and 2, the difference caused by the applied shear and moment at the ground surface in the deflection and moment in a long pile is not appreciable. It was further shown that one can make good predictions of the moment curves by using $k_x = n_h x$, even though variations may be quite nonlinear with respect to depth. However, the effect of the soil modulus variation close to the ground surface on the computed moments is very large.

In Figs. 7.14 and 7.15, A_y and B_y coefficients are plotted for values of Z_{max} 2, 3, 4, 5, and 10. It can be seen that the coefficients A_y and B_y vary almost in a linear fashion with the depth coefficient z for $Z_{max} = 2$. Because the deflections

Table 7.3 Coefficients A for long piles under lateral loads*

z	A_y	A_S	A_M	A_V	A_p
0.0	2.435	−1.623	0.000	1.000	0.000
0.1	2.273	−1.618	0.100	0.989	−0.227
0.2	2.112	−1.603	0.198	0.956	−0.422
0.3	1.952	−1.578	0.291	0.906	−0.586
0.4	1.796	−1.545	0.379	0.840	−0.718
0.5	1.644	−1.503	0.459	0.764	−0.822
0.6	1.496	−1.454	0.532	0.677	−0.897
0.7	1.353	−1.397	0.595	0.585	−0.947
0.8	1.216	−1.335	0.649	0.489	−0.973
0.9	1.086	−1.268	0.693	0.392	−0.977
1.0	0.962	−1.197	0.727	0.295	−0.962
1.2	0.738	−1.047	0.767	0.109	−0.885
1.4	0.544	−0.893	0.772	−0.056	−0.761
1.6	0.381	−0.741	0.746	−0.193	−0.609
1.8	0.247	−0.596	0.696	−0.298	−0.445
2.0	0.142	−0.464	0.628	−0.371	−0.283
3.0	−0.075	−0.040	0.225	−0.349	0.226
4.0	−0.050	0.052	0.000	−0.106	0.201
5.0	−0.009	0.025	−0.033	0.013	0.046

*After Matlock and Reese (1961 and 1962).

Table 7.4 Coefficients B for long piles under lateral loads*

Z	B_y	B_S	B_M	B_V	B_p
0.0	1.623	− 1.750	1.000	0.000	0.000
0.1	1.453	− 1.650	1.000	− 0.007	− 0.145
0.2	1.293	− 1.550	0.999	− 0.028	− 0.259
0.3	1.143	− 1.450	0.994	− 0.058	− 0.343
0.4	1.003	− 1.351	0.987	− 0.095	− 0.401
0.5	0.873	− 1.253	0.976	− 0.137	− 0.436
0.6	0.752	− 1.156	0.960	− 0.181	− 0.451
0.7	0.642	− 1.061	0.939	− 0.226	− 0.449
0.8	0.540	− 0.968	0.914	− 0.270	− 0.432
0.9	0.448	− 0.878	0.885	− 0.312	− 0.403
1.0	0.364	− 0.792	0.852	− 0.350	− 0.364
1.2	0.223	− 0.629	0.775	− 0.414	− 0.268
1.4	0.112	− 0.482	0.688	− 0.456	− 0.157
1.6	0.029	− 0.354	0.594	− 0.477	− 0.047
1.8	− 0.030	− 0.245	0.498	− 0.476	0.054
2.0	− 0.070	− 0.155	0.404	− 0.456	0.140
3.0	− 0.089	0.057	0.059	− 0.213	0.268
4.0	− 0.028	0.049	− 0.042	0.017	0.112
5.0	0.000	0.011	− 0.026	0.029	− 0.002

*After Matlock and Reese (1961 and 1962).

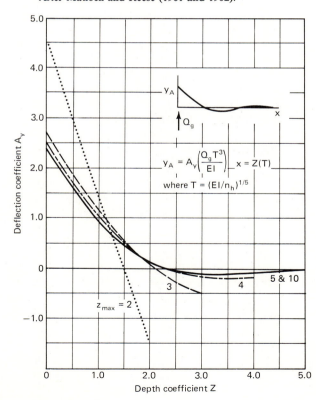

Figure 7.14 Deflection coefficient A_y due to lateral load at ground surface. *(After Reese and Matlock, 1956.)*

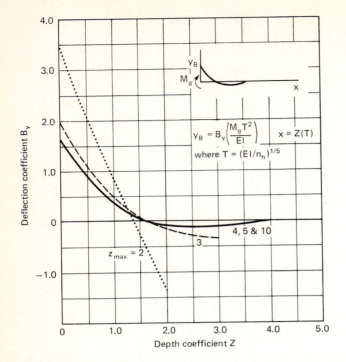

Figure 7.15 Deflection coefficient B_y due to moment at ground surface. (*After Reese and Matlock, 1956.*)

y_A and y_B are directly proportional to A_y and B_y for a given set of conditions, it is evident that both deflections y_A and y_B are linear with depth x. This shows that the pile undergoes only rigid-body deflections and that deflections caused by curvature are negligible. Hence, the piles with $Z_{max} \leq 2$ behave as rigid piles or poles.

Further, from the same figures, it can be seen that the deflection coefficients A_y and B_y for Z_{max} of 5 and 10 are identical. This means that pile length beyond $Z_{max} = 5$ is not effective in altering the deflections of the pile. Therefore,

$$L_\alpha = 5T \tag{7.32}$$

It will be seen that, in practice, most of the piles satisfy the condition $L_s > 5T$. Therefore, solutions for long piles are applicable. Coefficients A and B in Tables 7.3 and 7.4 can then be used. Also, the pile heads are usually fixed; that is, at $Z = 0$, $S = 0$. Therefore, Eq. (7.21) gives

$$S_0 = S_A + S_B = A_S \frac{Q_g T^2}{EI} + B_S \frac{M_g T}{EI} = 0 \tag{7.33a}$$

which gives

$$\frac{M_g}{Q_g T} = -\left(\frac{A_S}{B_S}\right)_{(z\,=\,0)} \tag{7.33b}$$

By substituting the values of A_S and B_S at $z = 0$ from Tables 7.3 and 7.4, we get

$$\frac{M_g}{Q_g T} = -0.93 \tag{7.33c}$$

Quantity $M_g/Q_g T$ has been defined as the *nondimensional fixity factor* by Prakash (1962). The expression for deflection [Eq. (7.20)] is modified for this case as

$$y = (A_y - 0.93B_y)\frac{Q_g T^3}{EI}$$

$$= C_y\frac{Q_g T^3}{EI} \tag{7.34a}$$

in which

$$C_y = A_y - 0.93B_y \tag{7.34b}$$

In a similar manner, the C coefficients for moment and soil reaction may be defined as

$$C_m = A_m - 0.93B_m \tag{7.35a}$$

which gives

$$M = C_m Q_g T \tag{7.35b}$$

and

$$C_p = A_p - 0.93B_p \tag{7.36a}$$

which gives

$$p = C_p\frac{Q}{T} \tag{7.36b}$$

The piles may undergo some rotation at the joints where their heads meet the caps. This results in partial fixity. In this case, the nondimensional fixity factor (NDFF) may be defined suitably, and the coefficients 'C' would also be modified accordingly.

Design Procedure

Based upon the discussion presented above, the following design procedure is recommended:

1. Determine the loads on the top of the pile.
2. Determine the soil profile and estimate a proper value of k or n_h for the type of soil.

3. Select a trial section with known EI and its width.
4. Compute

$$T = \sqrt[5]{\frac{EI}{n_h}} \qquad \text{and} \qquad Z_{max} = \frac{L_s}{T}$$

The term Z_{max} in practice is always greater than 5. Consideration of the vertical-load-carrying capacity determines the length.

5. Estimate the fixity λ of the pile head.
6. Compute the deflections from

$$y = C_y \frac{Q_g T^3}{EI} \qquad\qquad (7.34a)$$

in which

$$C_y = A_y - (\lambda \times 0.93 B_y)$$

The maximum deflection occurs at the top of the pile and should not be greater than the permissible value. In the absence of a specified permissible value, $\frac{1}{2}$ in (1.25 cm) may be adopted as a reasonable permissible value.

7. Determine the bending moment along the length of the pile by using

$$M_x = C_m Q T \qquad\qquad (7.35b)$$

in which

$$C_m = A_m - 0.93\lambda B_m$$

The following tabulation format is convenient for recording these computations.

Table for computation of M_x

Z	x	A_m	$0.93\lambda B_m$	C_m	M_x	Remarks
1	2	3	4	5	6	7

Plot the bending moment along the depth of the pile and determine M_{max}. Check the stresses in the section and compare them with the allowable stresses in the material of the pile.

8. Determine the soil reaction along the length of the pile by using the following equation:

$$P_x = C_p \frac{Q}{T} \qquad\qquad (7.36b)$$

in which

$$C_p = A_p - 0.93\lambda B_p$$

The following tabulation format is convenient for recording these computations.

Table of computations for p_x

z	x	A_p	$0.93\lambda B_p$	C_p	p_x	Remarks
1	2	3	4	5	6	7

Plot the soil reaction diagram along the depth of the pile. The permissible soil reaction at any depth x is given by

$$p_a = \frac{1 + \sin \phi}{1 - \sin \phi} \gamma \times b \tag{7.37}$$

in which γ = unit weight of soil and b = width of pile.

9. If the deflection, stress in the pile, and soil reactions indicate that the section adopted is safe and is not overly conservative, the selection of the section is permissible. Otherwise, select a new section and repeat steps 3 through 8.

Example 7.2 A pile in sand, 10 m long with head free to deflect and rotate is acted upon by a lateral load of 3000 kg. The EI of the section is 3.5×10^{10} kg·cm². The pile undergoes a deflection of 12 mm. If the piles in the group were restrained against rotation to the extent of 50 percent of the fully restrained piles, determine the maximum bending moment and the soil reaction on the piles. Also plot the deflected shape of the pile. Assume that the width of the pile is 30 cm and that the unit weight of soil is 1.8 g/cm³. Neglect group action.

SOLUTION   From the test data,

$$y_g = \frac{A_y Q_g T^3}{EI}$$

Therefore,

$$T = \sqrt[3]{\frac{EIy_g}{A_y Q_g}} = \sqrt[3]{\frac{(1.2)(3.5 \times 10^{10})}{2.435 \times 3000}} = 179.15 \text{ cm}$$

Because the pile head is restrained only 50 percent of the full restraint, the negative moment at the top of the pile is† $-0.465Q_g T$

therefore

$$M_g = -0.465 \times 3000 \times 179.15 \text{ kg·cm}$$

Now,

$$y = A_y \frac{Q_g T^3}{EI} + B_y \frac{M_g T^2}{EI} = (A_y - 0.465 B_y) \frac{Q_g T^3}{EI}$$

† (See Fig. 7.16a.)

Table 7.5 Computation of deflection y, bending moment M, and soil reaction p in Example 7.2

x, m	$Z = \dfrac{x}{T}$	A_y	$0.465B_y$	C_y	y, cm	A_m	$0.465B_m$	C_m	M, t·cm	A_p	$0.465B_p$	C_p	p, kg/cm
1	2	3	4	5	6	7	8	9	10	11	12	13	14
0	0.0	2.435	0.755	1.680	0.828	0	− 0.465	− 0.465	− 250	0.000	0	0	0
0.36	0.2	2.112	0.601	1.511	0.745	0.198	0.465	− 0.267	− 1,43	− 0.422	− 0.120	− 0.302	− 5.06
0.72	0.4	1.796	0.466	1.330	0.655	0.379	0.459	− 0.080	− 43	− 0.718	− 0.186	− 0.532	− 8.91
1.07	0.6	1.496	0.350	1.146	0.565	0.532	0.446	0.086	46	− 0.897	− 0.210	− 0.687	− 11.50
1.43	0.8	1.216	0.251	0.965	0.476	0.649	0.425	0.244	1,20	− 0.973	− 0.201	− 0.772	− 12.93
1.79	1.0	0.962	0.169	0.793	0.391	0.727	0.396	0.331	1,77	− 0.962	− 0.169	− 0.793	− 13.28
2.15	1.2	0.738	0.104	0.634	0.312	0.767	0.360	0.407	2,19	− 0.885	− 0.125	− 0.760	− 12.73
2.87	1.6	0.381	0.013	0.368	0.181	0.746	0.276	0.470	2,55	− 0.609	− 0.022	− 0.587	− 9.83
3.58	2.0	0.142	0.013	0.175	0.086	0.628	0.188	0.440	2,36	− 0.283	0.065	− 0.318	− 5.83
5.37	3.0	− 0.075	− 0.032	− 0.034	− 0.017	0.225	0.027	0.198	1,06	0.226	0.125	0.101	1.69
7.16	4.0	− 0.050	− 0.041	− 0.037	− 0.018	0.000	− 0.019	0.020	10	0.201	0.052	0.149	2.50
8.96	5.0	− 0.009	− 0.013	− 0.009	− 0.004	− 0.033	− 0.012	− 0.021	− 11	0.046	− 0.001	0.047	0.79

Similarly,

$$M = (A_m - 0.465B_m)Q_g T$$

and

$$p = (A_p - 0.465B_p)\frac{Q_g}{T}$$

The values of y, m, and p are computed in tabular form as shown in Table 7.5 and have been plotted in Fig. 7.16b.

The maximum $M = 255$ t·cm and $p_{max} = 13.5$ kg/cm.

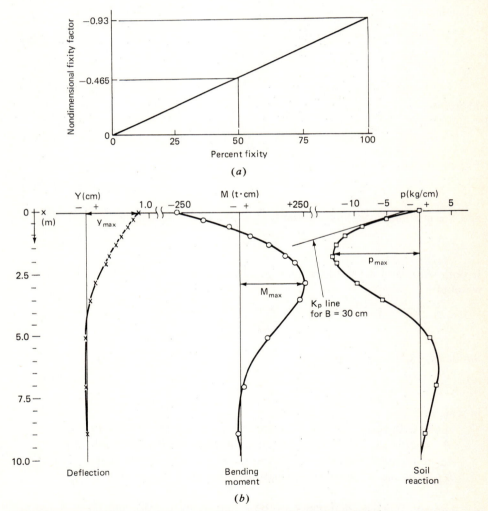

Figure 7.16 (a) Percent fixity vs. nondimensional fixity factor. (b) Deflection, moment and soil reaction with depth in Example 7.2.

k_p line for $\phi = 30°$ and $\gamma = 1.8$ g/cm³ [Eq. (7.37)] has been plotted on the soil reaction diagram.

7.8 PILES IN CLAY

Solutions similar to the ones presented in Sec. 7.7 have been obtained by Davisson (1962) and by Davisson and Gill (1963) for clays that occur in two layers. The stiffnesses of the top and bottom layers are defined by k_1 and k_2 respectively. For a particular case of $k_1 = k_2$, by using R in place of T for clay, letting $\phi(z) = 1$, and with A_{yc} in place of A_y in Eq. (7.28), we obtain the following equation:

$$\frac{d^4 A_{yc}}{dz^4} + \phi(z)A_{yc} = 0 \tag{7.38}$$

$$\phi(z) = \frac{kR^4}{EI} = 1 \tag{7.17}$$

Therefore,

$$R = \sqrt[4]{\frac{EI}{k}} \tag{7.39}$$

The depth coefficient is

$$z = \frac{X}{R} \tag{7.40a}$$

and the maximum depth coefficient is

$$Z_{max} = \frac{L_s}{R} \tag{7.40b}$$

If both shear and moment act on a pile head, and if one uses B_{yc} in Eq. (7.20), we obtain

$$y_x = A_{yc}\frac{Q_g R^3}{EI} + B_{yc}\frac{M_g R^2}{EI} \tag{7.41a}$$

Similarly, Eq. (7.22) becomes

$$M_x = A_{mc}Q_g R + B_{mc}M_g \tag{7.41b}$$

in which
A_{yc} = deflection coefficient for shear load on a free head pile in clay
B_{yc} = deflection coefficient for moment load on a free head pile in clay
A_{mc} = moment coefficient for shear load on free head pile in clay
B_{mc} = moment coefficient for moment load on free head pile in clay

The soil reaction diagram may be obtained by multiplying the y diagram with k, which is constant along the depth of embedment of the pile.

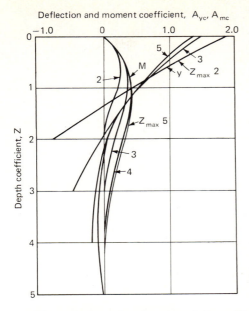

Deflection and moment coefficient, A_{yc}, A_{mc}

Depth coefficient, Z

Figure 7.17 Deflection and moment coefficients A_{yc} and A_{mc} due to lateral loads at ground surface. (*After Davisson and Gill, 1963.*)

The solutions for the A and B coefficients may be obtained by using either the technique described by Matlock and Reese (1962) or an analogue computer (Davisson and Gill, 1963). In Figs. 7.17 and 7.18, A_{yc}, A_{mc}, B_{yc}, and B_{mc} have been plotted for piles of different Z_{max}.

It may be seen from the deflection coefficients in Figs. 7.17 and 7.18 for $Z_{max} = 2$, that the plot is almost a straight line. Hence, the pile may be

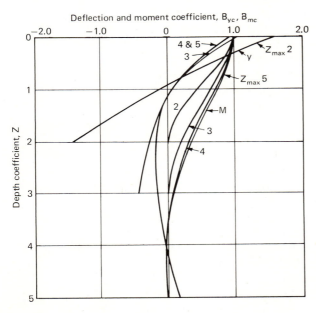

Deflection and moment coefficient, B_{yc}, B_{mc}

Depth coefficient, Z

Figure 7.18 Deflection and moment coefficients B_{yc} and B_{mc} due to moment at ground surface. (*After Davisson and Gill, 1963.*)

considered to be a rigid pile if $Z_{max} \leq 2$. Similarly, for $Z_{max} \geq 4$, the pile may be considered infinitely long pile. In practice, most piles in clays satisfy this condition.

7.9 DYNAMIC ANALYSIS

In current design practice, the total lateral load applied to a pile foundation is equal to the base shear computed in the dynamic analysis of the superstructure, which is considered to be fixed at the level of the foundation. Hayashi (1973), Prakash and Sharma (1969), and Prakash and Gupta (1970) attempted to determine the natural frequencies of the soil pile system by using an equivalent cantilever method. The soil-pile system is idealized as a massless equivalent cantilever with a single concentrated mass at the top. Its natural frequency is determined by using Rayleigh's method. The exciting frequency is used to check the frequency of the system for resonance. This approach is more or less arbitrary.

Generally, there are three techniques that can be used to solve problems of soil-pile superstructure interaction (Novak, 1977). The first represents soil as a continuum with linear elastic properties. It correctly represents geometric damping as well as soil layer resonance (Novak and Nogami, 1977; Novak, 1977). In the second, the finite element technique is used to represent the pile and the soil. This method offers a maximum flexibility for the variation of soil-pile properties (Novak, 1977; Kuhlemeyer, 1979). The third represents the soil-pile system by a set of discrete (lumped) masses, springs, and dashpots. This approach can be used to incorporate the depth and nonlinearity variations of the soil properties in more detail. These variations depend upon the definition of the local soil stiffness and geometric damping (Penzien et al., 1964; Penzien, 1970; Prakash and Chandrasekaran, 1973, 1977).

A reasonably practical solution for soil-pile interaction under dynamic loads has been proposed by Chandrasekaran (1974; Prakash and Chandrasekaran 1980). This analysis is based on the following assumptions:

1. The pile is divided into a convenient number of segments and mass of each segment is concentrated at its center point (Fig. 7.19).
2. The soil is assumed to act as a linear Winkler's spring. The soil reaction is separated into discrete parts at the center points of the masses in Fig. 7.19. The soil modulus variation is considered both constant with depth and linearly varying with depth (Fig. 7.20).
3. The mass of the superstructure is concentrated at the pile top as M_t.
4. The system is one-dimensional in its behavior.
5. The pile end conditions are either completely free to undergo translation and rotation or completely restrained against rotation but free to undergo translation.

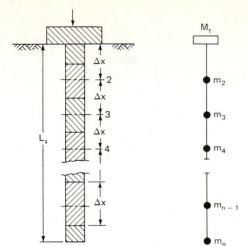

Figure 7.19 Pile-structure idealization. *(After Chandrasekaran, 1974.)*

For evaluating the free-vibration characteristics, the modal analysis is performed by using successive approximations of the natural frequencies of the system with an initially assumed value and related end conditions. The adopted end conditions are also utilized to generate the transfer equations and to evaluate the unknown quantities, either at the pile top or the pile bottom, in terms of the known quantities. These modal quantity values at different station points define the mode shapes. Values at the bottom or top of the piles assist in determining the natural frequencies of vibrations in different modes.

The forces and displacements in two different station points are illustrated in Fig. 7.21 (Prakash and Chandrasekaran, 1977).

The details of the idealization and the method of analysis and detailed parametric studies are presented elsewhere (Chandrasekaran, 1974).

Information has been obtained with these approaches for piles embedded in soils in which the soil modulus can be considered either to remain constant or to vary linearly with depth. In both of these cases, solutions have been obtained for natural frequency, modal displacements, slopes, bending moments, shear forces, and soil reactions along the lengths of the piles in the first three modes of vibrations (Chandrasekaran, 1974; Prakash and Chandrasekaran, 1980). Only typical solutions for handling a practical problem shall be discussed herein.

Natural Frequencies

Based on the parametric study, nondimensional frequency factors have been obtained with respect to the basic soil parameters.

The variables constituting F_{CL_1}, the *nondimensional frequency factor* for piles embedded in soils in which the soil modulus remains constant with depth, is

256

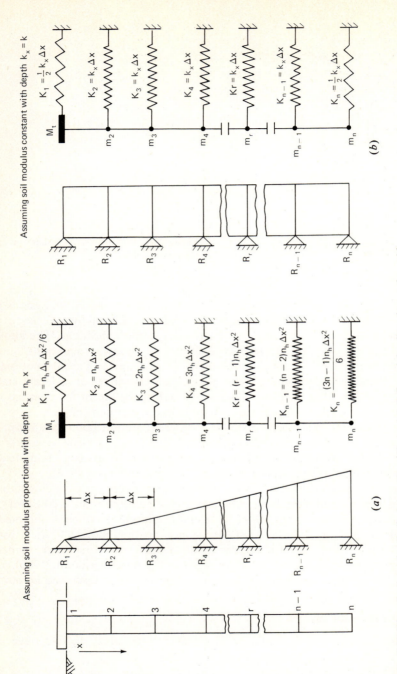

Figure 7.20 Discretization of soil-pile interaction effects. (*a*) Soil modulus proportional with depth. (*b*) Soil modulus constant with depth. (*After Chandrasekaran, 1974.*)

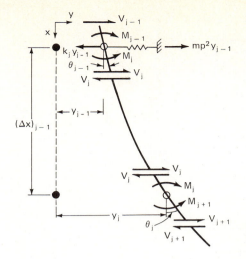

Figure 7.21 Deflections and forces at two adjoining nodal points. *(After Chandrasekaran, 1974.)*

given by

$$F_{CL_1} = \omega_{n_1} \sqrt{\frac{W}{gKR}} \qquad (7.42)$$

in which ω_{n1} is the first natural angular frequency in radians per second, W/g the lumped mass at the top of the pile, K the soil modulus, and R, the relative stiffness factor, defined as follows:

$$R = \sqrt[4]{\frac{EI}{k}} \qquad (7.39)$$

In Fig. 7.22a, the variation of frequency factor F_{CL_1} with Z_{max} has been plotted, in which $Z_{max} = L_s/R$. It may be seen that for a given soil with pile characteristics, such as flexural stiffness EI, soil stiffness in terms of k, sustained vertical load, W, and Z_{max}, unique frequency factor values exist.

In Fig. 7.22b and c, frequency factors F_{SL_1} and F'_{SL_1} for soils whose moduli vary linearly with depth have also been plotted for the pile top free to rotate and the pile top restrained against rotation, respectively. The definitions of F_{SL_1} and F'_{SL_1} for the pile tops free to rotate and the pile top restrained against rotation are identical and given by

$$F_{SL_1} \text{ or } F'_{SL_1} = W_{n1} \sqrt{\frac{W}{g} \frac{1}{n_h T^2}} \qquad (7.43)$$

in which n_h is the constant of horizontal subgrade reaction for $k_x = n_h x$ and

$$T = \sqrt[5]{\frac{EI}{n_h}} \qquad (7.31)$$

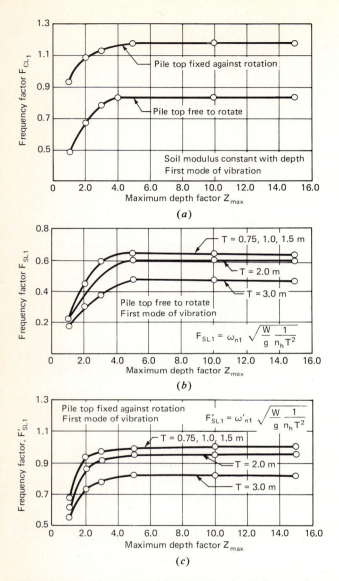

Figure 7.22 Nondimensional frequency factors in first mode of vibrations. (*a*) Soil modulus constant with depth. (*b*) Soil modulus linearly varying with depth and pile top free. (*c*) Soil modulus linearly varying with depth and pile top restrained against rotation. (*After Prakash and Chandrasekaran, 1977.*)

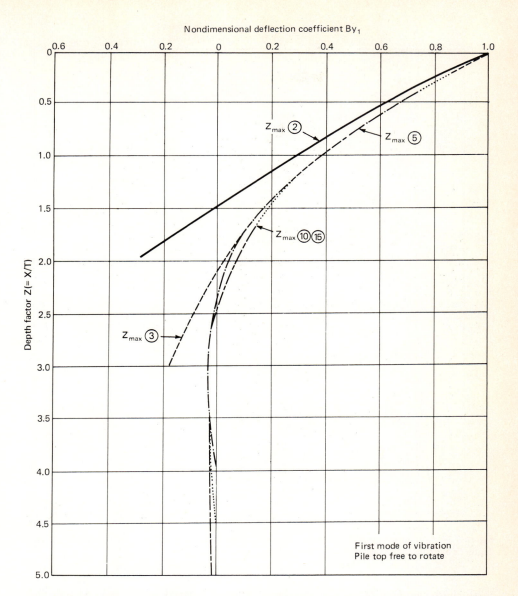

Figure 7.23 Nondimensional deflection coefficients assuming soil modulus proportional to depth. *(After Chandrasekaran, 1974.)*

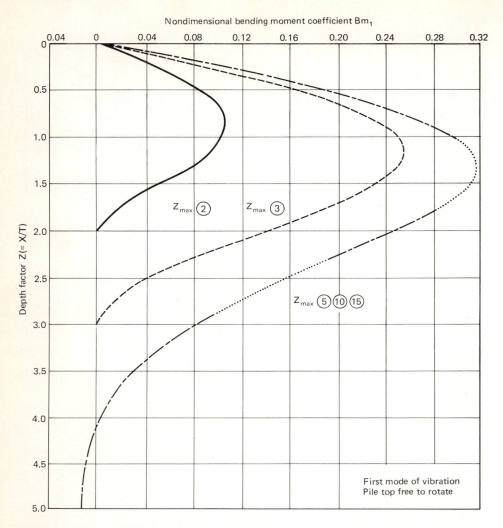

Figure 7.24 Nondimensional bending moment coefficient assuming soil modulus proportional to depth. *(After Chandrasekaran, 1974.)*

With these two sets of curves, the designer can predict the time period for the first mode of vibrations because the soil-pile characteristics, length, and fixity conditions are known. Similar frequency factors for determining natural frequencies in the second and third modes of vibrations have also been plotted by Chandrasekaran (1974). Also, mode shapes in the first three modes of vibrations have been evaluated. Once the mode shapes and frequencies of the system are determined, the system can be treated as an uncoupled system, and the individual modes can be superposed to determine the overall response. However, only the solutions of the first mode of vibrations will be examined and a design procedure based on these solutions formulated.

A plot of nondimensional displacement with depth factor $z (= x/T)$ in the first mode of vibration is shown in Fig. 7.23 for a pile top free to rotate and embedded in a soil with modulus proportional with depth. Similarly, the variation of nondimensional bending moment coefficient with the depth of the pile in the first mode of vibrations is shown in Fig. 7.24. In Fig. 7.23, it can be seen that for $Z_{\max} < 2$, the pile vibrates as a rigid body. Also, for $Z_{\max} \geq 5$, the pile is a "long" pile.

It can be seen from Fig. 7.24 that for a pile with $Z_{\max} \geq 5$, the maximum bending moment coefficient $B_{me_1} = 0.315$ and the maximum value occurs at approximately $x/T = 1.30$. For designing piles, these data are sufficient and one does not have to refer to the entire curve.

Method of Aseismic Analysis and Design of Piles

Based upon the above analysis and the concept of the spectral response technique (Chap. 2), the following method of analysis and design of piles against earthquakes is proposed.

For this analysis, it is assumed that the following data are known:

1. soil characteristics, nature and bore log of soils
2. pile characteristics, size, EI, length, type of pile
3. lateral load-deflection of the pile under static conditions

The steps in this analysis and design are:

1. Estimate the dynamic soil modulus k or n_h. In the absence of realistic data, the values from a static lateral load test may be modified based upon engineering judgment.
2. By using the soil modulus value, compute the relative stiffness factor R or T.
3. Calculate the maximum depth factor $Z_{\max}$ for a pile; $Z_{\max}$ should be > 5.
4. For the computed value of the maximum depth factor and the pile end condition, read the frequency factor (Fig. 7.22).
5. Estimate the dead load on the pile. This provides the mass at the pile top.
6. Using Eq. (7.42) or (7.43), determine the natural frequency ω_{n_1}.
   (*a*) Soil modulus constant with depth:

$$\omega_{n_1} = F_{CL_1} \div \sqrt{\frac{W}{gkR}} \qquad (7.42)$$

   (*b*) Soil modulus proportional to depth:

$$\omega_{n_1} = (F_{SL_1} \text{ or}) F'_{SL_1} \div \sqrt{\frac{W}{g} \frac{1}{n_h T^2}} \qquad (7.43)$$

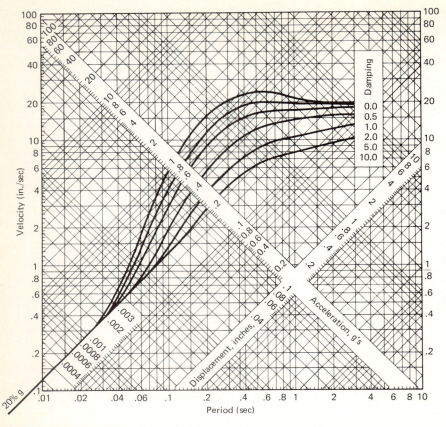

Figure 7.25 Combined plot of design spectrum giving S_a, S_v, and S_d as a function of period and damping, scaled to 20 percent of acceleration at zero period. *(Reproduced with permission of Prentice-Hall Inc., Englewood Cliffs, N.J., from "Design Spectrum" by G. W. Housner in Earthquake Engineering, ed., R. L. Wiegel.)*

7. Compute the time period $T_{n_1} = 2\pi/\omega_{n_1}$.
8. For the computed time period, determine the spectral displacement S_d for assumed damping from Fig. 7.25.† For the soil-pile system, 5 percent damping may be assumed. This is the maximum displacement of the pile head.
9. Estimate the maximum bending moment in the pile section.
   (a) Soil modulus constant with depth.

$$\text{Bending moment} = A_{me} \times KR^2 \times S_d \qquad (7.44)$$

The maximum values of A_{me} are given in Table 7.6.

---

† If an accelogram for a site has been selected, spectral response is determined for this ground motion.

Table 7.6 Maximum values of coefficient A_{me}*

Maximum depth factor Z_{max}	Coefficient A_{me}		
	Pile top free to rotate	Pile fixed at top against rotation	
		$-$ ive	$+$ ive
2	0.13	0.9	0
3	0.24	0.9	0.04
5–15	0.32	0.9	0.18

* After Chandrasekaran (1974).

(*b*) Soil modulus increasing linearly with depth.

$$\text{Bending moment} = B_{me} \times n_h T^3 \times S_d \tag{7.45}$$

The maximum values of B_{me} are given in Table 7.7.

Table 7.7 Maximum values of coefficient B_{me}*

Maximum depth factor Z_{max}	Coefficient B_{me}		
	Pile top free to rotate	Pile fixed at top against rotation	
		$-$ ive	$+$ ive
2	0.100	0.93	0
3	0.255	0.93	0.10
5–15	0.315	0.90	0.28

* After Chandrasekaran (1974).

The pile section needs to be checked against this moment.
10. For the maximum displacement at the ground computed above, the displacement all along the length of the pile may be determined approximately by assuming the deflections as per the solutions of Davisson and Gill (1963) and Reese and Matlock (1956) for the two cases of soil modulus. The soil reaction is then computed all along the pile lengths as follows:
(*a*) For soil modulus constant with depth.

$$p_x = k \cdot y_x \tag{7.46a}$$

(*b*) For soil modulus linearly varying with depth:

$$p_x = n_h \cdot x \cdot y_x \tag{7.46b}$$

The allowable soil reaction may be taken as that corresponding to the Rankine passive pressure at all depths (Terzaghi and Peck, 1967; Prakash et al., 1979).

It is recommended that the solution be obtained for the two cases of pile restraint—the pile top free to rotate and the pile top restrained against rotation. Once the fixity condition of the actual piles in the group is estimated, the solution is obtained for this case by linear interpolation.

The deflections, bending moments, and soil reactions under static loading are added to the corresponding values under earthquake loading to arrive at the final values.

Example 7.3 A pile carries a vertical load of 77.6 t and the base shear on the top of the pile cap is 3 t. If the soil is sandy in character with $\phi = 30°$ and $n_h = 1.612$ kg/cm^3 under dynamic loading, determine the

1. maximum displacement of the pile head
2. maximum bending moment in the pile
3. soil reaction diagram along the length of the pile

Assume that EI of the pile $= 3.8 \times 10^{10}$ kg·cm^2, that the diameter of the pile $= 30$ cm, and that the length of piles in groups $= 12.2$ m.

SOLUTION

Step 1

$$n_h = 1.612 \text{ kg/cm}^3$$

Step 2

$$T = \sqrt[5]{\frac{EI}{n_h}}$$

$$= \sqrt[5]{\frac{3.8 \times 10^{10}}{1.612}} = 118.7 \text{ cm}$$

$$= 1.187 \text{ m}$$

Step 3

$$Z_{max} = \frac{12.2}{1.187} = 10.27$$

Because $Z_{max} > 5$, it is a "long" pile.

Step 4 From Fig. 7.22b and c, for $Z_{max} > 5$ and $T = 1.187$ m,

$$F_{SL_1} = 0.65 \text{ for free pile head}$$

$$F'_{SL_1} = 1.00 \text{ for pile head restrained against rotation}$$

Step 5

$$M_t = 77.6 \times \frac{1 \text{ t/s}^2}{981 \text{ cm}}$$

Step 6 From Eq. (7.43),

$$\omega_{n_1} = F_{SL_1} \div \sqrt{\frac{W}{g} \frac{1}{n_h T^2}} \tag{7.43}$$

$$= 0.65 \times \sqrt{\frac{981}{77.6} \times \frac{1.612}{1000} \times 118.7^2}$$

$$= 11.014 \text{ rad/s}$$

therefore, $\qquad f_{n_1} = \dfrac{11.014}{2\pi} = 1.753 \text{ Hz}$

Step 7

$$T_{n_1} = \frac{2\pi}{\omega_{n_1}} = \frac{1}{1.753} = 0.570 \text{ s}$$

Step 8 From Fig. 7.25, for $T_{n_1} = 0.57$ s, $\xi = 5\%$ spectral displacement $S_d = 0.8$ in(2.0 cm).

The maximum deflection of the pile top is 2.0 cm.

Step 9 Maximum bending moment

$$= B_{me} \times n_h T^3 S_d \tag{7.45}$$

$$= 0.315 \times \frac{1.612}{1000} \times (118.7)^3 \times 2.0 = 1698 \text{ t} \cdot \text{cm}$$

Step 10

$$y_g = A_y \frac{Q_g T^3}{EI} = A_y B(\text{constant})$$

For soils with modulus increasing linearly with depth

$$A_y = 2.435$$

Therefore, (constant) in the above equation is $\dfrac{2.0}{2.435} = 0.821$. Therefore, $y_x = 0.821 \times A_y$.

The solution of deflection and soil reaction along the pile length is presented in Table 7.8.

Table 7.8 Computation of y_x and p_x along the pile length (Example 7.3)

x, cm	z	A_y	$y_x = 0.821\,A_y$, cm	$n_h x$ kg/cm^2	$p = n_h xy$, kg/cm
0	0	2.435	2.00	0	0
100	0.84	1.164	0.955	161.2	153.94
200	1.68	0.327	0.268	322.4	86.40
300	2.52	0.029	0.024	483.6	11.61
400	3.36	− 0.066	− 0.054	644.8	− 34.82
500	4.21	− 0.042	− 0.034	806.0	− 27.40
600	5.05	− 0.009	− 0.007	967.2	− 6.77

The soil reaction diagram can now be plotted.

By proceeding in a similar manner, the period, spectral displacement, and maximum bending moment need to be computed for the pile head restrained against rotation. The final results are as follows:

	Pile head free to rotate	Pile head restrained against rotation
T_n	0.57 s	0.370 s
S_d	2.00 cm	1.00 cm
M_{max}	1698 t cm	2426 t cm

A soil reaction diagram can then be computed as illustrated for the pile top that is free to rotate.

Check on Design

1. Estimate the fixity of the pile head. In the absence of a realistic estimate, 50 percent fixity may be assumed.
2. Compute displacement. For 50 percent fixity, the displacement under seismic loading condition is $\dfrac{2.0 + 1.0}{2} = 1.5$ cm. For any other fixity of the pile head, linear interpolation may be made.
3. Compute the maximum bending moment as for displacements.

$$M_{max} = 1213\ \text{t·cm}(-)$$

4. The soil reaction needs to be interpolated at each point and a new diagram obtained.

For the given static loads determine the deflections, bending moments, and soil reaction diagram, as illustrated in Example 7.2. The final values are the sum of static and dynamic quantities. The total displacements need to be checked against permissible displacements. Stresses in the materials of the pile need to be compared with the allowable stresses. Allowable soil reaction at any depth x is

$$p_a = \frac{1 + \sin \phi}{1 - \sin \phi} \, \gamma b x \text{ kg/cm} \qquad (7.37)$$

in which γ = unit weight of soil and b = width of pile.

7.10 SOIL MODULUS VALUES

Terzaghi (1955), based upon his experience, recommended values for the modulus of horizontal subgrade reaction k and the constant n_h.

A large number of lateral load tests have since been reported in the literature. On the basis of this analysis, Davisson (1963) recommended values of n_h and k for different types of soils. These were revised later by Davisson (1970c) on the basis of his further work (Table 7.9).

Table 7.9 Estimated Values for k or n_h*

Soil type	Value
Granular soils	n_h ranges from 1.5 to 100 lb/in^3, is generally in the range from 10 to 100 lb/in^3, and is approximately proportional to relative density.
Normally loaded organic silt	n_h ranges from 0.4 to 3.0 lb/in^3.
Peat	n_h is approximately 0.2 lb/in^3.
Cohesive soils	k is approximately 67 C_U, in which C_U is the undrained shear strength of the soil.

* After Davisson (1970c). The effects of group action and repeated and dynamic loadings are not included in these estimates.

For a preliminary design, it is recommended that the values of k or n_h be taken from the above table. For a more realistic estimate of the soil modulus for a given problem, a full scale test may be organized.

7.11 GROUP ACTION

Piles are most often used in groups. Therefore, the value of k needs to be corrected. The following guidelines may be used.

1. If the center-to-center spacing in the direction of loading is 8 d, in which d is the diameter of the pile, and the center-to-center spacing is at least 2.5 d in the direction perpendicular to the load, there is no group action.

2. If the spacing in the direction of the load is 3 d, the effective value of k (k_{eff}) is 0.25 k. For other spacing values, a linear interpolation may be made.
3. If the load is applied in a repeated manner, the deflections increase and k_{eff} decreases. It has been observed that the deflections after 50 cycles of load application are double the deflections under the first cycle (Prakash, 1962). The soil modulus is correspondingly reduced. The deflections after 800 cycles are increased to about 2.5 to 3 times the deflections in the first cycle (Prakash and Chandrasekaran, 1970). The soil modulus is further reduced.
4. If the load is applied in an oscillatory manner, the deflections increase about seven times that under the first cycle of loading (Prakash and Sharma, 1969). The soil modulus decreases to a larger extent in this case.

If group action and oscillatory loads are considered, the soil modulus is decreased on two counts, and the final value may be less than 10 percent of k for a single pile.

These recommendations may be regarded as tentative. When more data become available, these recommendations may need to be revised.

7.12 CODAL PROVISIONS

Very little has been provided in building design codes on aseismic design for pile foundations. The permissible increases in allowable bearing pressures or resistance of soils for piles resting on rock and friction piles are listed in Table 6.5 (page 192). In making use of these provisions, the total loads on the piles are worked out from considerations of vertical loads, frame moment, and local moment (Prakash and Sharma, 1969).

The Applied Technology Council (1978) makes the following recommendations: For seismic performance category B,†

> Construction employing posts or poles as columns embedded in earth or embedded in concrete footings in the earth may be used to resist both axial and lateral loads. The depth of embedment required for posts or poles to resist seismic loads shall be determined by means of the design criteria established in the foundation report.
> Individual pile caps shall be interconnected by ties. All ties shall be capable of carrying, in tension or compression, a force equal to $A_v/4$ of the larger pile cap or column load, unless it is demonstrated that equivalent restraint can be provided by other means.

For seismic performance category C, the following special requirements shall apply:

> (A) UNCASED CONCRETE PILES. Reinforcing steel shall be provided for uncased cast-in-place concrete piles, drilled piers or caissons with a minimum steel ratio of 0.005 with a minimum of four No. 6 bars. Ties shall be provided at eight-bar-diameter spacing with a

† See Chap. 6 for definitions.

maximum spacing of 3 inches in the top 4 feet. Ties shall be a minimum of No. 3 bars for up to 20-inch-diameter piles and No. 4 bars for piles of larger diameter.

(B) METAL-CASED CONCRETE PILES. Reinforcing steel shall be provided for metal-cased concrete piles for the full length of the pile. The upper two-thirds of the pile shall have a minimum of 4 bars with a minimum steel ratio of 0.0075 with a minimum of 1/4-inch diameter spiral ties at 9-inch maximum pitch. At the top 4 feet, the pitch shall be 3 inches maximum.

(C) PRECAST CONCRETE PILES. Ties in precast concrete piles shall conform to the requirements of members subjected to bending and axial load, for the top half of the pile. Precast concrete piles shall not be used to resist flexure caused by earthquake motions unless it can be shown that they will be stressed to below the elastic limit under the maximum soil deformations that would occur during an earthquake.

(D) STEEL PILES. The connection between the pile cap and steel piles or unfilled steel pipe piles shall be designed for a tensile force equal to ten percent of the pile compression capacity.

For Seismic Performance Category D,

Precast-prestressed piles shall not be used to resist flexure caused by earthquake motions.

7.13 FINAL COMMENTS

It must be appreciated that piles have been studied in greater detail under vibrations and earthquake-type loading than in corresponding studies on shallow footings. The question to be answered is, "What are the amounts of vertical settlement and lateral deflections under earthquake-type loading?" The question of settlement under vertical vibrations has been studied to a degree by Swiger (1948), Barkan (1957), and Prakash and Agarwal (1971). The results of detailed study by Ghumman (1981) have not yet been made available.

The question of lateral deflections under earthquake-type vibrations can be answered by the solutions presented in this chapter. These solutions are based upon the extension of the concept of modulus of subgrade reaction. Therefore, all the shortcomings of this concept are obviously inherent in this analysis (Terzaghi, 1955; Matlock et al., 1978). Another limitation of this method is that the mass of the superstructure is assumed to be concentrated at the top of the pile. How much is this concentrated mass? Is it the mass of the total load on each pile or a fraction of it? Because the load on the pile is not really a concentrated load but is transferred from several story heights, the interaction effects of the superstructure are not considered. Very little information is presently available on the subject, and it certainly does not qualify for inclusion in a text at this stage.

The next important question concerns the value of soil modulus. A very large refinement has been made since the values were first recommended by Terzaghi (1955). There is always room for refinements and improvements. The effect of group action and dynamic loading on the soil modulus also needs further study. The recommendations in this regard may undergo major revisions when more carefully conducted test data become available.

Piles embedded in layered soils (Davisson and Gill, 1963) and possible buckling of partially embedded soils (Davisson and Robinson, 1965) have been solved for the static case only. Simultaneous vertical and lateral oscillatory loads cause vertical settlement and lateral deflection. These problems are not amenable to solution by the principle of superposition. Their solution, in fact, presents a challenge to the profession.

Nevertheless, it is important to appreciate that we have reached a stage when reasonably practical solutions are available. The time spent by the profession in this direction is just about a decade, and the information available in the published literature is impressive.

PRACTICE PROBLEMS

7.1 (a) A pile is embedded 10 m into a soil whose modulus increases at the rate of 0.12 kg $cm^{-2}cm^{-1}$. The load acting at its top is 40 t vertical and 7.5 t lateral. The EI of the pile is 150×10^{10} kg·cm². The fixity of the pile head is characterized by the following relationships:

$$\frac{M_g}{S_g} = 20 \times 10^8 \text{ kg·cm rad}^{-1}$$

Determine the maximum bending moment in the pile.

(b) Determine also the maximum bending moment in the pile as if the pile head were completely free and fully restrained against rotation.

7.2 In Prob. 7.1b, the soil modulus is characterized by

$$k = 30 + 0.12 \text{ kg cm}^{-1}\text{cm}^{-1}$$

Determine the maximum bending moment in the pile.

7.3 A pile completely restrained against rotation carries a vertical load of 50 t and a lateral load of 10 t. The area of the pile is 100 cm¹² and $I = 6000$ cm⁴. The n_h value of the soil is 0.5 kg/cm³ and the E of the pile material is 2.1×10^6 kg·cm². The pile length is 10 m, and its width is 25 cm. Determine the maximum deflection, bending moment, and soil reaction.

7.4 A pile 45 cm in diameter is 10 m long. Under a lateral load of 3 t, it undergoes a deflection of 1.2 cm. Assuming that the damping in the soil-pile system is 5 percent of critical, determine the average spectral displacement of the pile-soil system. The pile carries a load of 50 t, and assume that the fixity of the pile head is 65 percent. The soil is noncohesive, and the water table is at a great depth.

7.5 From the load test data in Prob. 7.4, sketch the complete load-deflection curve approximately. Superimpose on this diagram the following load-deflection graphs by judgment. Justify your answer.

(a) Four-pile group, neglecting group action (spacing three times the diameter in both directions).

(b) Four-pile group considering group action.

(c) In (b) above, the pile heads undergo partial rotation say 50% fixity.

7.6 Outline a procedure for analysis of a pile carrying a vertical load and subjected to a North-South component of the El Centro earthquake of May 18, 1940.

REFERENCES

Agarwal, H. P.: "Effect of Vibrations on Skin Friction of Piles," Master of Engineering Dissertation, University of Roorkee, Roorkee, India, 1967.

American Society for Testing and Materials: "Standard Method of Testing Piles Under Axial Compressive Load," ASTM 1143-74.

Applied Technology Council: "Tentative Provisions for the Development of Seismic Regulations for Buildings," Pub. No. ATC-3-08, June, 1978.

Barkan, D. D.: Foundation Engineering and Drilling by Vibration Method, *Proc. Fourth Int. Conf. Soil Mech. Found. Engin.*, London, vol. 2, pp. 3–7, 1957.

Bowles, J. E.: "Foundation Analysis and Design," 2d ed., McGraw-Hill Book Co., New York, 1977.

Chandrasekaran, V.: "Analysis of Pile Foundations Under Static and Dynamic Loads," Ph.D. Thesis, University of Roorkee, Roorkee, India, 1974.

Chellis, R. D.: "Pile Foundations," McGraw-Hill Book Co., New York, 1961.

_____: Pile Foundations, in G. A. Leonards (ed.): "Foundation Engineering," McGraw-Hill Book Co., New York, 1962, chap. 7.

Dalmatov, B. I.: "Lectures on Vibration Driving of Sheet Piles and Use of Vibro-drivers in Construction Engineering," Department of Civil Engineering, University of Roorkee, Roorkee, UP, India, 1962.

Davisson, M. T.: "Behavior of Flexible Vertical Piles Subjected to Moment, Shear and Axial Load," Ph.D. Thesis, University of Illinois, Urbana, 1960:

_____: Estimating Buckling Loads for Piles, *Proc. Second Pan American Conf. Soil Mech. Found. Engin.* vol. 1, pp. 350–371, 1963.

_____: Static Measurement of Pile Behavior, *Proc. Conf. Design and Installation of Pile Foundations and Cellular Structures, Lehigh University*, pp. 159–164, 1970a.

_____: Design Pile Capacity, *Proc. Conf. Design and Installation of Pile Foundations and Cellular Structures, Lehigh University*, pp. 75–85, 1970b.

_____: Lateral Load Capacity of Piles, *Highw. Res. Rec.*, no. 333, pp. 104–112, 1970c.

_____: "Pile Load Capacity," Design, Construction and Performance of Deep Foundations, ASCE, Univ. of California, Berkeley, August, 1975.

_____ and H. L. Gill: Laterally Loaded Piles in a Layered Soil System, *J. Soil Mech. Found. Div., ASCE*, vol. 89, no. SM 3, pp. 63–94, 1963.

_____ and K. E. Robinson: Bending and Buckling of Partially Embedded Piles, *Proc. Sixth Int. Conf. Soil Mech. Found. Engin.*, Montreal, vol. 2, pp. 243–246, 1965.

_____ and S. Prakash: A Review of Soil Pole Behavior, *Highw. Res. Rec.*, no. 39, pp. 25–48, 1963.

Federal Highway Administration Reports on Pile Driving Analysis: Wave Equation Users Manual TT1 Program

IP-76-13.1   Background
IP-76-13.2   Computer Program and Sample Problems
IP-76-13.3   Program Documentation
IP-76-13.4   Narrative Presentation

Ghumman, M. S.: "Effect of Vertical Vibrations on the Penetration Resistance of Piles," Ph.D. Thesis, University of Roorkee, Roorkee, India, 1981 (under preparation).

Gumenskii, B. M., and N. S. Kamrov: "Soil Drilling by Vibrations," translated into English from original Russian by Consultants Bureau, New York, 1961.

Hayashi, S. C.: A New Method of Evaluating Seismic Stability of Steel Structures, *Proc. Fifth World Conf. Earthquake Engin.*, Rome, vol. 2, pp. 2602–2605, 1973.

Housner, G. M.: Design Spectrum in R. L. Wiegel (ed.), "Earthquake Engineering," Prentice-Hall, Englewood Cliffs, NJ, 1970, chap 5.

Hrennikoff, A.: Analysis of Pile Foundations with Battered Piles, *Trans. ASCE*, vol. 115, p. 351, 1950.

Indian Standard Criteria for Earthquake Resistant Design of Structures. 3d rev., IS 1893–1975, Indian Standards Institution, New Delhi.

Indian Standard Code of Practice for Design and Construction of Pile Foundations: Part I, Load Bearing Concrete Piles, IS 2911, (part 1), 1964, Indian Standards Institution, New Delhi.

Kuhlemeyer, R. L.: Static and Dynamic Laterally Loaded Piles, *J. Geot. Eng. Div., ASCE*, vol. 105, no. GT 2, pp. 289–304, February, 1979.

Levkin, M. M.: "Use of the Vibratory Method for Sinking Piles and Pile Shells in Bridge Construction in the USSR," H.R.B. Special Report 60, Pub. No. 80, 1960.

Matlock, H., and L. C. Reese: Foundation Analysis of Offshore Pile Supported Structures, *Proc. Fifth Int. Conf. Soil Mech. Found. Engin.*, Paris, vol. 2, pp. 91–97, 1961.

_____ and _____: General Solutions for Laterally Loaded Piles, *Trans. ASCE*, vol. 127, part 1, pp. 1220–1247, 1962.

_____, H. C. F. Stephen, and L. M. Bryant: Simulation of Lateral Pile Behavior Under Earthquake Motion, *Proc. ASCE Specialty Conference on Soil Dynamics and Earthquake Engineering*, Pasadena, vol. 2, pp. 600–619, June, 1978.

Menzenbach, E.: The Determination of the Permissible Point Load of Piles by Means of Static Penetration Tests, *Proc. Fifth Int. Conf. Soil Mech. Found. Engin.*, Paris, vol. 2, pp. 99–104, 1961.

Meyerhof, G. G.: Penetration Tests and Bearing Capacity of Cohesionless Soils, *Proc. ASCE, Soil Mech. Found. Div.*, vol. 91, no. SM1, pp. 1–19, January, 1965.

_____ : Bearing Capacity and Settlement of Pile Foundations, Eleventh Terzaghi Lecture, *J. Geot. Eng. Div. ASCE*, vol. 102, GT 3, pp. 197–228, March, 1976.

Novak, M.: "Foundations and Soil Structure Interaction," Theme Report, Topic 4, Proc. VI World Conference on Earthquake Engineering, vol. 2, pp. 1421–1448, New Delhi, 1977.

_____ and T. Nogami: Soil-Pile Interaction in Horizontal Vibration, *Int. J. Earthquake Eng. Structural Dynamics*, vol. 5, pp. 263–281, 1977.

Palmer, L. A., and J. B. Thompson: "The Earth Pressure and Deflection Along the Embedded Lengths of Piles Subjected to Lateral Thrust, *Proc. Second Int. Conf. Soil Mech. Found. Engin.*, vol. V, p. 156, 1948.

Peck, R. B., W. E. Hansen, and T. H. Thornburn: "Foundation Engineering," 2d ed., John Wiley and Sons, Inc., New York, 1974.

Penzien, J.: Soil-Pile-Foundation Interaction, in R. L. Wiegel (ed.): "Earthquake Engineering," Prentice-Hall, Inc., Englewood Cliffs, NJ, 1970.

_____ C. F. Scheffey, and R. A. Parmalee: Seismic Analysis of Bridges on Long Piles, *J. Eng. Mech. Div., ASCE*, vol. 90, no. EM 3, pp. 223–254, June, 1964.

Prakash, S.: "Behavior of Pile Groups Subjected to Lateral Loads," Ph.D. Thesis, University of Illinois, Urbana, 1962.

_____ and H. P. Agarwal: Effect of Vibrations on Skin Friction of Piles, *Proc. Fourth Asian Regional Conf. Soil Engin.*, Bangkok, vol. 1, July, 1977.

_____ and S. L. Agarwal: Effect of Pile Embedment on Natural Frequency of Foundations, *Proc. South East Asian Regional Conf. Soil Mech. Found. Engin.*, Bangkok, pp. 333–336, April, 1967.

_____ and V. Chandrasekaran: Deflections of Battered Piles Under Cyclic Lateral Loads, *Proc. Second South East Asian Conf. Soil Engin.*, Singapore, vol. 1, pp. 411–421, 1970.

_____ and _____: Pile Foundations Under Lateral Dynamic Loads, *Proc. Eighth Int. Conf. Soil Mech. Found. Eng.*, Moscow, vol. 2, pp. 199–203, 1973.

_____ and _____: Free Vibration Characteristics of Piles, *Proc. Ninth Int. Conf. Soil Mech. Found. Engin.*, Tokyo, vol. 2, pp. 333–336, 1977.

_____ and _____: Analysis of Piles in Clay Against Earthquakes, Preprint no. 80-109, ASCE, Convention and Exposition, Portland, Ore., April 14–18, 1980.

_____ and L. P. Gupta: A Study of Natural Frequency of Pile Groups, *Proc. Second South East Asian Regional Conf. Soil Engin.*, Singapore, vol. 1, pp. 401–410, 1970.

_____, G. Ranjan, and S. Saran: "Analysis and Design of Foundations and Retaining Structures," Sarita Prakashan, Meerut, UP, India, 1979.

_____ and D. Sharma: "Laboratory Study of a Flexible Pile Subjected to Reversible Load," Paper presented to Annual General Meeting, Indian Geotechnical Society, Warangal, AP, India, December, 1974.

_____ and H. D. Sharma: Analysis of Pile Foundations Against Earthquakes, *Indian Concr. J.*, pp. 205–220, June, 1969.

Reese, L. C., and H. Matlock: "Non-dimensional Solutions for Laterally Loaded Piles with Soil

Modulus Assumed Proportional to Depth," *Proc. Eighth Texas Conference on Soil Mechanics and Foundation Engineering, Spec. Publ. No. 29, Bureau of Engineering Research, University of Texas,* Austin, September, 1956.

Saul, W. E.: Static and Dynamic Analysis of Pile Foundations, *J. Structural Engin. Div., ASCE,* vol. 94, no. ST 5, pp. 1077–1100, May, 1968.

Sharma, H. D.: Uncertainties in Cone Penetration Tests for Design of Pile Foundations, *Proc. Symposium on Bearing Capacity of Piles,* Roorkee, pp. 11–19, 1964.

Smith, E. A. L.: Pile Driving Analysis by the Wave Equation, *Trans. ASCE,* pp. 1145–1193, 1962.

Sonics Drive a Pile 71 ft While Steam Drives Another 3 Inches, *Eng. News-Rec.,* November 9, 1961.

Swiger, W. F.: Effect of Vibration of Piles in Loose Sand, *Proc. Second Int. Conf. Soil Mech. Found. Engin.,* Rotterdam, vol. 2, p. 19, 1948.

Teng, W. C.: "Foundation Design," Prentice-Hall, Englewood Cliffs, NJ, 1962.

Terzaghi, K.: Evaluation of Coefficients of Subgrade Reaction, *Geotechnique,* vol. 5, pp. 297–326, 1955.

Tomlinson, M. J.: "Foundation Design and Construction," 2d ed., Pitman Publishing House, London, 1969.

Van der Veen, C., and L. Boersma: The Bearing Capacity of a Pile Predetermined by a Cone Penetration Test, *Proc. Fourth Int. Conf. Soil Mech. Found. Engin.,* London, vol. 2, pp. 72–75, 1957.

Winkler, E.: "Die Lehre von Elastizitat und Festigkeit," Prague, p. 182, 1867.

Winterkorn, H. F. and H. Y. Fang: "Foundation Engineering Hand Book", Van Nostrand Reinhold, New York, NY, 1976.

LIQUEFACTION OF SOILS

8.1 INTRODUCTION

One of the major causes of destruction during an earthquake is the failure of the ground structure. The ground may fail due to fissures, abnormal or unequal movements, or loss of strength. The loss of strength may take place in sandy soils due to an increase in pore pressure. This phenomenon, termed *liquefaction*, can occur in loose and saturated sands. The increase in pore pressure causes a reduction in the shear strength, which may even be lost completely. Soil that has lost all shear strength behaves like a viscous fluid. Liquefaction often appears in the form of "sand fountains" during earthquakes. A large number of such fountains were observed during the Bihar earthquake of 1934 (Housner, 1958; Dunn et al., 1939). When soil fails in this manner, a structure resting on it simply sinks into it.

It was shown in Fig. 1.1 that buildings tilted by as much as 30° due to liquefaction of sands in the Niigata earthquake of 1964. The Niigata and Alaska earthquakes of 1964 resulted in characteristic damage to buildings, embankments, and natural slopes and focused the attention of the profession on detailed study of the phenomenon of liquefaction.

8.2 THEORY

The strength of sand is due to internal friction only. In a saturated state, it may be expressed as

$$s = (\sigma_n - u)\tan\phi \tag{8.1}$$

where $s =$ strength
$\quad\quad \sigma_n =$ normal pressure on any plane at depth Z (Fig. 8.1)
$\quad\quad u = \gamma_w \cdot Z$
$\quad\quad \phi =$ angle of internal friction

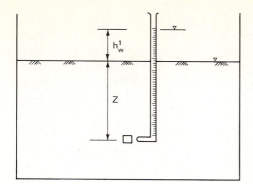

Figure 8.1 Pore-water pressure increase.

Considering stresses on a horizontal plane at depth Z,

$$\sigma_n = (\gamma_{sat} Z) \tag{8.2}$$

Equation (8.1) can now be expressed as

$$s = \bar{\sigma}_n \tan \phi \tag{8.3a}$$

or

$$s = \gamma_b Z \tan \phi \tag{8.3b}$$

in which γ_{sat} = unit weight of saturated soils and γ_b = submerged unit weight of soil.

Now if there is an increase in pore pressure $+ \Delta u = (\gamma_w \cdot h'_w)$ due to shaking of the ground, strength may be expressed as

$$s = (\gamma_b Z - \Delta u)\tan \phi$$

or

$$s = (\gamma_b Z - \gamma_w h'_w)\tan \phi \tag{8.4}$$

It is seen that with the development of additional positive pore pressures, the strength of sand is reduced.

For a complete loss of strength

$$\gamma_b Z = \gamma_w \cdot h'_w$$

or

$$\frac{h'_w}{Z} = \frac{\gamma_b}{\gamma_\omega} = \frac{S_s - 1}{1 + e} = i_{cr} \tag{8.5}$$

in which S_s = specific gravity of soil solids
        e = void ratio
     i_{cr} = critical hydraulic gradient

If the void ratio of soil is close to 0.6, and S_s is close to 2.6, i_{cr} = 1. From Eq. (8.5), $h'_w = Z$; that is, for a complete loss of strength to occur, an additional water head equal to the depth of the deposit is required.

It will be seen that a loss of strength occurs due to a transfer of intergranular stress from grains to pore water. Thus, if this transfer is complete, there is a complete loss of strength. However, if stress is only partially transferred from the grains to the pore water, only a partial loss of strength occurs. Since the stress condition is cyclic, a momentary transfer of all initial effective confining pressure to the pore water may not be of great engineering significance if the subsequent behavior of sand is satisfactory from considerations of load-carrying capacity, particularly in dense sands. In order to designate the behavior of saturated sand subsequent to the transfer of initial effective stress to the pore water, the following terminology will be used in this text (Seed 1976):

1. *Liquefaction*. This denotes a condition where a soil will undergo continued deformation at a constant low residual stress or with no residual resistance, due to the buildup and maintenance of high pore water pressures which reduce the effective confining pressure to a very low value; pore-pressure buildup leading to (true) liquefaction of this type may be due to either static or cyclic stress application.
2. *Initial liquefaction*. This denotes a condition where, during the course of cyclic stress applications, the residual pore-water pressure becomes equal to the applied confining pressure on completion of any full stress cycle. The development of initial liquefaction has no implications concerning the magnitude of the deformations that the soil might subsequently undergo; however, it defines a condition that is a useful basis for assessing various possible forms of subsequent soil behavior.
3. *Initial liquefaction with limited strain potential*; *cyclic mobility*; *or cyclic liquefaction*. These denote a condition in which cyclic stress applications develop a condition of initial liquefaction and subsequent cyclic stress applications cause limited strains to develop, either because of the remaining resistance of the soil to deformation or because the soil dilates, the pore pressure drops, and the soil stabilizes under the applied loads.

It must be appreciated at this stage that in case the complete transfer of initial effective stresses to the pore water is maintained for some time, the soil behaves as a viscous fluid. The phenomenon can be observed visually. In case of partial transfer of stresses, only internal changes occur in the soil and no apparent evidence of this phenomenon can be seen on the surface as in the former case. Figure 8.2 shows a plot of deviator stress $(\sigma_1 - \sigma_3)$ and axial strain on dry Ottawa sand having a uniformity coefficient of 1.3. The test data are on two densities, 101 lb/ft^3 and 109 lb/ft^3, corresponding to relative densities of 0 percent and 88 percent, and under confining pressures from 2.0 kg/cm^2 to 5.0 kg/cm^2 (Makhlouf and Stewart, 1965). The confining pressures on loose specimens were 5 kg/cm^2 and 2 kg/cm^2. The slope of the stress-strain plots decreases with decreasing confining pressure. In dense sand also, the slope of the stress-strain plot decreases, with a decrease in confining pressure from 3 kg/cm^2 to 2 kg/cm^2. Similar data have been obtained by Bishop et al. (1965) on Ham river

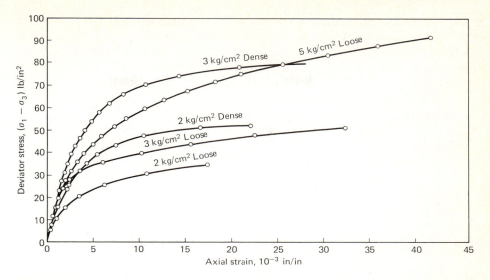

Figure 8.2 Effect of confining pressure on the slope of stress-strain plot of an Ottawa sand at 0% and 88% relative density. *(After Makhlouf and Stewart, 1965.)*

sand tested with very high confining pressures of 990 lb/in² to 100 lb/in². Thus, a decrease of effective stress means a reduction in rigidity and, hence, greater strains or settlement. Therefore, as soon as a partial transfer of stress occurs, settlement tends to start, resulting in possible surface settlement as well as settlement of structures founded on such soils. In case soil remains liquefied, it behaves as a viscous material. The structures resting on such a material start sinking into it. The rate of sinking depends upon the viscous properties of the suspension and its mass density. The total amount that a structure sinks† depends upon the time the sand remains liquefied.

It can thus be seen that structures may settle if the stress transfer from soil grains to pore water is partial and will sink if the soil is completely liquefied. Thus, as soon as liquefaction occurs, the process of consolidation starts, followed by surface settlement that results in closer packing of sand particles. During this process, the pore pressure starts dissipating and, in the field, water flows only upward. Because flow results in upward seepage forces, the effective stresses may be further reduced. This may cause liquefaction in layers that may not have liquefied initially.

8.3 CRITERION OF LIQUEFACTION

Figure 4.2 shows that in drained shear, dense sands expand in volume and loose sands decrease in volume. Therefore, between the two states there is a void ratio

† It was shown in Chap. 1 that light structures may float up.

at which there is no change in volume at failure. This void ratio is termed the *critical void ratio* (e_{cr}) (Casagrande, 1936). In consolidated undrained shear, there are negative pore-water pressures if $e_0 < e_{cr}$ and positive pore-water pressures if $e_0 > e_{cr}$.

Therefore, Casagrande (1936, 1976) proposed the critical void ratio as a possible criterion for deciding if sands in the field would liquefy or not. If the sands have a void ratio smaller than the critical void ratio, they will not liquefy. However, if the void ratio is larger than the critical void ratio, the soil is loose and the sands will liquefy during shear if drainage is prevented.

Casagrande (1938) proposed a method for determining the critical void ratio. Drained triaxial tests are performed at different initial void ratios. A plot of the change in volume Δv at its peak point is plotted against the initial void ratio. The void ratio corresponding to no volume change ($\Delta v = 0$) is the critical void ratio.

Figure 8.3 shows typical plots of volume change and the initial void ratio e_0 for saturated Fort Peck sand in drained tests (Taylor, 1948).

The critical void ratio is found to depend upon the confining pressure. The following values were obtained for Fort Peck sand:

Confining pressure, kg/cm^2	Critical void ratio
1.1	0.850
2.2	0.817
4.4	0.777

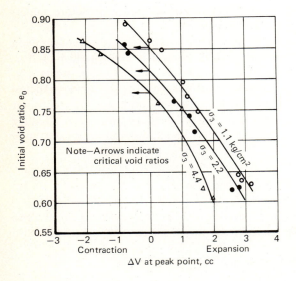

Figure 8.3 Plots of initial void ratio and volume changes at constant σ_3 on washed Fort Peck sand in triaxial compression tests in dense and loose state. *(After Taylor, 1948.)*

Thus, the critical void ratio is not a unique property of the soil.

The concept of liquefaction implies the sudden application of a load as in an earthquake or due to a bomb blast. The critical void ratio is determined in drained static tests. Since loading conditions in a laboratory are entirely different from those in nature during an earthquake or bomb blast, laboratory results may not be applicable to field problems. Taylor (1948) suggested that since the effect of shocks is not determined in tests for the critical void ratio, all laboratory constant-volume test results and all data on critical void ratios obtained from such tests can be accepted as representing sudden liquefaction conditions in nature only to that degree to which such conditions in nature are free of the dynamic effects that are not present in the laboratory tests. This introduces a serious gap in applying laboratory test results to field problems.

Maslov (1957) proposed the concept of *critical acceleration*. According to this concept, sand will liquefy if the acceleration of attendant motion is greater than the critical acceleration. The value of critical acceleration depends upon the density of the sand, the amplitude and frequency of oscillations, and the normal load or externally applied pressure. Thus, it appears that critical acceleration is not a unique property of a particular sand. Also, an engineer will be interested in liquefaction problems if the acceleration levels associated with the loss of strength are comparable to those occurring during earthquakes. If critical acceleration is too high, it may have no practical significance.

Florin and Ivanov (1961) suggested that because of the great variety of factors causing the collapse of sand structure, the criterion for the collapse of the soil structure should not be the critical void ratio or the density of sand, but the critical values of the intensity of dynamic disturbance, stress condition of the soil, or weight of surcharge and hydraulic gradient of water passing through it. Even if the factors listed above are considered, no ready index for liquefaction of sands can be evolved.

A field criterion for liquefaction of saturated sandy soils in relation to standard blasting in the field was also proposed. A 5-kg weight of explosive is fired at a depth of 4.5 m. The average settlement of the soil surface is measured in a radius of 5 m, as is the ratio of settlement resulting from successive blasting at one place. If the average settlement is less than 8 to 10 cm in a radius of 5 m, there is no need to take measures to prevent liquefaction. Also, if the average settlement is greater after three successive blasts, the sand will be looser and the possibility of liquefaction will be greater. If the ratio between two successive blasts is greater than 1:0.6, then there is danger of an undesirable spreading of the soil due to liquefaction.

Studies of Seed and Lee (1966), Seed and Idriss (1967, 1971), Prakash and Gupta (1970), Finn et al. (1970), Castro and Poulos (1976), Casagrande (1976), Seed (1976), Finn et al. (1976), and Gupta (1979) have demonstrated that liquefaction characteristics of a soil depend upon a larger number of factors. Although it may not be possible at this stage of our knowledge to determine an index in terms of one parameter, it appears that the standard penetration value N may ultimately solve this riddle (Christian and Swiger, 1975).

8.4 FACTORS AFFECTING LIQUEFACTION CHARACTERISTICS

The factors that affect liquefaction characteristics of sands are the following:

1. grain-size distribution of sand
2. density of deposit (initial relative density D_R)
3. vibration characteristics
4. location of drainage and dimensions of deposit
5. magnitude and nature of superimposed loads
6. method of soil formation (soil structure)
7. period under sustained load
8. previous strain history
9. entrapped air

Liquefaction characteristics of sands are affected by each of these factors as discussed below.

Grain-size distribution of sands Grain-size distribution affects the behavior of sand masses during vibrations. Fine and uniform sands are believed to be more prone to liquefaction than coarse sands under otherwise identical conditions. Since the permeability of a coarse sand is greater than that of a fine sand, the pore pressure developed during vibrations dissipates more easily in coarse sand than in fine sand. Hence, the chances of liquefaction are reduced with coarseness of the sand grains. Also, uniformly graded sands are more susceptible to liquefaction than well-graded sands.

Initial relative density Initial relative density is one of the most important factors controlling liquefaction. Both settlement and pore pressures are considerably reduced during vibrations with the increase in initial relative density. Typical stress-strain curves for a loose and a dense sand appear in Fig. 8.4. The slope of the stress-strain curve, which is a measure of the rigidity of the soil, is smaller for loose sand than it is for dense sand. Hence, under otherwise identical stress conditions, sands having smaller initial relative density will undergo larger strains and larger settlements than those having higher initial relative density. Chances of liquefaction and excessive settlement are therefore reduced with increased relative density.

Vibration characteristics Liquefaction and settlement depend on the nature, magnitude, and type of dynamic loading. The whole stratum may be liquefied at the same time under shock loading, while liquefaction may start from the top and proceed downward under steady-state vibrations (Florin and Ivanov, 1961). Under steady-state vibrations, the maximum pore pressure develops only after a certain number of cycles have been imparted to the deposit (Seed and Lee, 1966; Lee and Seed, 1967; Peacock and Seed, 1968; Prakash and Gupta, 1970a; Yoshimi, 1967). In general, it has also been found that horizontal vibrations in

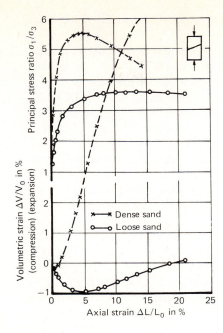

Figure 8.4 Plots of typical triaxial compression tests on Fort Peck sand. Dense $e_0 = 0.605$, loose $e_0 = 0.834$, $\sigma_3 = 30$ lb/in^2. *(After Taylor, 1948.)*

dry sand lead to larger settlements than vertical vibrations (Prakash and Gupta, 1967c). Similar behavior is anticipated in saturated sands.

The amount of damage to structures on soils undergoing liquefaction depends on how long the sand remains in a liquefied state. In coarse sand, due to the high coefficient of permeability, the duration of liquefaction may be shorter than it is for fine sands.

The landslides in Anchorage during the Alaska earthquake were triggered about 90 s after the start of the ground motion (Seed and Idriss, 1971). Therefore, if the ground motion had lasted less than 90 s—say, 45 s— liquefaction or soil instability would not have developed.

Multidirectional shaking as in an earthquake is more severe than one-directional loading. Seed (1976, 1979) reports that under multidirectional shaking or stress conditions, pore-water pressures build up faster than under unidirectional stress conditions, and that the stress ratio required to cause a peak cyclic pore-pressure ratio of 100 percent under multidirectional shaking conditions is about 10 percent less than that required under unidirectional shaking conditions. Accordingly, a correction factor of about this magnitude should be applied to the results of conventional cyclic-loading simple shear tests to account for this effect.

Location of drainage and dimensions of deposit Sands are generally more pervious than fine-grained soils. However, if a pervious deposit has large dimensions, the drainage path increases and, under quick loading during an earthquake, the deposit may behave as if it were undrained. Therefore the chances of liquefaction are increased in such a deposit.

The introduction of gravel drains to stabilize a potentially liquefiable sand deposit has been proposed by Yoshimi and Kuwabara (1973). Seed and Booker (1976) and Seed (1976) have proposed an analytical procedure for designing such drainage. The drains are considered fully effective if the material of which they are constructed is about 200 times more permeable than the soil in which they are installed. The drainage path is reduced by the introduction of drains.

Magnitude and nature of superimposed loads An isotropic stress condition constitutes the initial effective stress on a sample. To transfer a large initial effective stress to the pore water, either the intensity of vibrations must be large or the number of particular stress cycles must be large. Hence, large initial effective stress reduces the possibility of liquefaction.

If the initial stress condition is not isotropic, as is the case in the field, the stress condition causing liquefaction depends upon the coefficient of earth pressure at rest K_0 of the deposit. For K_0 greater than 5, the stress condition required to cause liquefaction was increased by at least 50 percent (Seed, 1976). This leads to a very important conclusion that triaxial test data do not simulate the field conditions for study of liquefaction and give results on the conservative side. However, if large initial intergranular stress has been applied in the field by loading, it is necessary that it should be composed of free draining material like boulders or concrete blocks so that pore pressure gets easily dissipated through this material.

Method of soil formation Sands are generally known not to display a characteristic structure as do fine-grained soils, such as clays. But recent investigations of Ladd (1976) and others have demonstrated that liquefaction characteristics of saturated sands under cyclic loading are significantly influenced by the method of sample preparation and by soil structure. It is shown by Seed (1976) that, depending on the method of sample preparation, the stress condition required to cause liquefaction in a given number of stress cycles for samples of the same sand at the same density may vary as much as 200 percent. It will, therefore, be necessary to simulate the orientation of soil particles and the soil fabric in the laboratory. More research is needed on the definition of soil fabric in quantitative terms and on the methods of reproducing it in the laboratory.

Period under sustained load The age of a sand deposit may influence its liquefaction characteristics. A study of the liquefaction of an undisturbed sand and its freshly prepared sample indicates that the liquefaction resistance may increase by 75 percent (Seed, 1976). Lee (1975) explains this strength increase as being due to some form of cementation or welding, which may occur at contact points between sand particles, and as being associated with secondary compression of the soil. This effect must be recognized as different from that due to orientation of soil particles in the soil fabric.

Previous strain history Sands may be subjected to some strains due to earthquakes. To determine the effect of previous strain history, studies were made of the liquefaction characteristics of freshly deposited sand and of a similar deposit previously subjected to some strain history in simple shear by Finn et al. (1970). It was found that liquefaction characteristics were influenced by the strain undergone previously. Seed (1976) showed that although the prior strain history caused no significant change in the density of the sand, it increased the stress that causes liquefaction by a factor of about 1.5. Much larger increases have been shown to result from more severe prestrain conditions (Bjerrum, 1973; Lee and Focht, 1975).

Trapped air If air is trapped in water in which pore pressures develop, part of it is dissipated due to compression of air. Hence, trapped air helps reduce the possibility of liquefaction.

The interaction of all of the factors discussed above is quite complex. Sufficient test data on loose sands under vibrations are available to warrant some quantitative and many more qualitative conclusions. Guidelines are now available, too, that will help researchers to confidently plan and rationally interpret both laboratory and field investigations. Also, several significant studies have been made of damage to soils and structures resting on soils that liquefied. Typical laboratory investigations of liquefaction are presented in this chapter, followed by a discussion of the methods of analysis.

8.5 LABORATORY STUDIES ON LIQUEFACTION

Two types of laboratory tests have been used for studies of liquefaction of sands: triaxial or simple shear tests and vibration-table tests. In triaxial tests, the sample is consolidated isotropically and then pulsating stress is applied. In a simple shear test, vertical stress is applied on the sample and then oscillatory shear stresses of predetermined magnitude are applied. In vibration-table studies, sand is deposited in a tank mounted on a vibration table and vibrated with known frequency and amplitude of motion under steady-state or programmed motions. The sand deposit is consolidated under the applied surcharge simulating field loading conditions.

Typical studies in both categories of laboratory tests are described in the following sections.

8.6 LIQUEFACTION STUDIES IN TRIAXIAL SHEAR

In the 1960s, a comprehensive laboratory investigation program on liquefaction of sands was initiated at the University of California in Berkeley. A series of publications originated from Seed and his group.

Seed and Lee (1966) reported the first set of comprehensive data on a sand. They advocated that a major part of the soil deformation in many earthquakes may be attributed to the upward propagation of shear waves from underlying layers, as explained in Figs. 4.22 and 4.23. During an earthquake, the soil is considered to be subjected to a series of cyclic shear strains that reverse directions many times. If the ground surface is horizontal, then there is no shear stress on a horizontal plane. The total normal stress on this plane remains constant and cyclic shear stresses are induced during the earthquake.

Such deformation conditions can best be reproduced in the laboratory by a simple shear test conducted under cyclic loading conditions. However, they may also be approximately reproduced by the cyclic-loading triaxial-compression tests illustrated in Fig. 8.5. In this figure, col. 1 shows three stress conditions at different stages of a cyclic loading test. In condition a, the sample is subjected to an all-around pressure. The Mohr diagram for this stress condition is a point (see col. 2) and the stress on plane XX is equal to σ_3. In condition b, the vertical stress is increased by an amount $\sigma_{dp}/2$ and the horizontal stress is decreased by an equal amount; the resulting Mohr diagram is shown in col. 2. It may be seen that the normal stress on plane XX is still equal to σ_3, but a shear stress equal to $\sigma_{dp}/2$ has been induced. Finally, in condition c, the vertical stress is reduced by $\sigma_{dp}/2$, but the horizontal stress is increased by this amount. Again, the resulting stress condition produces a stress equal to σ_3 on plane XX, but a shear stress of $\sigma_{dp}/2$ acts in the opposite direction to that for condition b.

Thus, by bringing a sample to equilibrium under an ambient stress condition and then cycling the vertical and horizontal stresses between conditions b and c in Fig. 8.5, the stress conditions on plane XX will be the same as those on a horizontal plane in Fig. 4.23.

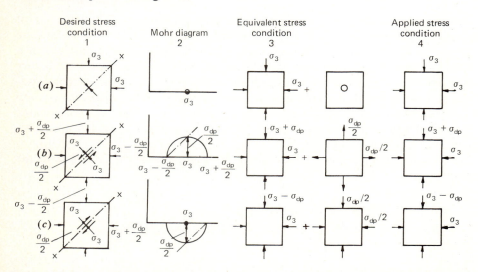

Figure 8.5 Stress conditions for triaxial test on a saturated sand under simulated earthquake loading conditions. *(After Seed and Lee, 1966.)*

The cyclic stress changes required to induce the desired stress conditions require that at all stages of loading, the mean of the major and minor principal stresses should be maintained constant. This condition might be termed as constant-mean-extreme-principal stress and, if the effects of the intermediate principal stress are neglected, maintenance of this condition would provide the desired stress condition.

The application of simultaneous cyclic changes in both the vertical and horizontal stresses acting on a test specimen, to maintain a constant-mean-extreme-principal stress condition, is a difficult test procedure. However, in working with saturated soils, this difficulty can readily be overcome. For example, the desired stress condition shown by condition b (Fig. 8.5, col. 1) can be induced on a test specimen by simultaneously applying the two stress conditions shown in col. 3; directly adding the two stress conditions in col. 3 produces the same stresses as indicated in col. 1. Thus, the desired stress condition can be induced by increasing the axial stress on the specimen by an amount σ_{dp}, keeping the lateral stress constant, and simultaneously reducing the all-around confining pressure on the specimen by an amount $\sigma_{dp}/2$. However, the reduction in all-around confining pressure would simply reduce the pore-water pressure in the saturated sample by $\sigma_{dp}/2$ without causing any change in effective stresses in the sample. Because deformation of a sample is only caused by changes in effective stress, the deformation would be the same whether the change in confining pressure was made or not. In fact, if the reduction in confining pressure were omitted from the test procedure, the effective stresses and the strains in the sample would be just the same as if it were included, except that pore-water pressures would be too high by $\sigma_{dp}/2$. Thus, the effects of the desired stress condition b in col. 1 can be determined by applying the stress conditions shown in col. 4 and simply correcting the measured pore-water pressures as explained above. Strains and effective stresses would require no correction at all.

Similarly, the desired stress condition shown by condition c (Fig. 8.5, col. 1) can be induced by the application of the two conditions shown in col. 3.; that is, by reducing the vertical stress by σ_{dp} and applying an increase in all-around pressure equal to $\sigma_{dp}/2$. The effects of the desired stress conditions can therefore be determined by reducing the vertical stress and correcting the pore-water pressure by increasing it by $\sigma_{dp}/2$. It is, of course, necessary that the cyclic stress σ_{dp} not exceed the initial confining pressure σ_3, as the vertical stress must remain compressive at all times.

The tests were performed on Sacramento River sand with minimum and maximum void ratios of 0.61 and 1.03, respectively. The grain size ranged between 0.149 mm and 0.297 mm.

Behavior of Loose Sand under Cyclic Loading

The results of a typical cyclic loading test on a sample of loose sand are shown in Fig. 8.6a. In this test, a cyclic deviator stress, σ_{dp}, of constant amplitude

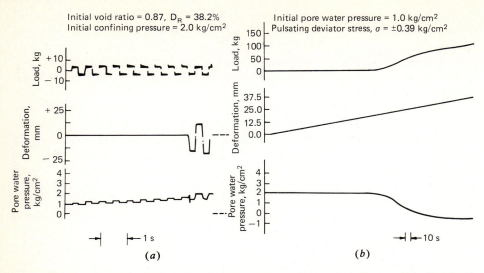

Figure 8.6 (*a*) Cyclic triaxial test on loose sand. (*b*) Static test after liquefaction. (*After Seed and Lee, 1966.*)

(± 0.39 kg/cm^2), was applied with a frequency of 2 Hz to a sample of saturated sand under a confining pressure of 1 kg/cm^2, and the resulting changes in axial strain and pore-water pressure were recorded. The sand was sufficiently pervious for the pore-pressure in the sample to be equalized almost immediately after the stress applications. The test data in Fig. 8.6*a* show the changes in stress, strain, and pore-water pressure with time.

It will be noted that, during the first six cycles of stress application, the sample showed no noticeable deformation although the pore-water pressure built up gradually. However, during the ninth stress cycle, the pore pressure suddenly increased to a value equal to the externally applied confining pressure and the sample developed large strains which, in the tenth cycle, exceeded 20 percent. In fact, the soil had liquefied and the effective confining pressure had been reduced to zero. Over a wide range of strains, the soil could be observed to be in a fluid condition.

Based on test data shown in Fig. 8.6*a*, Fig. 8.7 shows the changes in axial strain amplitude, the observed changes in pore-water pressures, and the pore-water pressure changes corrected to mean extreme principal stress conditions with an increasing number of stress cycles. Axial strains are negligible until liquefaction occurs; then they are relatively symmetrical in extension and compression and their amplitude is quite large. Pore-water pressure continues to build up steadily as the number of stress cycles increases, until there is a sudden increase denoting the onset of initial liquefaction. The different values of pore-water pressure developed during increases and decreases in deviator stress reflect the influence of the applied stress conditions. However, even when the

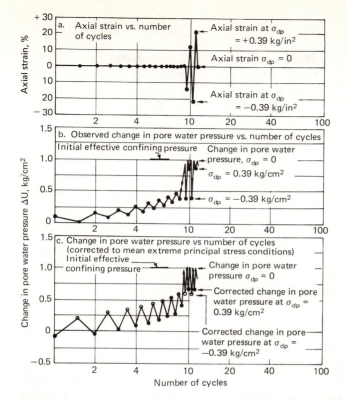

Figure 8.7 Typical pulsating load test on loose sand; $e = 0.87$, $D_R = 38\%$, $\sigma_3 = 1$ kg/cm^2, $\sigma_{dp} = 0.39$ kg/cm^2. *(After Seed and Lee, 1966.)*

pore pressures are corrected to constant-mean-extreme-principal-stress conditions, the pore pressures are still different during axial compression and axial extension, reflecting the influence of the intermediate principal stress on the test results. (During axial compression, the intermediate principal stress, σ_2, is equal to the minor principal stress, σ_3, but during axial extension it is equal to the major principal stress, σ_1.)

After liquefaction, pore-water pressures are lowest when the deviator stress is at a maximum, and they have their highest values (equal to the external confining pressure on the specimen) when the cyclic deviator stress is zero.

Liquefaction occurred suddenly after eight cycles of motion, during which the deformation of the sample was negligible. When the level of pulsating deviator stress was increased, the number of cycles needed to cause liquefaction decreased, and vice versa (Fig. 8.8). In these cases, the samples withstood from 8 to 200 stress cycles with no noticeable deformation, but liquefied completely in the course of one or two more cycles as demonstrated in Fig. 8.7.

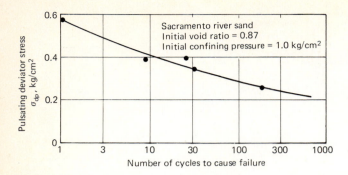

Figure 8.8 Relationship between pulsating deviator stress and number of cycles required to cause failure in loose sand. *(After Seed and Lee, 1966.)*

Effect of Static Loading Following Liquefaction of Sand

After the sand had liquefied, a static test was performed on loose sand (Fig. 8.6b). The sample was considerably deformed without mobilizing any resistance to deformation and without any change in pore-water pressure. Finally, when the strain was about 20 percent, the sample tended to dilate, the pore-water pressure decreased, and the resulting increase in effective stress led to the development of an appreciable resistance to deformation.

It may be concluded that, in cases where there is no upward seepage through a liquefied sand mass, the application of static shear stress following a series of cyclic motions will significantly displace the liquefied sand and will simultaneously develop a high resistance to further deformation. Thus, it is expected that such a liquefied sand layer would immediately become firm again when the cyclic stresses or earthquake ground motions stop.

Effect of Confining Pressure on Liquefaction

It has already been shown how the initial confining pressure affects liquefaction characteristics of sand. In this test series, three samples of sand (prepared so they had the same void ratio after consolidation) were initially consolidated under confining pressures of 0.5, 0.75, and 1.0 kg/cm^2, respectively. They were then subjected to cyclic stress applications of the same magnitude and the resulting pore pressure and deformations were recorded.

It was found that as the confining pressure got higher, a greater number of stress cycles were required to induce liquefaction, which is obvious.

Lee and Seed (1967) performed a large number of tests on Sacramento sand to establish quantitative relationships between various factors affecting liquefaction. The tests were performed on sand with the following properties:

Density	D_R	e_0
Relatively loose	38%	0.87
Medium dense	60%	0.78
Dense	94%	0.71
Very dense	100%	0.66

A large amount of quantitative data on the factors affecting liquefaction, initial liquefaction, and predetermined strain conditions, under oscillatory load in the Sacramento sand has been presented.

8.7 LIQUEFACTION STUDIES IN OSCILLATORY SIMPLE SHEAR

A simple oscillatory shear device is described in Chap. 4 as are tests on soils in such a device to obtain the dynamic shear moduli. This device has been extensively used by research workers to study liquefaction characteristics of soils. Peacock and Seed (1968) reported the first comprehensive information in this regard. The stress condition in the sample is as shown in Fig. 4.23.

The sand used was clean, uniform Monterey, California, sand, classified as SP according to the Unified Soil Classification System. Individual grains were hard and durable and medium in size. The minimum and maximum void ratios of this sand were 0.53 and 0.83, respectively, with a uniformity coefficient of 1.22 and D_{10} of 0.54 mm. The sample size was 6 cm square and 2 cm thick. The samples were tested at initial void ratios of 0.68, 0.59, and 0.56, corresponding to relative densities of 50 percent (loose), 80 percent (medium dense), and 90 percent (dense), respectively. All samples were tested while saturated and under a back pressure of 1 kg/cm^2. During the tests, the predetermined normal stress was kept constant and the oscillatory shear stress was applied at a frequency of 2 Hz in most of the tests.

Figure 8.9 shows a typical cyclic load test on loose sand conducted in the simple shear apparatus. A cyclic shear stress, τ_{hp}, of constant amplitude (± 0.33 kg/cm^2) was applied with a frequency of 1 Hz to a sample of loose saturated sand under a vertical consolidation load, σ_v, of 5 kg/cm^2, and the resulting changes in horizontal shear strain and pore-water pressure were recorded.

As seen from Fig. 8.9b, there was no significant deformation of the sample during the application of the first 24 cycles of stress. However, during the twenty-fifth stress cycle, the deformation suddenly increased to a value of about 15 percent double-amplitude strain. During the twenty-sixth cycle, the strain increased to 23 percent. Thus, excessive strains developed suddenly following the twenty-fourth cycle.

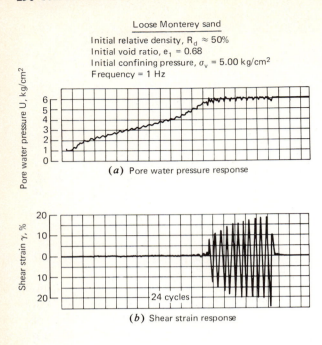

Loose Monterey sand

Initial relative density, $R_d \approx 50\%$
Initial void ratio, $e_1 = 0.68$
Initial confining pressure, $\sigma_v = 5.00 \text{ kg/cm}^2$
Frequency = 1 Hz

Pore water pressure U, kg/cm²

(*a*) Pore water pressure response

Shear strain γ, %

24 cycles

(*b*) Shear strain response

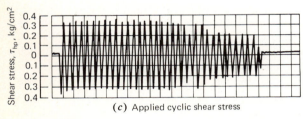

Shear stress, τ_{hp}, kg/cm²

(*c*) Applied cyclic shear stress

Figure 8.9 Record of a typical pulsating load test on loose sand in simple shear conditions. (*After Peacock and Seed, 1968.*)

From Fig. 8.9*a*, it is apparent that there was a gradual increase in pore-water pressure until the effective confining pressure had practically been reduced to zero. At this point, the resulting deformations became extremely large, and the soil had essentially liquefied. It is interesting to note that, in the initial stage of the test (that is, during the first 24 cycles of stress application), the gradual increase in pore-water pressure did not produce a significant increase in the shear deformation even though the effective stress was constantly being reduced. However, as soon as the effective stress within the sample had been reduced to zero, the deformations increased rapidly and liquefaction occurred within about two cycles. This sudden failure is characteristic of the behavior of loose sands whether tested under cyclic-loading–simple-shear or cyclic-loading–triaxial conditions. Figure 8.9*b* is very similar to the deformation-time record in a triaxial test on a loose sand in Fig. 8.6*a*. Thus, the general nature of the behavior of loose sands in triaxial and simple shear under dynamic loading is similar.

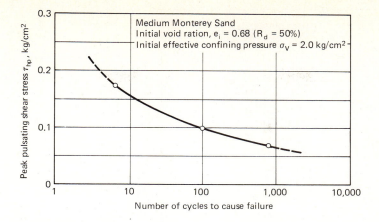

Figure 8.10 Typical form of relationship between pulsating shear stress and number of cycles to cause failure—simple shear conditions. *(After Peacock and Seed, 1968.)*

Relationship Between Peak Pulsating Shear Stress and Number of Cycles Required to Cause Liquefaction

The results of a series of tests performed on loose sand are shown in Fig. 8.10. It is apparent from this figure that, for a sand at a given void ratio under a given initial effective confining pressure, the number of stress cycles required to cause liquefaction increases as the applied pulsating shear decreases. This plot is typical of the relationship that occurs when sand is tested under cyclic-loading–triaxial conditions (see Fig. 8.8).

Influence of Confining Pressure on the Cyclic Stresses Required to Cause Liquefaction

In Fig. 8.11a, the effect of confining pressure σ_v on the liquefaction of a Monterey sand has been studied. The tests were performed at three confining pressures of 3, 5, and 8 kg/cm^2.

While the curves are similar in shape, their position is governed by the initial effective confining pressure. As the confining pressure increases, the curves become progressively steeper and shift upward on the diagram.

This effect of confining pressure is clearly illustrated in Fig. 8.11b. For a given number of cycles, the pulsating shear stress required to cause liquefaction increases linearly with increasing confining pressure. This is consistent with the behavior of sand under cyclic-loading–triaxial conditions (Lee and Seed, 1967).

Comparison of Cyclic Stresses Causing Liquefaction under Simple Shear Conditions and Triaxial Conditions

To compare the relative magnitudes of the cyclic shear stresses required to cause liquefaction of saturated sands under triaxial compression and simple shear

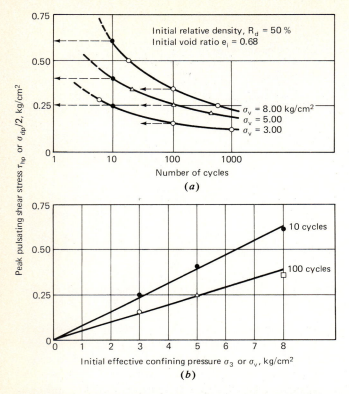

Figure 8.11 (*a*) Cyclic stresses required to cause initial liquefaction of loose Monterey sand at three confining pressures. (*b*) Effect of confining pressure on cyclic stress required to cause failure in 10 cycles and 100 cycles. *(After Peacock and Seed, 1968.)*

conditions, samples with a relative density of 50 percent were tested at confining pressures of 3, 5, and 8 kg/cm² in both types of test. The results are plotted in Fig. 8.12. It is seen from this figure that, at all confining pressures, the cyclic stress required to cause initial liquefaction under simple shear conditions is considerably less than the cyclic stress required to cause initial liquefaction under triaxial test conditions.

To obtain a quantitative comparison of the data for the two types of tests, the results have also been plotted as shown in Fig. 8.13. It may be seen from this figure that the cyclic stress required to cause liquefaction of loose sands under simple shear conditions is about 35 percent of the cyclic stress required to cause liquefaction under triaxial loading conditions.

Tests were performed at frequencies of 1/6 Hz, 2 Hz, and 4 Hz on this sand in oscillatory shear test, and the effect of frequency on the stress causing liquefaction was negligible. Test data on this sand were also obtained at relative densities of 80 and 90 percent. It was found that dense sand exhibits somewhat similar behavior as loose sand. Initially, there was virtually no noticeable

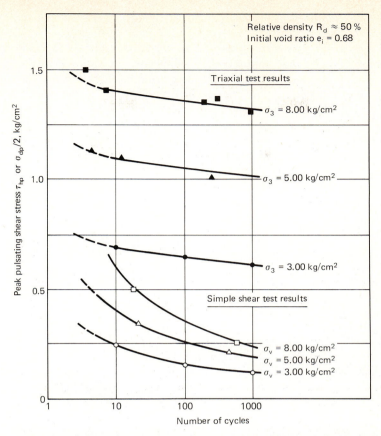

Figure 8.12 Cyclic stresses required to cause initial liquefaction of Monterey sand at three confining pressures in triaxial and simple shear tests. *(After Peacock and Seed, 1968.)*

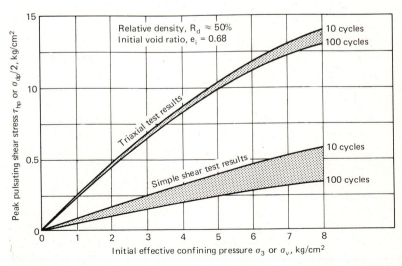

Figure 8.13 Comparison of pulsating shear strengths of loose Monterey sand under cyclic-loading–simple-shear and –triaxial conditions. *(After Peacock and Seed, 1968.)*

deformation with increasing pore-water pressure. However, in contrast to loose sand, the strain amplitude of dense sand increased somewhat more slowly as the number of stress cycles increased. Thus, there was no sudden failure of the sample as in the case of loose sand. The gradual increase in strain amplitudes is characteristic of the behavior of dense sand, whether tested in cyclic-loading–simple-shear or cyclic-loading–triaxial conditions.

The question of liquefaction of dense sand under cyclic loading conditions will be examined in detail later in this chapter.

8.8 EVALUATION OF LIQUEFACTION POTENTIAL

It has been shown in Sec. 8.5 that the following factors influence the liquefaction characteristics of a sand:

1. soil type
2. relative density or void ratio
3. initial confining pressure
4. intensity and duration of ground shaking

Based upon the above factors, Seed and Idriss (1967, 1971) proposed a general method for evaluation of liquefaction potential involving the following steps:

1. After establishing soil conditions and the design earthquake, determine the time history of shear stresses induced by earthquake ground motions at different depths within the deposit.
2. By appropriate weighting of the stress levels involved in the various stress cycles throughout the earthquake, convert the stress history into an equivalent number of uniform stress cycles and plot the equivalent uniform stress level as a function of depth, as shown in Fig. 8.14. By this means, the intensity of ground shaking, the duration of shaking, and the variation of shear stress with depth within the deposit are taken into account.
3. By means of available field data or laboratory soil tests on representative samples, conducted under various confining pressures, determine the cyclic shear stresses that would have to be developed at various depths to cause liquefaction in the same number of stress cycles as that determined in step 2 to be representative of the particular earthquake under consideration. Either cyclic-load–triaxial-compression tests or cyclic-load–simple-shear tests may be used for this purpose.
4. By comparing the shear stresses induced by the earthquake with those required to cause liquefaction, determine whether any zone exists within the deposit where liquefaction can be expected to occur (induced stresses exceed those causing failure).

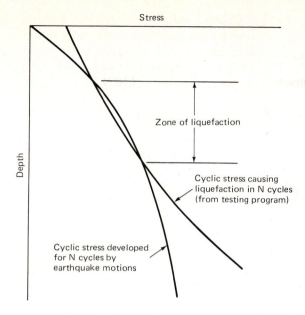

Stress

Zone of liquefaction

Depth

Cyclic stress causing
liquefaction in N cycles
(from testing program)

Cyclic stress developed
for N cycles by
earthquake motions

Figure 8.14 Method of evaluating
liquefaction potential. *(After Seed
and Idriss, 1967, 1971.)*

A ground response analysis is performed (Seed and Idriss, 1971) to evaluate
the stress history at various depths and to determine how pore pressure dissipates during an earthquake and after earthquake motion has ceased. Other
factors listed in Sec. 8.5 also affect the liquefaction characteristics of soils in situ.
However, the simplified method described below takes into account only the
four factors listed above. To evaluate the effect of other factors, Seed (1976) has
proposed multiplying factors as correction coefficients. Also, in this analysis, the
laboratory test data are not necessary for a particular sand.

The method of analysis consists of the following steps.

Computation of maximum shear stresses in the deposits The shear stresses
developed at any point in a soil deposit during an earthquake appear to be due
primarily to the upward propagation of shear waves in the deposit. If the soil
column above a soil element at depth h behaved as a rigid body and the
maximum ground surface acceleration was a_{max}, the maximum shear stress
$(\tau_{max})_r$ on the soil would be

$$(\tau_{max})_r = \frac{\gamma h}{g} a_{max} \qquad (8.6a)$$

in which γ = total unit weight of the soil. Since the soil column behaves as a
deformable body, the actual shear stress at depth h, $(\tau_{max})_d$, as determined by a
ground response analysis, will be less than $(\tau_{max})_r$ and might be expressed by

$$(\tau_{max})_d = r_d(\tau_{max})_r \qquad (8.6b)$$

in which r_d = a stress reduction coefficient with a value of less than 1.

Computations of the value of r_d for a wide variety of earthquake motions and soil conditions having sand in the upper 50 ft have shown that r_d falls within the range of values shown in Fig. 8.15 (Seed and Idriss, 1971). The scatter of the results in the upper 30 ft or 40 ft is not great, and the error involved in using the average values shown by the dashed line would generally be less than about 5 percent. Thus, a reasonably accurate assessment of the maximum shear stress developed during an earthquake can be made to depths of about 40 ft from the relationship

$$\tau_{max} = \frac{\gamma h}{g} a_{max} r_d \qquad (8.6c)$$

in which values of r_d are taken from the dashed line in Fig. 8.15. The critical depth for development of liquefaction, if it is going to occur, will normally be in the depth covered by this relationship.

Determination of equivalent number of significant stress cycles N_c The actual time history of shear stress at any point in a soil deposit during an earthquake will have an irregular form such as that shown in Fig. 8.16. From such relationships, it is necessary to determine the equivalent uniform average shear stress. By appropriately weighting individual stress cycles, based on laboratory data, it has been found (with a reasonable degree of accuracy) that the average equivalent uniform shear stress τ_{av} is about 65 percent of the maximum shear

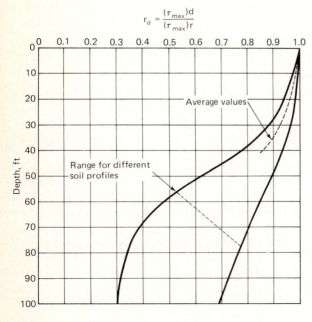

Figure 8.15 Range of values of r_d for different soil profiles in liquefaction analysis. (*After Seed and Idriss, 1971.*)

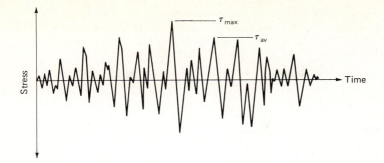

Figure 8.16 Time history of shear stresses during earthquakes for liquefaction analysis. *(After Seed and Idriss, 1971.)*

stress τ_{max}. Therefore,

$$\tau_{av} \simeq 0.65 \times \frac{\gamma h}{g} a_{max} \times r_d \qquad (8.7)$$

The appropriate number of significant stress cycles N_c will depend on the duration of ground shaking and thus on the magnitude of the earthquake. Representative numbers of stress cycles are:

Earthquake magnitude	Number of significant stress cycles N_c
7	10
7.5	20
8	30

   Further details on the "equivalent uniform cycles" from random motion, have been described by Ishihara and Yasuda (1973), Lee and Chan (1972), Lee and Focht (1975a), Seed et al. (1975), and Prakash and Gupta (1970).

Determination of stresses causing liquefaction A cyclic triaxial or simple shear apparatus is used to determine stresses that cause liquefaction within a given number of cycles of motion, depending on the magnitude of the earthquake.
   The results of a number of triaxial tests with different grain sizes, represented by the mean grain size D_{50}, and at a relative density of 50 percent are summarized in Figs. 8.17 and 8.18 (Seed and Peacock, 1971). The results of these tests are expressed in terms of the stress ratio $\sigma_{dc}/2\sigma_a$ causing liquefaction in 10 cycles and 30 cycles, where σ_{dc} is the cyclic deviator stress and σ_a is the initial ambient pressure under which the sample was consolidated. The stresses required to cause liquefaction for sands at other relative densities may be estimated from the fact that for relative densities up to about 80 percent, the shear stress required to cause initial liquefaction is approximately proportional to the relative density.

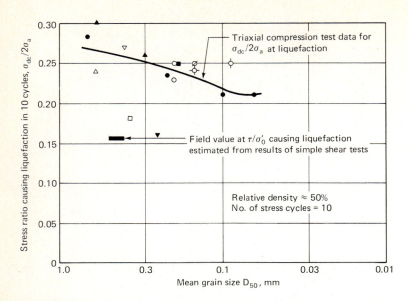

Figure 8.17 Stress condition causing liquefaction of sands in 10 cycles. *(After Seed and Idriss, 1971.)*

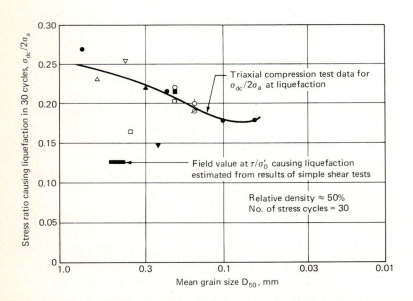

Figure 8.18 Stress conditions causing liquefaction of sands in 30 cycles. *(After Seed and Idriss, 1971.)*

The values of the stress ratio τ/σ_0' causing liquefaction under field conditions, estimated from the results of simple shear tests where τ is the shear stress developed on a horizontal plane and σ_0' is the initial effective overburden pressure, have shown that the field value of τ/σ_0' is less than the corresponding value of $\sigma_{dc}/2\sigma_a$. However, the two stress ratios may be related by

$$\left(\frac{\tau}{\sigma_0'}\right)_\ell = \left(\frac{\sigma_{dc}}{2\sigma_a}\right)_\ell c_r \tag{8.8}$$

in which c_r is a correction factor to be applied to laboratory triaxial test data to obtain the stress conditions causing liquefaction in the field.

Thus the test data adopted in Figs. 8.17 and 8.18, together with the values of c_r, give the stress conditions likely to cause liquefaction of different soils in the field. The stress ratio causing liquefaction in the field for a given soil at a relative D_r may be estimated from

$$\left(\frac{\tau}{\sigma_0'}\right)_{\ell D_r} \simeq \left(\frac{\sigma_{dc}}{2\sigma_a}\right)_{\ell 50} c_r \frac{D_r}{50} \tag{8.9}$$

where D_r and 50 denote relative densities D_r and 50%, respectively.

The following values of c_r[†] may be adopted in preliminary analysis:

Relative density $D_r\%$	Correction factor c_r
0–50	0.57
60	0.60
80	0.68

Evaluation of liquefaction potential To evaluate the liquefaction potential of a deposit, it is necessary to determine whether the shear stress [determined from Eq. (8.7)] induced at any depth by the earthquake is sufficiently large to cause liquefaction at that depth, as indicated by the relationship in Eq. (8.9). For deposits in which the water table is at a depth of 0 ft to 10 ft, the critical depth will often be about 20 ft, and for those in which the water table depth is about 15 ft, the critical depth may be about 30 ft.

The use of the above procedure will be explained with the help of an example.

Example 8.1 During an earthquake, severe damage to buildings and other structures occurred due to extensive liquefaction of sands. The maximum intensity of ground shaking is 0.1 g, the magnitude of the earthquake is 7.5

[†] After Seed and Idriss (1971)

on the Richter scale and D_{50} of the sand is 0.2 mm and its relative density is 45 percent. The water table occurs at a depth of 3 ft and the depth of the sand deposit is assumed to be up to 60 ft. The unit weight of sand is 112 lb/ft³ when moist and 50 lb/ft³ in a submerged state. Determine the zone of liquefaction.

SOLUTION   (a) Computation of shear stress (τ_{av}) in the deposit

$$\tau_{av} = 0.65\gamma h \frac{a_{max}}{g} r_d \tag{8.7}$$

Depth, ft	$\gamma^* h$, lb/ft²	$\dfrac{a_{max}}{g}$	r_d	τ_{av} lb/ft²
10*	1,123.5	0.1	0.98	71.6
20	2,248.5	0.1	0.96	140.3
30	3,373.5	0.1	0.94	206.1
35	3,939.0	0.1	0.90	230.4
40	4,498.5	0.1	0.85	248.4
60	6,748.5	0.1	0.70	307.0

*γ is 112 lb/ft³ up to 3-ft depth and (50 + 62.5) below 3-ft depth.

(b) Determination of equivalent number of significant stress cycles
From the table on page 297, for an earthquake of magnitude 7.5, the number of significant stress cycles N_c is 20.
(c) Determination of stress causing liquefaction
The stress causing liquefaction is given by Eq. (8.9):

$$\left(\frac{\tau}{\sigma_0'}\right)_{\ell D_r} = \left(\frac{\sigma_{dc}}{2\sigma_a}\right)_{\ell 50} c_r \frac{D_r}{D_{50}} \tag{8.9}$$

For a relative density of 0 to 50 percent, the value of c_r is 0.57 (see p. 299).

From Figs. 8.17 and 8.18, the stress causing liquefaction for soil of $D_{50} = 0.2$ mm is as follows:

$$\left(\frac{\sigma_{dc}}{2\sigma_a}\right) = 0.242 \qquad \text{for 10 cycles}$$

$$= 0.210 \qquad \text{for 30 cycles}$$

Therefore, $\sigma_{dc}/2\sigma_a$ for 20 cycles is $\dfrac{0.242 + 0.210}{2} = 0.226$. The value of shear stress causing liquefaction is now calculated with the aid of Eq. (8.9) as follows:

$$\tau = \sigma_0' \times 0.226 \times 0.57 \times \frac{45}{50} = 0.1159\sigma_0'$$

where $$\sigma_0' = \Sigma\gamma_b h$$

Depth, ft	$\sigma_0' = \gamma_b\,{}^*h$, lb/ft^2	τ, lb/ft^2
10	686	79.53
20	1,186	137.50
30	1,686	195.47
35	1,936	224.45
40	2,186	253.44
60	3,186	369.37

*γ_b is 112 lb/ft^3 up to 3-ft depth and 50 lb/ft^3 below this depth.

Maximum shear stress and the shear stress causing liquefaction have been plotted with depth in Fig. 8.19. It will be seen that the maximum shear stress is larger than the stress causing liquefaction between 15 ft and 37.5 ft. Therefore, liquefaction occurs in this zone first. Since the pore pressures are dissipated in the upward direction, the soil may liquefy in the zone between 0 and 15 ft also. Below 37.5 ft, the maximum shear stress is smaller than the stress causing liquefaction. Therefore, liquefaction does not occur below this depth.

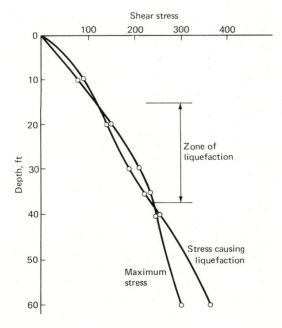

Figure 8.19 Plot of maximum shear stress causing liquefaction in Example 8.1.

8.9 VIBRATION-TABLE STUDIES

The liquefaction studies of large saturated sand samples excited on a shaking table appear to offer the following general advantages over the cyclic loading triaxial and simple shear tests commonly used (Finn, 1972).

1. Large homogeneous samples of saturated sand that simulate the field condition of K_0-consolidation may be prepared. Since the inertia effects of embedded instruments should be negligible for such large samples, internal strains and accelerations may be measured.
2. Uniform accelerations will be developed throughout the sample at low frequencies under plane-strain conditions that correspond to the propagation of shear waves in situ.
3. It is possible to use displacement, velocity, or acceleration modes of control to provide a wide range of acceleration records and frequencies for the shaking table.
4. It is possible to trace the actual pore-water pressure distribution in a large mass of saturated sand during liquefaction.
5. A visual examination of the sample during vibration is possible.

The chief disadvantages of shake-table tests on large samples of saturated sand are the initial high cost and the even higher cost of obtaining the data.

Matsuo and Ohara (1960), reported results of tests on saturated loose sands performed on a horizontal vibration table, 40 cm × 90 cm × 100 cm high. They found that a sudden increase in pore pressure occurred at a definite acceleration. This confirmed the concept of "critical acceleration." Also, the settlement-versus-acceleration plots were found to rise sharply, initially, and then to level off at higher values of acceleration.

Florin and Ivanov (1961) reported results of vibration tests on a 20-cm thick sand deposit, under both steady-state and transient vibrations. Their findings were:

1. If sand is subjected to shock loading, the whole stratum liquefies at the same time, while under steady-state vibrations, the liquefaction starts from the top and proceeds downward. In this case, initial vibrations liquefy the upper layer, which carries a comparatively light load. This reduces the overburden pressure on the lower layers and, as a result, the latter also passes into a liquefied state with subsequent vibrations. Thus, the zone of liquefaction spreads downward.
2. Some of their further studies showed that the theoretically computed time during which a 5-m thick deposit of fine sand remains in a liquefied state is 27 min. The time reduces to 2 min if a free-draining surcharge of 5 kg/cm^2 is acting. Further, with supplementary drainage at the base of the stratum, it ranges from 20 s to 15 s. This reduction in the time during which sand remains liquefied improves the stability of liquefied soil and of the structures built over it.

3. An increase in initial loads requires a considerable increase in the dynamic disturbance needed for the structure of the sand to completely collapse and to liquefy. As a result of many field observations, it was concluded that at depths ranging from about 10 m to 15 m below ground level, even very loose sand can hardly be liquefied. Therefore, surcharge with any material can be used as a method of reducing liquefaction.

Finn (1972) describes shake-table studies on a 9-ft × 6-ft table. The table was constrained to allow movement in one horizontal direction only and was actuated by a hydraulic ram mounted on a fixed base frame and connected to the table through a rigid link. The desired motions were transmitted to the table under the control of an MTS earthquake simulator control console. The table accelerations were measured with an accelerometer-amplifier system and recorded on a 12-channel light-beam oscillographic recorder and a storage oscilloscope.

Inside dimensions of the sample were 72 × 18 × 7 in, and surcharge pressures of 50 to 100 lb/in² could be applied. These pressures corresponded to 100 and 200 feet of saturated overburden.

The sample was prepared by depositing sand uniformly in water, carefully leveled to a 7-in height and sealed in a 0.01-mm-thick rubber membrane.

The uniformity of samples prepared in this manner was checked by recovering intact gelatin-impregnated samples and determining the distribution of the void ratio. The variation between the void ratio and the mean value in a sample was less than 2 percent.

Wedron silica sand is a uniformly graded, well-rounded, natural sand with these properties: specific gravity $S_S = 2.66$; maximum void ratio $e_{max} = 0.77$; minimum void ratio $e_{min} = 0.47$; and $D_{50} = 0.55$ mm.

The required total surcharge pressure on the sealed sample was applied by air pressure. The sample was then allowed to drain to a back pressure of 15 lb/in². When drainage was completed, the effective surcharge pressure on the sample was the total pressure minus the back pressure. The drainage line to the back-pressure container was then turned off and the sealed sample was ready for testing with the desired excitation.

Pore-water pressures during each test were monitored at five different locations in the middle of the sample (Fig. 8.20).

The degree of saturation was determined by comparing the pore-water pressure increase (measured in the sample by probes 1, 2, 3, and 4) with the total applied pressure (measured with an extra transducer and indicated by the initial tracing for probe 5). For 100 percent saturation, the pressure increase in the sample was equal to the total applied pressure.

The pore-pressure response curves shown in Fig. 8.20 are typical of those observed in all tests that resulted in liquefaction. Three features of the pore-water pressure behavior during liquefaction are important:

1. There was a rapid rise in the pore pressure at the beginning of the excitation and then a steady, gradual increase to about 70 percent of the effective

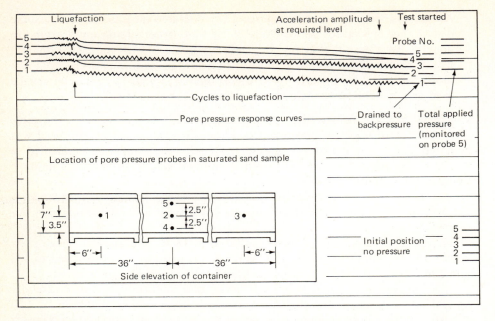

Figure 8.20 Typical pore-pressure response curves for initial liquefaction surcharge pressure of 1 lb/in^2 sinusoidal acceleration of ± 0.25 g at 2 hz. *(After Finn, 1972.)*

overburden pressure at the level of the probe. At this point, there was a rapid increase in pore-water pressure to a value close to the total overburden pressure, at which point liquefaction occurred. After liquefaction, the pore-water pressure decreased to the applied surcharge pressure.

2. The increase in pore pressure for each of the probes was about the same at any stage of the test; hence, the final total pore-pressure increase was approximately the same for each probe at liquefaction.

3. Liquefaction occurred at the same time for the three middle probes (2, 4, and 5) but lagged by up to a half cycle for the end probes (1 and 3).

The pore-water pressure data indicated that free field conditions existed over much of the sample.

A series of tests were carried out in which the surcharge pressure was varied from 0.25 to 10 lb/in^2 (corresponding to about 0.5 to 20 ft of saturated overburden) (Fig. 8.21). As the surcharge pressure increased, the number of cycles required to cause liquefaction of the saturated sand sample increased.

Examination of deformation of the sample on 8-mm movie films indicates that individual sand grains may move up to ± 1 in at liquefaction.

At a surcharge pressure of 2 lb/in^2 and a frequency of 2 Hz, acceleration to first liquefaction varied from ± 0.10 g to ± 0.50 g (Fig. 8.22). The resistance to liquefaction decreased with the increase in acceleration amplitude. Since the

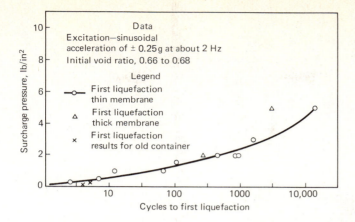

Figure 8.21 Effect of surcharge pressure on resistance to initial liquefaction in vibration-table studies. *(After Finn, 1972.)*

shear stresses induced in the sample are a function of the acceleration amplitude, this decrease in the resistance to liquefaction with increasing acceleration amplitude was as anticipated.

These results are in general qualitative agreement with the data obtained from triaxial and simple shear tests (Seed and Lee, 1966; Peacock and Seed, 1968). However, the surcharge loads were noninertial. Table 8.1 summarizes the different shake tables that have been used lately for studying liquefaction of soils and settlement of sands.

Typical results of Gupta (1979) and DeAlba (1976) will now be presented and then conclusions will be drawn on the use of shake-table tests for studying liquefaction potential.

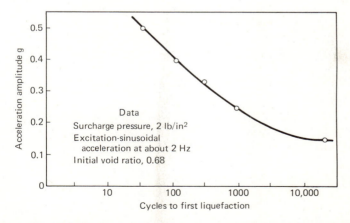

Figure 8.22 Effect of acceleration amplitude on resistance to liquefaction on vibration-table studies. *(After Finn, 1972.)*

Table 8.1 Inventory of shake tables

Serial	Size of table	Self weight	Sample size	Frequency, Hz	Amplitude, in	Maximum Accel- eration n	Maximum Velocity, in/s	Surcharge, lb/in²	Reference
1	9' × 6'	1,000 lb	6' × 1.5' × 7"	2	± 2	—	17	50†	Finn (1972)
2	10' × 7'	—	10' × 7' × 12"	4	—	0.3	—	2.43†	Seed and Silver‡ (1972)
3	30' × 13.3' × 5'	—	—	—	—	—	—	—	Kubo et al. (1975), Yoshimi (1977)
4	7.5' × 3.6'	—	(2' 2" × 1' 2" × 4")*	4	—	—	—	8†	DeAlba et al. (1976)
5	4' × 4'	—	4Φ × 3" (Area = 8.79 ft²)*	4, 6	—	—	—	2.56	Pyke et al. (1975)
6	3'3" × 2' × 2'4"	—	3'3" × 2' × 21"	5	—	0.6	—	5.5	Gupta (1979)

* Effective zone of free field stress.
† Noninertial surcharge.
‡ Report on settlement of sand.

At the University of Roorkee, a comprehensive program of liquefaction and settlement studies of sands was initiated in 1962 under the supervision of the author. The problem arose because of anticipated liquefaction of sands below 30-m-high Obra Dam (Krishna et al., 1967). Loose sand occurs up to about 24 m deep in the foundation of this dam. The design seismic coefficient (ratio of design acceleration to acceleration due to gravity) for the dam is about 10 percent. The ground, however, is likely to experience a few shocks of considerably larger intensity (Krishna and Prakash, 1968).

Tenughat Dam is 55 m high and a loose deposit in the bed of the river extends to about 15 m in depth. The design acceleration in this case was also 10 percent of acceleration due to gravity (Prakash and Gupta, 1967b, 1968a).

The problem at Ukai was a little different. The proposed dam was to be an 80.77-m-high earthfill in the river portion (Prakash and Gupta, 1968b). There was a standing pool of water created by the backwater of an existing weir. Therefore, it was decided to construct a 6.71-m-high sand platform under water. The deposited sand mass was loose and the design seismic coefficient for this site was 0.05. Since this platform constituted a part of the main dam, it was necessary to study the possibility of its liquefaction or its undergoing excessive settlements.

In still another case, loose fine sand, similar to Solani sand, existed up to a depth of 24 m. The design seismic coefficient was 0.15 g horizontally and 0.1 g vertically.

The problem, therefore, in all of the above cases was almost identical. The grain-size distributions of the four sands are shown in Fig. 8.23. Other properties of the four sands are listed in Table 8.2. All of the sands belonged to the SP

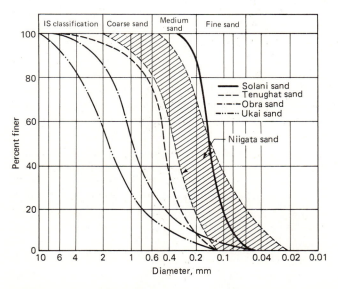

Figure 8.23 Grain-size distribution of sands tested at Roorkee. *(After Gupta, 1979.)*

Table 8.2 Properties of sands*

Particulars	Ukai sand	Obra sand	Tenughat sand	Solani sand
Specific gravity of grains S_s	2.76	2.61	2.62	2.59
Uniformity coefficient C_u	5.7	5.45	2.27	1.9
Coefficient of curvature C_c	1.2	1.42	1.24	1.07
Grain size D_{50}	1.8 mm	1.0 mm	0.47 mm	0.15 mm
Maximum void ratio e_{max}	0.57	0.68	0.79	0.86
Minimum void ratio e_{min}	0.34	0.40	0.49	0.48
Initial relative density D_{Ri}	40	28	20	20
For initial liquefaction $\frac{h'_w}{z}$ (Eq. 8.5)	1.18	1.00	0.96	0.89
Grain shape	Rounded	Angular	Sub-angular	Angular

* After Gupta (1979).

group, according to the Indian Standard on Classification of Soils.† These sands vary considerably in grain size and grading. A microscopic examination of the four sands is shown in Fig. 8.24.

A series of comprehensive tests were performed on samples by simulating initial field conditions with respect to relative density and initial effective surcharge. This was done by depositing sand in a container mounted on a horizontal steady-state vibration table.

The tests were performed on the table, which was driven by a 3-hp motor and which had the following characteristics:

Maximum horizontal acceleration	2 g
Frequency	0–20 Hz
Amplitude of motion	0–20 mm peak to peak
Platform size	60 cm × 105 cm

Figure 8.25 shows the time required for the increase and dissipation of excess pore-water pressure during vibrations of Solani sand at 10 percent *g*. It was observed that there was no change in pore-water pressure in the first three cycles and that it increased to the maximum in about 10 cycles. The maximum pore pressure for Solani sand (a fine sand) remained constant for about 35 s (175 cycles) and then it started dissipating slowly. Since this sample represents a condition near the surface in the field, pore pressures may be expected to remain constant for about 35 s before they start dissipating during an earthquake.

Figure 8.26 shows the maximum pore pressure versus acceleration for 10 cycles at a relative density of 25 percent and at depths of 25 cm, 15.5 cm, and 6 cm from the surface. The ratio of excess pore pressure $u = \gamma_w h'_w$ to the initial effective overburden pressure $\bar{\sigma}_i$ is also plotted. A value of one for this ratio represents initial liquefaction.

It can be seen from Fig. 8.26 that pore pressure increases initially with an increase in acceleration and becomes constant at all three depths with further

† The classification is SP also according to the Unified Soil Classification System.

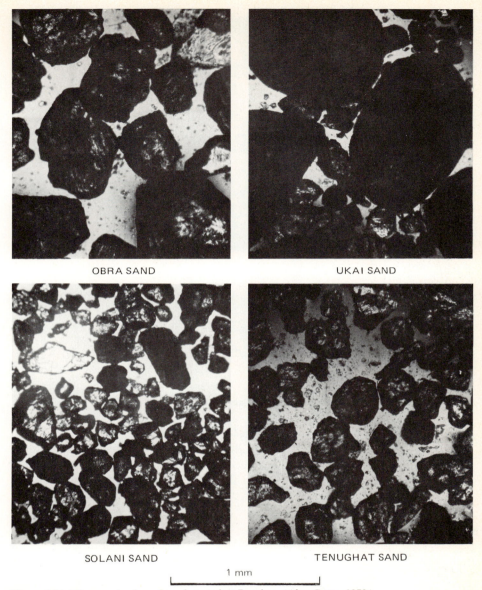

OBRA SAND · UKAI SAND

SOLANI SAND · TENUGHAT SAND

1 mm

Figure 8.24 Microscopic view of sands tested at Roorkee. *(After Gupta, 1979.)*

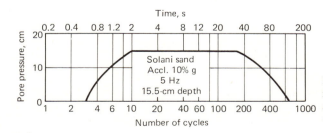

Figure 8.25 Pore pressure vs. number of cycles in Solani sand at 10% g acceleration. *(After Gupta, 1979.)*

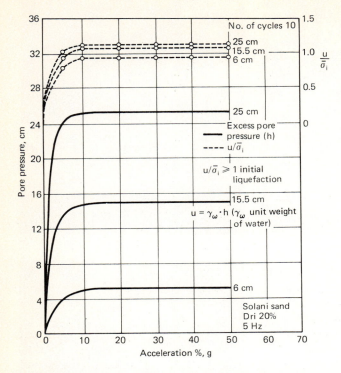

Figure 8.26 Pore pressure vs. acceleration on Solani sand. *(After Gupta, 1979.)*

increases in acceleration. Also, with accelerations larger than about 5 percent g, the values of $u/\bar{\sigma}_i$ are close to unity at all three depths. This showed that initial liquefaction had occurred in the soil mass. It was also observed that the sand/water mixture started ejecting in the form of a fountain up to about a centimeter above the top surface of the sample.

Effect of Coarseness

Figure 8.27 shows the time required for the increase and dissipation of excess pore-water pressure during vibration of Tenughat, Obra, and Ukai sands at 10 percent g. The maximum pore-water pressure developed in about 6 to 7 cycles. It started dissipating immediately after attaining a maximum value. The total time required for dissipation was about 6 s for Ukai sand and 20 s for Obra and

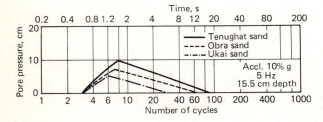

Figure 8.27 Pore pressure vs. number of cycles for different sands. *(After Gupta, 1979.)*

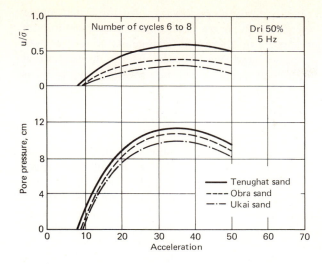

Figure 8.28 Pore pressure at 25-cm depth vs. acceleration in vibration-table studies in three sands. *(After Gupta, 1979.)*

Tenughat sands. The corresponding value for Solani sand was 120 s; it remained constant for about 35 s. Thus, it can be seen that the time required for dissipation decreases with increased coarseness.

Figure 8.28 shows the increases in pore pressure with acceleration for Tenughat, Obra, and Ukai sands at a 25-cm depth and at a relative density of 50 percent. The values of $u/\bar{\sigma}_i$ are also plotted in this figure to indicate the extent of liquefaction. It can be seen that pore pressure increases initially with an increase in acceleration and starts decreasing with further increases in acceleration after attaining a maximum value. The values of $u/\bar{\sigma}_i$ are much less than one in this case. It can also be seen that there was no change in the deposit when it was vibrated at an acceleration below a certain value. This suggests that there is a threshold value of acceleration below which sand is not disturbed. A similar phenomenon was reported earlier also (Bazant, 1965; Maslov, 1957). Table 8.3 shows the threshold values of acceleration obtained in these investigations for Tenughat, Obra, and Ukai sands at 40 percent and 50 percent relative density.

A marked difference has been observed between the behaviors of saturated fine sand and coarse sand under vibrations. In the case of fine sand, the maximum pore pressure remained constant with increased acceleration after initial liquefaction occurred, while in the case of coarse sand, it started decreas-

Table 8.3 Threshold values of accelerations

Sand	Threshold value of acceleration at 5 Hz	
	D_{Ri} 40%	D_{Ri} 50%
Tenughat	5% g	9% g
Obra	4.5% g	9% g
Ukai	—	9.5% g

ing after attaining a maximum value. Also, the pore-water pressure lasted longer in the case of fine sands as compared with coarse sand. Since the maximum pore pressures were found to decrease with increased coarseness and the pore pressures dissipated quickly in coarse sand, the chances of large movements of structures on coarse sands are less. This suggests that the problem may not be as severe in coarse sand as it is in fine sand.

Effect of Relative Density

Figure 8.29 shows the effect of relative density on an increase in pore pressure at 10 percent g for Solani sand. It can be observed that, with increased initial relative density, the excess pore pressure decreases under vibrations. In this case, no pore-pressure increase was observed when initial relative density equaled 62 percent. The corresponding values of initial relative density for accelerations of 20 percent g, 40 percent g, and 50 percent g were 62.5 percent, 66 percent, and 66.5 percent, respectively, for this sand (Gupta, 1979). Table 8.4 shows the relative density beyond which no pore-pressure increase was observed for all the sands used in this investigation. Thus, the chances of liquefaction were reduced with increases in the initial relative density. These sands may not liquefy if relative density is more than 65 percent.

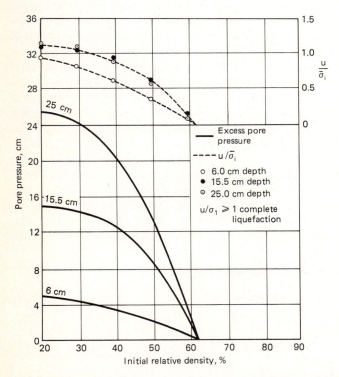

Figure 8.29 Pore pressure vs. initial relative density in Solani sand. *(After Gupta, 1979.)*

Table 8.4 Relative density beyond which no excess pore pressure develops*

Acceleration, (g) percent	Initial relative density beyond which no pore pressure increases during vibrations at 5 Hz			
	Solani sand	Tenughat sand	Obra sand	Ukai sand
10	62.0	52.0	51.5	50.5
20	62.5	61.5	60.0	59.5
40	66.0	64.0	62.5	62.0
50	66.5	65.0	64.0	63.0

*After Gupta (1979).

Studies With Initial Surcharge

The development and dissipation of pore pressure with an initial effective surcharge of 0.023 kg/cm^2 at 10 percent g for Solani sand is shown in Fig. 8.30. This surcharge corresponds to a 23-cm-thick soil cover above the top of the specimen in the tank. Thus, conditions at 25-cm depth in the tank correspond to a depth of 0.48 m in the field if the submerged unit weight of the deposit is considered to be one. The maximum pore pressure developed in 10 to 12 cycles and remained constant for about 90 s (450 cycles) before it started to dissipate. In the laboratory, partial drainage was provided, but undrained conditions might prevail in the field. Therefore, it is likely that the pore pressures may remain constant for more than 90 s in the field if vibrations continue for that time. The corresponding time was 35 s in tests without surcharge. In most cases, however, earthquakes in alluvial deposits have been observed to last from 20 to 40 s. Therefore, it is expected that excess pore-water pressure will remain constant for the duration of the earthquake.

Similar tests were performed with different values of initial effective surcharge. Test results in Fig. 8.31 show the effect of overburden pressure on the increase in pore pressure. The surcharge was provided by dead weights. The pore pressure increased with effective overburden pressure, up to about 200 g/cm^2, but further increases in effective overburden caused it to start decreas-

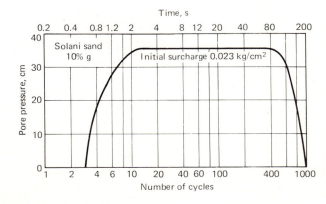

Figure 8.30 Pore pressure vs. number of cycles with initial surcharge. *(After Gupta, 1979.)*

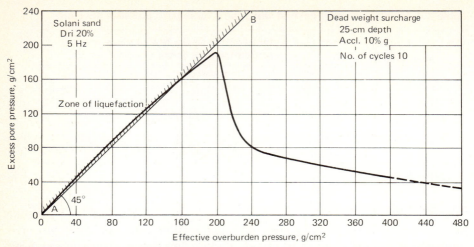

Figure 8.31 Excess pore pressure vs. effective overburden pressure on Solani sand. *(After Gupta, 1979.)*

ing. Line AB represents initial liquefaction. Although sand has been observed to completely liquefy at smaller surcharge intensities, the chances of liquefaction are reduced with increased surcharge intensity. It can also be seen in this figure that the pore pressure at an effective overburden of 480 g/cm² is about 30 cm. This means that only about 6 percent of intergranular stress is transferred to the pore water, which is of no great practical significance.

DeAlba, Seed and Chan (1976) performed liquefaction studies on a bed of sand, 90 in × 42 in × 4 in deep (2300 mm × 1100 mm × 100 mm) placed on a shaking table. A rubber membrane was placed over the sand to prevent drainage, and an inertial reaction mass (with a flexible base to provide uniform seating on the sand but a rigid lateral resistance) was placed on top of the sand. This reaction mass consisted of an open grill with the compartments fitted with a ballast of steel shot. Horizontal movements of the base thus produced cyclic stress conditions in the sand; the dimensions were selected to provide a free-field condition in most of the central section of the sample. By capping the sample container with a rigid box, air pressures could be applied to the sand to produce confinement representative of different depths in the ground.

The sand tested was Monterey no. 0 sand, a uniform sand with a mean grain diameter of about 0.36 mm (0.014 in) and a uniformity coefficient of 1.5.

Figure 8.32 shows a normalized plot of $\Delta u / \sigma_0'$ versus N_c / N_1, in which Δu = the pore pressure increase after N_c stress cycles, σ_0' = the initial effective normal stress, and N_1 = the number of cycles required to cause initial liquefaction for the test for a relative density of 54 percent and 68 percent.

The cyclic shear stress at the base of the sample is given from the relationship

$$\tau_h = \frac{W}{g} a_m \tag{8.10}$$

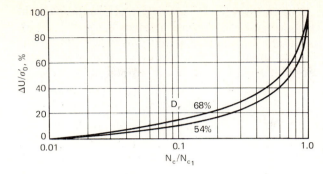

Figure 8.32 Normalized dynamic pore-pressure curves from a shake-table test. *(After DeAlba, Seed, and Chan, 1976.)*

in which W = the total pressure exerted on the base by the specimen and the inertia mass, a_m = the peak acceleration of the uniform cyclic motion, and g = the acceleration of gravity. The values of τ_h determined in Eq. (8.10) were corrected for the effects of small volume changes that take place in the testing system (termed *compliance effects*).

The corrected relationship between τ_h/σ_0' and the number of cycles required to cause initial liquefaction is shown in Fig. 8.33. This is considered to be a good representation of the results that would be obtained in an ideal noncompliant testing system for shaking in one horizontal direction.

The stress data in Fig. 8.33 were compared with simple shear test results of Seed and Peacock (1971) for a relative density of 50 percent. Where test data were not determined at this relative density, they were corrected to this condition by using the observation that stress ratios required to cause liquefaction are, for practical purposes, directly proportional to the relative density, up to relative densities of about 75 percent.

It would seem that there is very good agreement between the two sets of results. This indicates that test errors due to stress concentrations in small-scale tests may not be as large as has often been claimed (Castro, 1975), or they are counterbalanced by some other feature of the test.

It has already been shown in Fig. 8.12 that cyclic-loading triaxial tests lead to different stress ratios that cause initial liquefaction than do cyclic simple shear tests. A similar conclusion was drawn by comparing the test results from shake-table tests and the triaxial tests of Seed and Lee (1966).

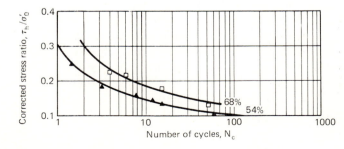

Figure 8.33 Corrected τ_h/σ_0' vs. N_c for initial liquefaction from shake-table studies. *(After DeAlba, Seed, and Chan, 1976.)*

In the field, the motion is multidirectional. The effects of multidirectional shaking were determined by comparing the volume changes occurring in dry sand under one-directional and multidirectional shaking conditions (Seed, Pyke, et al., 1975 and 1978). Such studies indicated that the stress ratios determined for one-directional shaking should be reduced by about 10 percent to produce results representative of multidirectional shaking conditions. Accordingly, the correction factors C_r in Eq. (8.8) should be reduced in the same proportion to determine stress ratios applicable to field conditions.

8.10 LIQUEFACTION BEHAVIOR OF DENSE SANDS

Figure 8.4 shows that dense sand increases in volume in drained tests. Therefore, if such a sand is tested in undrained shear, the pore-water pressure is negative, which increases effective stress and results in a higher shear strength. This is in accordance with the concept of the critical void ratio of Casagrande (1936). However, Seed and Lee (1966) and Lee and Seed (1967) appear to have demonstrated that dense sand does liquefy.

Typical results of a cyclic loading test on a sample of dense sand with a relative density of about 78 percent are shown in Fig. 8.34. In this case, the sample was initially consolidated under a confining pressure of 2 kg/cm² and then subjected to a cyclic deviator stress, σ_{dp}, of 0.7 kg/cm². The changes in stress, strain, and pore-water pressure, with time, are shown in Fig. 8.34a. As in the case of loose sand, the sample withstood a number of stress cycles with no

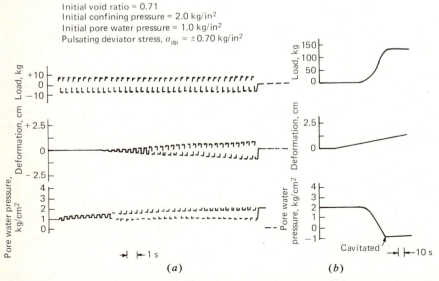

Figure 8.34 (a) Cyclic triaxial test on a dense sand. (b) Static test after initial liquefaction (*After Seed and Lee, 1966.*)

significant deformations. However, after about 12 stress cycles the pore water reached values equal to the confining pressure at certain instants during each stress cycle, and the strain amplitude increased markedly. However, in contrast to loose sand, the strain amplitude increased relatively slowly as the number of stress cycles increased.

The changes in axial strain amplitude, and the pore-pressure changes corrected to constant-mean-extreme-principal-stress conditions, are shown graphically in Fig. 8.35. After about 13 stress cycles, the pore-water pressure in the sample had increased to a value equal to the confining pressure at those stages in the cycle when the deviator stress was zero. However, the pore pressure dropped as the deviator stress amplitude increased, so that although the sample might be considered to have liquefied at some stages of the test, it was able to withstand the applied stresses without significant strains developing. In fact, although the sample might be considered to have liquefied after 13 cycles in the sense that at some stage in the test the effective confining pressure was zero, the strain amplitude did not exceed 10 percent after an additional 20 cycles. Thus, there was no sudden failure of the sample as in the case of loose sand.

The effect of a static stress application to a sample of relatively dense sand after cyclic mobility is shown in Fig. 8.34b. The dense sand begins to dilate and to resist deformation at application of much smaller strain (about 5 percent). The behavior of dense sand after initial liquefaction is quite different from that of loose sand.

DeAlba, Seed, and Chan (1976) report that when dense sand was tested in an isotropically consolidated, cyclic triaxial compression test, accurate data on the strains that developed after initial liquefaction was reached, were difficult to obtain due to necking in the test specimen. The large-scale shaking-table tests provided data on the behavior of dense sand at relatively high stress ratios and with large strain values.

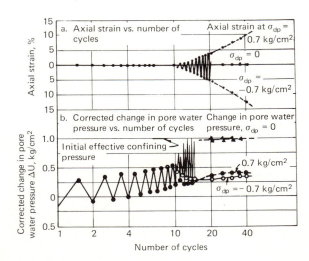

Figure 8.35 Typical pulsating load test on a dense sand. (*After Seed and Lee, 1966.*)

From the measured displacements of the inertia mass during shaking, average single-amplitude cyclic shear strain values γ could be obtained using the relationship

$$\text{shear strain } \gamma = \pm \frac{\Delta}{2h} \tag{8.11}$$

in which Δ = the peak-to-peak amplitude of the relative displacement and h = the specimen height.

The cyclic displacements increased rapidly when initial liquefaction was reached. However, they did not build up indefinitely, but were observed to reach a limiting value that depended on the tendency of the specimen to dilate as shear strain increased. This, in turn, was in proportion to the relative density of the specimen.

Figure 8.36 shows the relationships between cyclic stress ratio and the number of stress cycles required to produce average shear strains of 5 percent, 10 percent, 15 percent, and 20 percent calculated from the displacements measured in the shaking-table tests.

The data in Fig. 8.36 are replotted as values of cyclic stress ratio τ_h / σ_0' causing initial liquefaction, or different levels of shear strain, in 10 cycles versus relative densities (Fig. 8.37a). The data indicated that each of the curves is asymptotic to a certain relative density value, and that a curve of limiting shear strain versus relative density might, therefore, be established as shown in Fig. 7.37b.

Figures 8.36 and 8.37 show that for sand at any given relative density, there was a limited amount of shear strain that could be developed regardless of the applied stress ratio *or the number of stress cycles* unless the full undrained

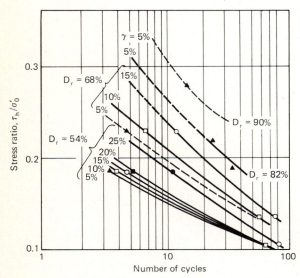

Figure 8.36 Relationship between τ_h / σ_0' and number of cycles causing different levels of strain. *(After DeAlba, Seed, and Chan, 1976.)*

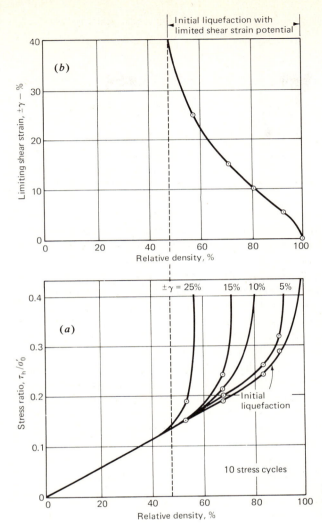

Figure 8.37 Limiting shear strains —10 stress cycles. *(After DeAlba, Seed, and Chan, 1976.)*

strength of the soil was exceeded (Seed 1976). For relative densities of less than about 45 percent, the application of cyclic stress ratios that were high enough to cause initial liquefaction also caused extremely high and probably unlimited strains in the soil. This corresponds to liquefaction. However, for relative densities greater than about 45 percent, the application of stress ratios and enough cycles to cause initial liquefaction would result in only limited shear strain. The limiting strain potential decreases with increasing relative density.

Gupta (1979) reports test data on dense sand at a relative density of 70 percent and 80 percent on all four sands. Figure 8.38 shows the test results. It is observed that no pore-pressure change in the sand occurred at low acceleration

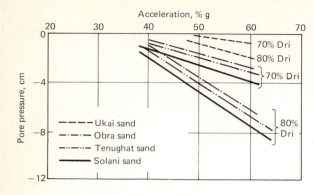

Figure 8.38 Pore pressure vs. acceleration on four sands in dense condition. *(After Gupta, 1979.)*

of less than about 35 percent g and the sand was not disturbed when vibrated below this acceleration. However, when the intensity of accelerations increased, negative pore pressure developed and dilation of the sample was observed. Under these conditions, it is obvious that liquefaction will not occur. However, the possibility of some reduction in shear strength from vibrations is not ruled out because of the reduction in internal friction angle, if such a reduction did occur. No pore-pressure increase was observed beyond the 65 percent initial relative density; a negative pore-water pressure with dilation was observed when the sand had a relative density of more than 70 percent.

In dense sand and under undrained shear, negative pore pressures develop resulting in increased shear strength, while under cyclic stress, the initial effective confining pressures become zero, as in loose sand that decreases in volume. Casagrande (1976) advocates that results similar to the ones observed by Seed and Lee (1966) be viewed with caution. Dense sand, according to him, would not show this behavior in the field, and, hence, sands above a certain value of relative density would not liquefy in the field. Seed (1976) defines this state of soil as *"initial liquefaction with limited strain potential"* (p. 276). Casagrande (1975, 1976) and Castro (1975) have termed this state as *"cyclic mobility."* The fact still remains that dense sands do not liquefy in the field.

8.11 FIELD TESTS

Florin and Ivanov (1961) proposed a field blasting test to predict liquefaction (Sec. 8.1).

Field blast tests were performed at Obra and Tenughat Dam sites under the supervision of the author (Krishna and Prakash, 1968; Prakash and Gupta, 1967*a*, 1970*b*). The purposes of these tests were:

1. To ascertain if these sands would liquefy under simulated earthquake loading
2. To compare the field results with those obtained in the laboratory
3. To ascertain if the sands at the two sites could be economically compacted, by blasting if necessary

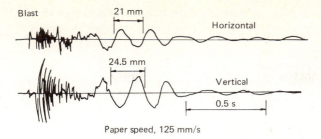

Blast   21 mm   Horizontal

24.5 mm   Vertical

0.5 s

Paper speed, 125 mm/s

Figure 8.39 Record of acceleration for 1 kg (60%) gelatin at a distance of 50 m from point of observation at Obra Dam site. *(After Krishna and Prakash, 1968.)*

Tests at both of the sites were performed in the beds of the rivers. Predetermined charges, ranging from 1 kg to 3 kg, along with electric detonators were installed at predetermined depths, usually 6 m to 8 m in cased bore holes. The holes were later filled with sand and the casing was withdrawn. Lead wires from the detonators were connected with the blaster so that the charges might be fired at any desired moment. Acceleration records were taken at distances of 10 m to 50 m from the blast point. The amplification and recording was done by Brush Universal Amplifier and Brush Pen Recorder. The pickups were embedded about 20 cm into the ground in such a manner that one of these recorded horizontal acceleration and the other vertical acceleration.

A typical record of ground vibrations is shown in Fig. 8.39. Figure 8.40 shows acceleration versus distance for a 1-kg blast at the Obra Dam site.

In an artificial blast of this kind, the longitudinal waves (direct, surface, refracted, or reflected longitudinal waves) dominate the ground vibrations. In such a case, the shear produced in the elastic medium is small compared with the change in volume; hence, in this case, most of the wave energy was propagated in the form of longitudinal waves. Since their angle of emergence at

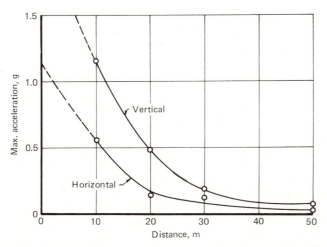

Figure 8.40 Acceleration vs. distance for 1-kg blast at Obra Dam site. *(After Krishna and Prakash, 1968.)*

Table 8.5 Maximum increase in pore pressure after the blasting of a charge of 2 kg*

Depth of piezometer, m	2.5 m from center of blasting		5.0 m from center of blasting		10 m from center of blasting		15 m from center of blasting		30 m from center of blasting	
	h'_w cm	% of effective stress	h'_w cm	% of effective stress	h'_w cm	% of effective stress	h'_w cm	% of effective stress	h'_w cm	% of effective stress
2.5	170	48.0	132	37.0	69	19.0	49	14.0	21	6
5.5	181	29.0	130	20.5	55	8.7	18	2.8	0	0
8.5	140	15.2	80	8.8	10	1.1	0	0	0	0

*After Krishna and Prakash (1968).

short distances of observation deviates only slightly from vertical, the vertical acceleration of ground motion is more than the horizontal acceleration. As distance increases, the difference between horizontal and vertical acceleration gradually diminishes.

The pore pressures and settlement observations at the time of blasting were also taken. Table 8.5 gives the change in pore pressure as a percentage of the initial intergranular stress from 2-kg blasts.

The maximum observed pore pressure at a depth of 2.5 m and at a distance of 2.5 m from the blast point is 48 percent of the initial intergranular stress. The pore pressure increases when projected to the blast point. Figure 8.41 shows that the increase in pore pressure is about 60 percent of the initial intergranular stress. For initial liquefaction, the increase in pore pressure should equal the intergranular stress. Hence, the Obra Dam sand did not undergo initial liquefaction in the field. The horizontal acceleration in this case was about 3.36 g and the vertical acceleration was 5.2 g (Krishna and Prakash, 1968).

It will be noticed that the Obra Dam sand did not liquefy under such heavy acceleration. But it must be remembered that there was only one impulse of shock loading. Therefore, any conclusion regarding the behavior of this sand under earthquake loading can be arrived at only if the effect of number of cycles is also accounted for.

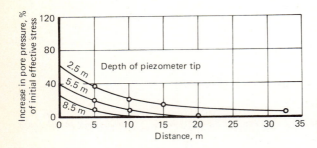

Figure 8.41 Pore pressure vs. distance at Obra Dam site with 2-kg blast. *(After Krishna and Prakash, 1968.)*

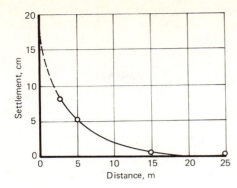

Figure 8.42 Settlement vs. distance at Obra Dam site with 2-kg blast. *(After Krishna and Prakash, 1968.)*

Since series blasting was not resorted to in the field, information on the effects of number of cycles on liquefaction was obtained from laboratory tests.

Figure 8.42 shows the settlement with distance due to a 2-kg blast. The acceleration at the blast point was 3.36 g (horizontal) and 5.2 g (vertical) and settlement at the blast point was 17.5 cm. Assuming that the depth of soil contributing settlement is 6 + 2, that is, 8 m.

Percentage of settlement (for a blast giving a single pulse)

$$= \frac{17.5 \times 100}{800} = 2.2\%$$

Considering that vertical acceleration is half as effective as horizontal acceleration away from critical value (Prakash and Gupta, 1967c), which for coarse sand is likely to be less than 1 g, effective horizontal acceleration is $(3.36 + \frac{5.2}{2}) g = (3.36 + 2.6) g = 5.96 g$.

Figure 8.43 is a plot of horizontal acceleration versus percent settlement of Obra sand for different cycles of motion (Krishna and Prakash, 1967).

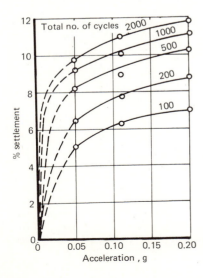

Figure 8.43 Acceleration vs. percent settlement from laboratory test on Obra sand. *(Krishna and Prakash, 1967.)*

Table 8.6 Values of acceleration and number of cycles of motion for 2.2 percent settlement*

Acceleration, g percent	No. of cycles
1.50	100
0.75	200
0.50	50

*After Krishna and Prakash (1967).

From this figure, a settlement of 2.2 percent occurs with the sets of acceleration and cycles of motion in Table 8.6.

These values are plotted in Fig. 8.44 along with the field value of 5.96 g and 1 cycle.

No liquefaction of the sand occurred either in the laboratory or in the field.

The design acceleration for the Obra Dam site is 0.10 g for the dam and 0.05 g for other structures. The maximum ground acceleration at such a site during an earthquake may reach 0.20 g in an extreme case. However, there are likely to be only a few cycles of higher acceleration. Also, there are usually a large

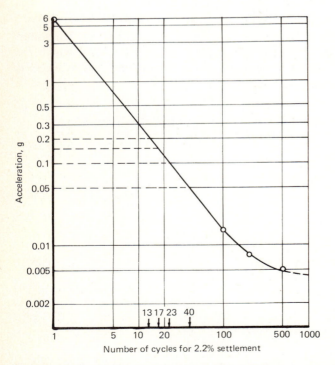

Figure 8.44 Acceleration vs. number of cycles for 2.2 percent settlement for Obra sand. *(Krishna and Prakash, 1968.)*

Table 8.7 Number of cycles to which Obra Dam site may be subjected in its lifetime*

Number of earthquakes	Maximum ground acceleration	Total no. of cycles of 5% equivalent to† horizontal acceleration
1	0.20 g, 5 cycles + 0.15 g, 10 cycles + 0.10 g, 20 cycles + 0.05 g, 50 cycles	1(16 + 24 + 35 + 50) = 125
2	0.15 g, 10 cycles + 0.10 g, 20 cycles + 0.05 g, 30 cycles	2(24 + 35 + 30) = 178
3	0.10 g, 10 cycles + 0.05 g, 20 cycles	3(18 + 20) = 114
10	0.05 g, 10 cycles	10 × 10 = 100
	Total number of cycles of 0.05 g	say 500 cycles of 0.05 g

*After Krishna and Prakash, 1968.

†Equivalent cycles of 0.05 g have been computed from Fig. 8.44. For 2.2% settlement at 20% g, no. of cycles = 13. For 2.2% settlement at 5% g, no. of cycles = 40. Therefore, 5 cycles of 0.20 g ≡ $\left(\dfrac{40}{13} \times 5\right)$, that is, 16 cycles of 0.05 g.

number of cycles of acceleration that are smaller than the design acceleration. Based on this concept, it is assumed that, in the life of the dam, it will be subjected to the number of cycles given in Table 8.7.

The settlement of a deposit with an initial relative density of about 20 percent for 500 cycles of 0.05 g is about 8 percent, that is, $24 \times \dfrac{8}{100} = 1.92$ m (Fig. 8.43).

The average relative densities of Obra sand may be taken as in Table 8.8.

The total settlement of a deposit with variable density is as given below (Krishna, Prakash, et al., 1967):

1. Maximum settlement of a deposit with 30 percent initial relative density is about 80 percent of the maximum settlement with 20 percent initial relative density.

Table 8.8 Variation of average relative density with depth of deposit at Obra Dam site

Relative density %	Thickness of deposit, m
30	3.6
50	12.0
70	8.4
Total depth of overburden	24.0

2. Maximum settlement of a deposit with 50 percent initial relative density is about 67 percent of the maximum settlement with 20 percent initial relative density.
3. Maximum settlement of a deposit with 70 percent initial relative density is about 25 percent of the maximum settlement with 20 percent initial relative density.

The total settlement of a deposit of 20 percent initial relative density with 5 percent acceleration and 500 cycles is 8 percent.

The total settlement of a deposit of 30 percent initial relative density with 5 percent acceleration and 500 cycles is 6.4 percent.

The total settlement of a deposit of 50 percent initial relative density with 5 percent acceleration and 500 cycles is 5.33 percent.

The total settlement of a deposit of 70 percent initial relative density with 5 percent acceleration and 500 cycles is 2 percent.

Hence,

$$\text{Total settlement} = \frac{3.6 \times 6.4}{100} + \frac{12 \times 5.33}{100} + \frac{8.4 \times 2}{100}$$
$$= 0.230 + 0.640 + 0.168$$
$$= 1.038 \text{ m, say } 1.1 \text{ m}$$

This settlement is not excessive and is not likely to occur during one earthquake.

Figure 8.45 shows acceleration versus number of cycles for 2.4 percent of settlement of Tenughat sand. This figure was obtained in an identical manner to that employed for Fig. 8.44 and similar conclusions were derived (Prakash and Gupta, 1970b).

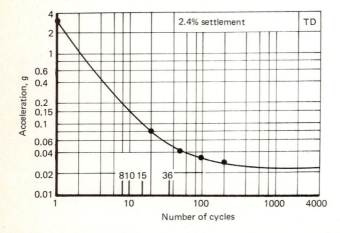

Figure 8.45 Acceleration vs. number of cycles for 2.4 percent settlement for Tenughat sand. *(After Prakash and Gupta, 1970b.)*

It may be appropriate to mention here that field blasting tests are not popular in the United States at present. However, it is believed that such testing techniques may become popular in the future. Also, their interpretation may need refinement.

The standard penetration test data and their correlation with soil behavior where liquefaction had occurred and with sites where liquefaction had not occurred have also engaged the attention of several researchers. Following the Niigata earthquake, Kishida (1966), Kuizumi (1966), and Ohasaki (1966) studied the areas in Niigata where liquefaction had and had not occurred and developed criteria for differentiating between liquefiable and nonliquefiable conditions in that city, based primarily on the standard penetration resistance of the sand deposits (Seed, 1976, 1979). The results of these studies for Niigata are shown in Fig. 8.46. These results are not likely to be applicable to other areas where shaking intensities may be stronger or where water tables may be at different depths than those in the Niigata area.

Subsequently, a more comprehensive collection of site conditions at various locations, where there was some evidence of either the presence or absence of liquefaction, was presented by Seed and Peacock (1971). To determine the relationship between field values of cyclic stress ratio at these locations, they used τ_h / σ_0' (in which $\tau_h =$ the average horizontal shear stress induced by an earthquake and $\sigma_0' =$ the initial effective overburden pressure on the soil layer

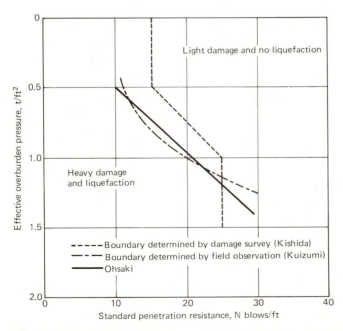

Figure 8.46 Analysis of liquefaction potential at Niigata for earthquake of June 16, 1964. *(After Seed, 1979.)*

• Liquefaction, stress ratio based on estimated acceleration
● Liquefaction, stress ratio based on good acceleration data
○ No liquefaction, stress ratio based on estimated acceleration
⊙ No liquefaction, stress ratio based on good acceleration data

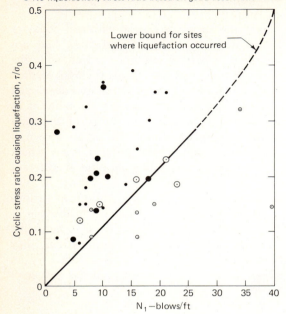

Figure 8.47 Correlation between stress ratio causing liquefaction in the field and penetration resistance of sand. *(After Seed, Mori, and Chan, 1977.)*

involved) and the relative density of the sand (as determined from the standard penetration resistance and its correlation with relative density). This collection of field cases has subsequently been supplemented by a few additional site studies (Christian and Swiger, 1975) to determine other correlations between liquefaction-producing parameters and penetration resistance. These data are shown in Fig. 8.47 (Seed, Mori et al., 1977). Values of stress ratios known to be associated with some evidence of liquefaction or no liquefaction in the field are plotted as a function of the corrected average penetration resistance N_1 of the sand deposit. In this form of presentation, N is the measured penetration resistance corrected to an effective overburden pressure of 1 t/ft². This can be determined using

$$N_1 = C_N N \tag{8.12}$$

in which C_N, a correction factor, may be determined by the relationship proposed by Peck, Hanson and Thornburn (1974):

$$C_N = 0.77 \log_{10} \frac{20}{\bar{p}} \tag{8.13}$$

where $\bar{p}$ = effective overburden pressure in t/ft^2 at the elevation of the penetration test.

The maximum value of C_N is 2.0. The cyclic stress ratio causing liquefaction at any depth in the ground can be determined with acceptable accuracy from Eq. (8.7).

Thus, for any given site and a given value of maximum ground surface acceleration, the possibility of liquefaction can readily be obtained on an empirical basis, with the aid of this chart. This is done by determining the appropriate values of N_1 for the sand layers involved, reading off a lower bound value of τ_{av}/σ_0' for sites where some evidence of liquefaction is known to have occurred (such as the line shown in Fig. 8.47), and comparing this value with that induced by the design earthquake for the site under investigation [computed from Eq. (8.7)].

This procedure suffers from the following limitations (Seed, 1979):

1. The lower boundary of conditions causing cyclic mobility or liquefaction at high values of τ_{av}/σ_0' needs to be more clearly defined with more field data.
2. Empirical charts of this type do not take into account all of the significant factors affecting liquefaction, such as duration of shaking and magnitude of the earthquake.
3. Penetration resistance may not be an appropriate index of the cyclic mobility characteristics of soils.
4. The standard penetration resistance of a soil cannot always be reliably determined in the field, and its value may vary significantly, depending on the boring and sampling conditions used in the determination.

Seed (1979) reported that this lower boundary line is strongly supported by data from Niigata, Japan, where liquefaction was probably more extensive than in any other recent earthquake, and by recent data obtained from investigations in China, where extensive studies of earthquakes and their effects have been recently found to have been under way for many years (State Capital Construction Commission, 1974).

For earthquakes with lesser magnitudes and involving shorter durations of shaking, values taken from Fig. 8.47 would be quite conservative, and stress ratios for earthquakes of magnitude 6 might be expected to be at least 25 percent higher than those indicated by the lower boundary line in Fig. 8.47 (Seed, Arango, and Chan, 1975).

It is of interest to note that for earthquakes of magnitude 7.5, the lower boundary value of the stress ratio required to cause cyclic mobility or liquefaction, based on this field-data approach, is approximately expressed by $(\tau_{av}/\sigma_0')_1 \approx N_1/90$ for values of N_1 up to about 35 bpf or cyclic stress ratios up to about 0.4.

Ohasaki (1970) describes a useful Japanese rule of thumb that says liquefaction is not a problem if the blow count from a standard penetration test exceeds twice the depth of the sample in meters.

8.12 LIQUEFACTION ANALYSIS FROM STANDARD PENETRATION DATA

There is a scarcity of reliable field data on the liquefaction potential of sands with high densities or high penetration resistance values and subjected to high cyclic stress ratios by earthquake ground motions. Such data can be collected only during large earthquakes, which cannot be made to order (Peck, 1979). DeAlba et al. (1976) performed large-scale simple shear tests, and the data collected (Fig. 8.36) was suitably modified to account for significant factors known to affect the results under field conditions, such as multidirectional shaking or aging. Also, to correlate the data in Fig. 8.36 with those in Fig. 8.47, a relationship between relative density and standard penetration values must be known. Seed (1979) used such a relationship established by Bieganousky and Marcuson (1977) from tests at the Waterways Experiment Station (WES), and, after applying the various correction factors to the data in Fig. 8.36, obtained the results for earthquakes of different magnitudes, involving equivalent numbers of uniform stress cycles of 5, 15, and 25 (Table 8.9).

These results were superimposed on the field data from Fig. 8.47 as shown in Fig. 8.48 for earthquakes of magnitude 7.5. The degree of agreement between the test data and the field data is excellent, indicating that the values of the overall correction factors selected are of the correct order of magnitude or that their relative value is approximately correct (Seed, 1979). More important, it suggests that comparable relationships might be obtained by following the same procedure for earthquakes of other magnitudes.

Proceeding in the same manner, Fig. 8.49 is obtained; combining all reliable data from field studies and the data presented in Table 8.9 leads to the data set shown in the figure. This permits lower bound relationships to be drawn for earthquakes with magnitudes of about 6, 7.5, and 8.25. The stress ratios in Figs. 8.48 and 8.49 are those required to cause peak cyclic pore-pressure ratios of 100 percent and shear strains of ± 5 percent for sands with different penetration resistance values. The development of such conditions for the denser sands will

Table 8.9 Data from large-scale simple shear tests on freshly deposited sand*

Relative density	N_1, bpf	M ≈ 5–6 5 cycles		M ≈ 7–7.5 15 cycles		M ≈ 8–8.25 25 cycles	
		$(\tau/\sigma_0')_{test}$[†]	$(\tau/\sigma_0')_{field}$	$(\tau/\sigma_0')_{test}$	$(\tau/\sigma_0')_{field}$	$(\tau/\sigma_0')_{test}$	$(\tau/\sigma_0')_{field}$
54	13.5	0.22	0.25	0.17	0.19	0.155	0.175
68	23	0.30	0.335	0.24	0.27	0.21	0.235
82	33	0.44	0.49	0.32	0.36	0.28	0.315
90	39	0.59	0.66	0.41	0.46	0.36	0.406

*After Seed (1979).

[†]Values of $(\tau/\sigma_0')_{test}$ listed are those required to cause a peak cyclic pore-pressure ratio of 100% and a cyclic shear strain of $\pm 5\%$.

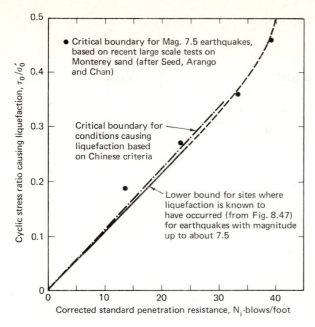

Figure **8.48** Comparison of field liquefaction correlation of Seed with correlation based on Chinese liquefaction criteria *(Seed, 1979.)*

clearly be accompanied by only limited shear strains, the magnitude of these strains depending on the relative density, the confining pressures, and possibly other factors. Accordingly, the limited strains observed in the tests by DeAlba et al. (1976), and the estimated range believed to be applicable for field conditions at confining pressures on the order of 1 t/ft², are also shown on Fig. 8.49 (Seed, 1979).

Method of Analysis

Based upon these correlations, the following procedure may be adopted for liquefaction analysis of a site with level ground surface:

Design Data The following data of a site must be known:

1. standard penetration record with depth, corrected for overburden
2. unit weights
3. location of water table
4. magnitude of earthquake expected at site

Analysis The following steps may be adopted:

1. Determine the shear stress τ_{av} caused by earthquake with the help of Eq. (8.7).

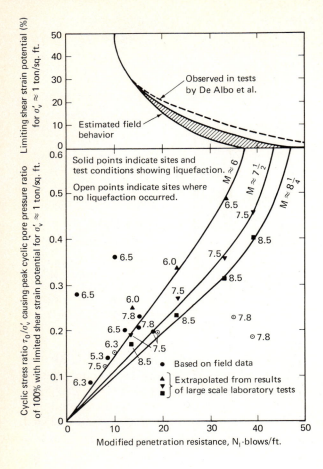

y-axis (outer, top): Limiting shear strain potential (%) for $\sigma_v' \approx 1$ ton/sq. ft.

y-axis (lower): Cyclic stress ratio τ_0/σ_v' causing peak cyclic pore pressure ratio of 100% with limited shear strain potential for $\sigma_v' \approx 1$ ton/sq. ft.

Observed in tests by De Albo et al.

Estimated field behavior

Solid points indicate sites and test conditions showing liquefaction.

Open points indicate sites where no liquefaction occurred.

$M \approx 6$ $M \approx 7\frac{1}{2}$ $M \approx 8\frac{1}{4}$

• Based on field data

▲
▼ } Extrapolated from results
■ } of large scale laboratory tests

x-axis: Modified penetration resistance, N_1-blows/ft.

Figure 8.49 Correlation between field liquefaction behavior of sands for level ground conditions and penetration resistance supplemented by data from large scale tests. *(After Seed, 1979.)*

2. Determine $\dfrac{\tau_0}{\sigma_v'}$ from Fig. 8.49 and compute τ_0.

3. A comparison of τ_{av} and τ_0 shows if liquefaction occurs or not. If $\tau_{av} > \tau_0$, liquefaction occurs; if not, liquefaction does not occur.

Example 8.2 A uniform deposit of sand occurs up to great depth. The observed N values are 20. The water table occurs at the ground surface. Assuming unit weight of saturated soil of 125 lb/ft^3, estimate if liquefaction occurs at this site for an earthquake of magnitude 7.5.

SOLUTION

   1. Correction of N with depth and computation of shear stress τ_0 causing liquefaction. The computations are done in a tabular form:

Depth, ft	σ_v', t/ft²	C_N [Eq. (8.13)]	N	$N_1 =$ $N \times C_N$	$\dfrac{\tau_0}{\sigma_v'}$ (Fig. 8.49)	τ_0 (col. 2 × col. 6)
1	2	3	4	5	6	7
10	0.312	1.39	20	27.8	0.300	0.094
20	0.625	1.15	20	23.0	0.275	0.172
30	0.937	1.02	20	20.4	0.225	0.211
40	1.249	0.92	20	18.4	0.180	0.225
50	1.561	0.85	20	17.0	0.16	0.25

2. Computation of shear stress developed during earthquake τ_{av}. The quantity τ_{av} is computed with Eq. (8.7):

$$\tau_{av} = 0.65 \gamma h \frac{a_{max}}{g} \times r_d \tag{8.7}$$

Depth, ft	$\dfrac{a_{max}}{g}$	γ, t/ft³	r_d	τ_{av}, t/ft²
10	0.1	0.0625	0.98	0.0398
20	0.1	0.0625	0.96	0.078
30	0.1	0.0625	0.94	0.114
40	0.1	0.0625	0.85	0.138
50	0.1	0.0625	0.70	0.142

A comparison of shear stress developed τ_{av} and shear stress causing liquefaction τ_0 shows that τ_0 is larger than τ_{av} at all depths. Hence, liquefaction does not occur.

8.13 FINAL COMMENTS

The question of liquefaction of sands has been extensively investigated in different parts of the world in the previous two decades. The understanding of the phenomenon has advanced to a degree that analytical procedures have been formulated to predict if liquefaction would occur at a site.

It is very clearly recognized that there are many factors that control the liquefaction of sands, as described in Sec. 8.4. These are:

1. grain-size distribution of sand
2. density of deposit (initial relative density D_R)
3. vibration characteristics

4. location of drainage and dimensions of deposit
5. magnitude and nature of superimposed loads
6. method of soil formation (soil structure)
7. period under sustained load
8. previous strain history
9. trapped air

The effect of these factors on the liquefaction potential of a sand has been discussed in this chapter.

In all of the studies discussed so far, the vibration of sand was in one direction only. Earthquakes may cause vibrations in all three directions, for example, longitudinal, transverse horizontally, and vertically. Seed, Pyke, and Martin (1975) determined from tests on a shaking table with two-directional motion that the shear stresses causing liquefaction under multidirectional shaking with two equal components are 10 and 20 percent less than shear stresses causing initial liquefaction under one-directional shaking. Since, in practice, it is unlikely that a second component of motion would be equal to the single component used for design purposes, it is suggested that a reduction of 10 percent in the shear stresses causing initial liquefaction may be used.

Thus the value of C_r is reduced by 10 percent in Eq. (8.9).

The analysis proposed by Seed and Idriss (1971) is based upon the assumption that no pore pressures dissipate during the shaking of the deposit. Seed, Martin, and Lysmer (1976) extended the studies to include consideration of the pore-water pressure redistribution that may take place during the period of earthquake shaking, as well as the period following the earthquake.

According to eyewitness accounts during the Niigata earthquake of 1964, the sand boils or the settlement of the buildings began to take place some time after the ground shaking had stopped (Yoshimi, 1977). In the case of a two-story, reinforced concrete building at the Niigata airport, which settled about 1 m, the time interval between the first major shock and the settlement was estimated to be about 40 s by reenacting the scene of evacuation from the office upstairs.

The time lag probably indicates that the soil at some depth was first liquefied during the earthquake, and that the excess pore-water pressure in the liquefied zone caused an upward seepage through the surface soil and a subsequent loss in the bearing capacity. This transient seepage problem was analyzed by applying the Terzaghi consolidation theory by Ambraseys and Sarma (1969) and Yoshimi and Kuwabara (1973). Yoshimi and Ohaka (1975), using soil properties determined from large-scale consolidation tests of liquefied sand, showed that the maximum pore pressure in the layer overlying the liquefied layer is primarily governed by the ratio of the coefficients of permeability of the two layers.

Gupta (1979) proposed a method for computing the step-by-step progress of liquefaction in a deposit of sand.

Structures settle when the soils on which they are constructed undergo liquefaction. Even before initial liquefaction takes place, there may be some settlement of structures. Needed analytical procedures are not yet available in readily usable form.

The question of the settlement of structures after initial liquefaction depends upon the time that the soils remain in a liquefied state. Loose sand tends to undergo large deformation after initial liquefaction.

Liquefaction of slopes and embankments is also an important problem. Seed (1968) demonstrated that the slides during the Alaskan earthquake of 1964 were initiated by liquefaction of seams or lenses of saturated sandy soils. In the process, he enlightened the profession by illustrating the importance of minor geologic details in determining the occurrence and characteristics of landslides during earthquakes due to soil liquefaction.

Slumping of embankments is quite common during earthquakes because even dense cohesionless soils may be affected. Youd (1973) identified this type of failure as a lateral-spreading landslide caused by cyclic liquefaction, and recognized the possibility that migration of pore water into a zone of soil that had dilated during cyclic shear could cause loosening, leaving the soil vulnerable to subsequent stress applications.

Casagrande (1976) reports that the progressive increase of cyclic pore pressures and softening in test specimens in various types of cyclic tests, and cyclic liquefaction in triaxial tests, is caused by radical redistribution of the water content, which is generated by mechanisms that are normally not active in situ. Also, it is unlikely that a laboratory test can be devised that will produce in test specimens the type of uniform stress distribution that exists during cyclic loading in a typical element in situ. In order to close the great gap between laboratory and in situ response, comprehensive field investigations of many full-scale tests that nature may perform in highly seismic regions will be required. Such investigations will have to be carried out with the best possible investigational tools and with meticulous attention to details, lest they create misleading information (Casagrande, 1976).

In a similar tone, Peck (1979) indicates that the laboratory tests fail to take into account several favorable factors that are likely to be present in the field.

"Disturbance" of sample is one such factor. In fact, absolutely undisturbed sample is a myth!

It would thus appear that correlation of standard penetration records with the behavior of sands (Fig. 8.49) may be the solution to liquefaction problems of the future.

It may be appropriate to mention that excellent reviews on the subject have been presented by Seed (1976a, 1976b), Casagrande (1976), Yoshimi (1977), Seed (1979) and Gupta (1979).

PRACTICE PROBLEMS

8.1 List and discuss the factors on which liquefaction of saturated sands depend.

8.2 What do you understand by the following:
    (*a*) initial liquefaction
    (*b*) complete liquefaction
    (*c*) cyclic mobility

8.3 Illustrate with neat diagrams the difference in behavior of (*a*) loose and (*b*) dense saturated sand under cyclic triaxial tests.

8.4 Discuss the difference in behavior of dense saturated sands in the laboratory and in situ, during cyclic loading.

8.5 "Dense sands do not liquefy in situ." Do you agree or disagree with this statement? Justify your answer fully.

REFERENCES

Ambraseys, N. N., and S. Sarma: Liquefaction of Soils Induced by Earthquakes, *Bull. Seismol. Soc. Am.*, vol. 59, no. 2, pp. 651–664, 1969.

Bazant, S: Stability of Saturated Sand During Earthquake, *Proc. Third World Conference on Earthquake Engineering, Auckland*, vol. 1, pp. 16–21, 1965.

_____, and A. Dvorak: Effects of Vibrations on Sand and the Measurement of Dynamic Properties, *Proc. Sixth Int. Conf. Soil Mech. Found. Engin.*, Montreal, vol. 1, pp. 161–164, 1965.

Bieganousky, W. A., and W. F. Marcuson III: Liquefaction Potential of Dams and Foundations, Report 2. Laboratory Standard Penetration Test on Platte River Sand and Standard Concrete Sand, WES Report no. 76-2, Vicksburg, Miss., March 1977.

Bishop, A. W., D. L. Webb, and A. E. Skinner: Triaxial Tests on Soil at Elevated Cell Pressure, *Proc. Sixth Int. Conf. Soil Mech. Found. Engin.*, Montreal, vol. 1, pp. 170–174, 1965.

Bjerrum, L.: Geotechnical Problems Involved in Foundation of Structures in the North Sea, *Geotechnique*, vol. 23, no. 3, pp. 319–358, 1973.

Casagrande, A.: Characteristics of Cohesionless Soils Affecting the Stability of Earth Fills, *J. Boston Soc. Civ. Eng.*, January, 1936, reprinted in "Contributions to Soil Mechanics, 1925–1960," Boston Society of Civil Engineers.

_____: "Liquefaction and Cyclic Deformation of Sands—A Critical Review," Paper presented at Fifth Pan American Conference on Soil Mechanics and Foundation Engineering, Buenos Aires, Argentina, November, 1975.

_____: "Liquefaction and Cyclic Deformation of Sands—A Critical Review," Harvard Soil Mechanics Series No. 88, Harvard University, Cambridge, Mass, 1976.

Castro, G., and S. J. Poulos: "Factors Affecting Liquefaction and Cyclic Mobility," Symposium on Soil Liquefaction, ASCE National Convention, Philadelphia, October 2, 1976, pp. 105–138, 1976.

Christian, J. T., and W. F. Swiger: Statistics of Liquefaction and S.P.T. Results, *J. Geotech. Engin. Div., ASCE*, vol. 101, no. GT 11, pp. 1135–1150, November, 1975.

DeAlba, P., H. B. Seed, and C. K. Chan: Sand Liquefaction in Large Scale Simple Shear Tests, *J. Geotech. Engin. Div., ASCE*, vol. 102, no. GT9, pp. 909–927, 1976.

Dunn, J. A., J. B. Auden, and A. M. N. Ghosh: The Bihar Nepal Earthquakes of 1934, *Mem. Geol. Surv. India*, vol. 73, p. 32, 1939.

Finn, W. D. L.: Soil-Dynamics-Liquefaction of Sands, *Proc. First Int. Conf. Microzonation, Seattle*, vol. 1, pp. 87–111, 1972.

_____, P. L. Bransby, and D. J. Pickering: Effect of Strain History on Liquefaction of Sands, *J. Soil Mech. Found. Div., ASCE*, vol. 96, no. SM 6, pp. 1917–1934, 1970.

_____, J. J. Emery, and Y. P. Gupta: A Shaking Table Study of the Liquefaction of Saturated Sands During Earthquakes, *Proc. Third Europ. Symp. Earthquake Engin.*, pp. 253–262, 1970.

_____, _____, and _____: Soil Liquefaction Studies Using a Shaking Table, *Closed Loop*, MTS Systems Corporation, Fall/Winter, 1971.

_____, K. W. Lee, and G. R. Martin: "An Effective Stress Model for Liquefaction," Symposium on Soil Liquefaction, ASCE National Convention, Philadelphia, pp. 169–198, 1976*a*.

_____, _____, and _____: "Seismic Pore-Water Pressure Generation and Dissipation," Symposium on Soil Liquefaction, ASCE National Convention, Philadelphia, pp. 169–198, 1976.

Florin, V. A., and P. L. Ivanov: Liquefaction of Saturated Sandy Soils, *Proc. Fifth Int. Conf. Soil Mech. Found. Engin.*, Paris, vol. 1, pp. 107-111, 1961.

Gupta, M. K.: "Liquefaction of Sands During Earthquakes," Ph.D. Thesis, University of Roorkee, Roorkee, India, 1979.

Housner, G. W.: Mechanics of Sand Blows, *Bull. Seismol. Soc. Am.*, vol. 48, no. 2, pp. 155–168, 1958.

Indian Standards on Classification of Soils for General Engineering Purposes, IS 1498–1971, 1st rev., Indian Standards Institution, New Delhi.

Ishihara, K., and S. Yasuda: "Sand Liquefaction Under Random Earthquake Loading Conditions," *Proc. Fifth World Conference on Earthquake Engineering*, *Rome*, 1973.

Kishida, H.: Damage to Reinforced Concrete Buildings in Niigata City with Special Reference to Foundation Engineering, *Soil Found. Engin.* (*Tokyo*), vol. 9, no. 1, pp. 75–92, 1966.

Krishna, J., S. Prakash, et al.: Study of Liquefaction of Obra Sands, *J. Inst. Engin.* (*India*), vol. 47, no. 1, pt CI1, pp. 36–50, September, 1967.

_____ and _____: Blast Tests at Obra Dam Site, *J. Inst. Engin.* (*India*), vol. 47, no. 9, pt. CI5, pp. 1273–1284, May, 1968.

Kubo, K., et al.: "Report on Aseismic Design of Akashi Bridge," *Japan Soc. Civil Engineers*, 40 pp (in Japanese, 1975).

Kuizumi, Y.: Change in Density of Sand Subsoil Caused by the Niigata Earthquake, *Soil Found. Engin.* (*Tokyo*), vol. 8, no. 2, pp. 38–44, 1966.

Ladd, R. S.: "Effects of Specimen Preparation on the Cyclic Structural Stability of Sands," Symposium on Soil Liquefaction, ASCE National Convention, Philadelphia, pp. 197–226, 1976.

Lee, K. L.: "Formation of Adhesion Bonds in Sands at High Pressures," Report No. UCLA-ENG-7586, UCLA School of Engineering and Applied Science, October, 1975.

_____: "Fundamental Considerations for Cyclic Triaxial Tests on Saturated Sands," International Conference on Behavior of Off-Shore Structures, Trondheim, Norway, August 2–5, 1976.

_____ and C. K. Chan: Number of Equivalent Significant Cycles in Strong Motion Earthquakes, *Proc. First Int. Conf. Microzonation*, Seattle, vol. 2, pp. 609–627, 1972.

_____ and J. A. Focht, Jr.: "Cyclic Testing of Soil to Ocean Wave Loading Problems," Seventh Annual Offshore Technology Conference, Houston, Texas, May 5–8, 1975a.

_____ and _____: Liquefaction Potential at Ekofisk Tank in North Sea, *J. Geotech. Engin. Div.*, *ASCE*, vol. 101, no. GT 1, pp. 1–18, 1975b.

_____ and H. B. Seed: Cyclic Stress Conditions Causing Liquefaction of Sand, *J. Soil Mech. Found. Div.*, ASCE, vol. 93, no. SM 1, pp. 47–70, January, 1967.

Makhlouf, H. M., and J. J. Stewart: Factors Influencing the Modulus of Elasticity of Dry Sand, *Proc. Sixth Int. Conf. Soil Mech. Found. Engin.*, Montreal, vol. 1, pp. 298–302, 1965.

Maslov, N. N.: Questions of Seismic Stability of Submerged Sandy Foundations and Structures, *Proc. Fourth Int. Conf. Soil Mech. Found. Engin.*, London, vol. 1, pp. 368–372, 1957.

Matsuo, H., and S. Ohara: Lateral Earth Pressure and Stability of Quay Walls, *Proc. Second World Conference on Earthquake Engineering*, Tokyo, vol. 1, pp. 165–182, 1960.

Ohasaki, Y.: Niigata Earthquake 1964, Building Damage and Soil Conditions, *Soil Found.* (Tokyo), vol. 6, no. 2, pp. 14–37, 1966.

_____: Effects of Sand Compaction on Liquefaction During the Tokachioki Earthquake, *Soil Found.* (Tokyo), vol. 10, no. 2, pp. 112–128, June, 1970.

Peacock, W. H., and H. B. Seed: Sand Liquefaction under Cyclic Loading Simple Shear Conditions, *J. Soil Mech. Found. Div.*, *ASCE*, vol. 94, no. SM 3, pp. 689–708, 1968.

Peck, R. B.: Liquefaction Potential—Science Versus Practice, *J. Geotech. Engin. Div.*, *ASCE*, vol. 105, no. GT 3, pp. 393–398, 1979.

_____, W. E. Hansen, and T. H. Thornburn: "Foundation Engineering," 2d ed., John Wiley & Sons, Inc., New York, 1974.

Prakash, S., and M. K. Gupta: "Final Report on Blast Tests at Tenughat Dam Site," Earthquake Engineering Studies, Roorkee University, Soil Dynamics ser. no. 14, 1967a.

_____ and _____: "Final Report on Liquefaction and Settlement Characteristics of Tenughat Dam," Earthquake Engineering Studies, Roorkee University, Soil Dynamics ser. no. 13, 1967b.

_____ and _____: Compaction of Sand Under Vertical and Horizontal Vibrations, *Proc. First Southeast Asian Regional Conference on Soil Engineering*, Bangkok, pp. 201–210, 1967c.

_____ and _____: "Liquefaction and Settlement Characteristics of Tenughat Dam Sand,"

Thirty-eighth Annual Research Session, Central Board of Irrigation and Power, Bangalore, 1968a.

_____ and _____: "Final Report on Liquefaction and Settlement Characteristics of Ukai Sand," Earthquake Engineering Studies, Roorkee University, Soil Dynamics ser. no. 21, 1968b.

_____ and _____: "Final Report on Liquefaction and Settlement Characteristics of Farrakka Sand," Earthquake Engineering Studies, Roorkee University, Soil Dynamics ser. no. 22, 1968c.

_____ and _____: Liquefaction and Settlement Characteristics of Loose Sand Under Vibrations, *Proc. International Conference on Dynamic Waves in Civil Engineering*, Swansea, pp. 323–338, 1970a.

_____ and _____: Blast Tests at Tenughat Dam Site, *J. Southeast Asian Soc. Soil Mech. Found. Engin.* (Bangkok), vol. 1, no. 1, pp. 41–50, 1970b.

_____ and _____: Liquefaction and Settlement Characteristics of Ukai Dam Sand, *Bull. Indian Soc. Earthquake Tech.* (Roorkee), vol. 7, no. 3, pp. 123–132, 1970c.

Pyke, R. M., H. B. Seed and C. K. Chan: "Settlement of Sands Under Multidirectional Shaking," *J. Geot. Engg. Div.*, ASCE, vol 101, no. GT 4, pp. 379–398, April 1975.

Seed, H. B.: The Fourth Terzaghi Lecture: Landslides During Earthquakes Due to Liquefaction, *J. Soil Mech. Found. Div.*, ASCE, vol. 94, no. SM 5, pp. 1053–1122, 1968.

_____: "Some Aspects of Sand Liquefaction Under Cyclic Loading," *Conference on Behavior of Off-Shore Structures*, The Norwegian Institute of Technology, Norway, 1976a.

_____: "Evaluation of Soil Liquefaction Effects on Level Ground During Earthquakes," *State of the Art Paper*, Symposium on Soil Liquefaction, ASCE National Convention, Philadelphia, pp. 1–104, 1976b.

_____: Soil Liquefaction and Cyclic Mobility Evaluation for Level Ground During Earthquakes, *J. Geotech. Engin. Div.*, ASCE, vol. 105, no. GT 2, pp. 201–255, February, 1979.

_____, I. Arango, and C. K. Chan: "Evaluation of Soil Liquefaction Potential During Earthquakes," Report no. EERC 75-28, Earthquake Engineering Research Center, University of California, Berkeley, October, 1975.

_____ and J. R. Booker: "Stabilization of Potentially Liquefiable Sand Deposits Using Gravel Drain Systems," Report No. EERC 76-10, Earthquake Engineering Research Center, University of California, Berkeley, April, 1976.

_____ and I. M. Idriss: Analysis of Soil Liquefaction, Niigata Earthquake, *J. Soil Mech. Found. Div.*, ASCE, vol. 93, no. SM 3, pp. 83–108, 1967.

_____ and _____: Simplified Procedure for Evaluating Soil Liquefaction Potential, *J. Soil Mech. Found. Div.*, ASCE, vol. 97, no. SM 9, pp. 1249–1273, 1971.

_____, _____, F. Makdisi, and N. Banerjee: "Representation of Irregular Stress Time Histories by Equivalent Uniform Stress Series in Liquefaction Analyses," Report no. EERC 75-29, University of California, Earthquake Engineering Research Center, Berkeley, October, 1975.

_____ and K. L. Lee: Liquefaction of Saturated Sands During Cyclic Loading, *J. Soil Mech. Found. Div.*, ASCE, vol. 92, no. SM 6, pp. 105–134, 1966.

_____, G. R. Martin, and J. Lysmer: Pore Water Pressure Changes During Soil Liquefaction, *J. Geotech. Engin. Div.*, ASCE, vol. 102, no. GT 4, pp. 327–346, 1976.

_____, K. Mori, and C. K. Chan: Influence of Seismic History on Liquefaction of Sands, *J. Geotech. Engin. Div.*, ASCE, vol. 103, no. GT 4, pp. 246–270, April, 1977.

_____ and W. H. Peacock: Test Procedures for Measuring Soil Liquefaction Characteristics, *J. Soil Mech. Found. Div.*, ASCE, vol. 97, no. SM 8, pp. 1099–1119, August, 1971.

_____, R. M. Pyke, and G. R. Martin: "Analysis of the Effect of Multi-directional Shaking on the Liquefaction Characteristics of Sands," Report no. EERC 75-41, Earthquake Engineering Research Center, University of California, Berkeley, December, 1975.

_____, _____, and _____: Effect of Multidirectional Shaking on Pore Pressure Development in Sands, *J. Geotech. Engin. Div.*, ASCE, vol. 104, no. GT 1, pp. 27–44, January, 1978.

_____ and M. L. Silver, "Settlement of Dry Sands During Earthquakes," *J. Soil Mech. Found. Div.* ASCE, vol. 98, no. SM-4, pp. 381–397, 1972.

State Capital Construction Commission: "Earthquake-Resistant Design Code for Industrial and Civil Buildings," TJ114, People's Republic of China, China Building Publishing House, Peking, China, December, 1974 (translated from Chinese by Andrew C. S. Chang).*

Taylor, D. W., Fundamentals of Soil Mechanics, John Wiley and Sons, New York, NY, 1948.

Yoshimi, Y.: Experimental Study of Liquefaction of Saturated Sands, *Soil Found.* (Tokyo), vol. 7, no. 2, pp. 20–32, 1967.

_____ : Liquefaction and Cyclic Deformation of Soils Under Undrained Conditions, *State of the Art Report, Proc. Ninth Int. Conf. Soil Mech. Found. Engin.*, vol. 2, pp. 613–623, 1977.

_____ and F. Kuwabara: Effect of Subsurface Liquefaction on the Strength of Surface Soil, *Soil Found.* (Tokyo), vol. 13, no. 2, pp. 67–81, 1973.

_____ and H. Ohaka: Influence of Degree of Shear Stress Reversal on the Liquefaction Potential of Saturated Sands, *Soil Found.* (Tokyo), vol. 15, no. 3, pp. 27–40, 1975.

Youd, T. L.: "Liquefaction, Flow and Associated Ground Failure," Geological Survey Circular 688, Washington, D.C., 1973.

*Referred by Seed, 1979.

MACHINE FOUNDATIONS

9.1 INTRODUCTION

Machine foundations require the special attention of a foundation engineer. In addition to static loads due to the weight of the machine and the foundation, loads acting on such foundations are dynamic in nature. In general, a foundation weighs several times as much as a machine. Also, a dynamic load associated with the moving parts of a machine is generally small as compared to its static load. In machine foundation a dynamic load is applied repetitively over a very large period of time but its magnitude is small, and it is therefore necessary that the soil behavior be elastic, or else deformation will increase with each cycle of loading until the soil becomes practically unacceptable. The amplitude of motion of a machine at its operating frequency is the most important parameter to be determined in designing a machine foundation, in addition to determining the natural frequency of a machine foundation soil system.

There are many kinds of machines that generate different periodic forces. The three most important categories are:

1. Reciprocating machines: Machines that produce periodic unbalanced force (such as compressor and reciprocating engines) belong in this category. The operating speeds of such machines are usually less than 600 r/min. For analysis of their foundations, the unbalanced forces can be considered to vary sinusoidally.
2. Impact machines: Included in this category are machines that produce impact loads, for instance, forging hammers. Their speeds of operation are

usually from 60 to 150 blows per minute. Their dynamic loads attain a peak in a very short interval and then practically die out.
3. Rotary machines: High-speed machines like turbogenerators or rotary compressors may have speeds of more than 3,000 r/min and up to 10,000 r/min.

A suitable foundation is selected, depending upon the type of machine being installed. For compressors and reciprocating machines, a block foundation is provided (Fig. 9.1a). Such a foundation consists of a pedestal resting on a footing. If two or more machines of similar characteristics are to be installed in a shop, these can profitably be mounted on one continuous mat.

A block foundation has a large mass and, therefore, a smaller natural frequency. However, if a relatively lighter foundation is to be provided, a box or a caisson type may be provided (Fig. 9.1b). The mass of the foundation is reduced and its natural frequency is increased. Hammers may also be mounted on block foundations, but their detail would be quite different than those for reciprocating machines.

Steam turbines have complex foundations that may consist of a system of wall columns and beam slabs (Fig. 9.1c). Each element of such a foundation is relatively flexible as opposed to a rigid mass of blocks and a box or a caisson-type foundation.

The analysis of a block foundation is quite different from that of a complex foundation. There are several methods of analysis for both the block and the

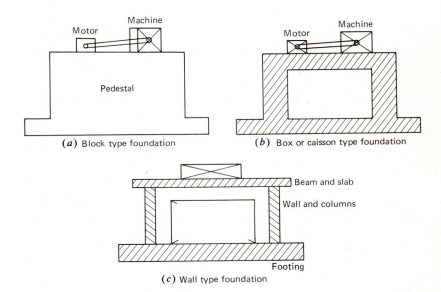

Figure 9.1 Types of machine foundations. (a) Block foundations. (b) Box or caisson foundations. (c) Complex foundations.

complex foundations. The criteria for designing machine foundations shall be discussed first, followed by their methods of analysis.

9.2 CRITERIA FOR A SATISFACTORY MACHINE FOUNDATION

A machine foundation should meet the following conditions in order to be satisfactory:

For static loads

1. It should be safe against shear failure.
2. It should not settle excessively.

These requirements are the same for all footings.

For dynamic loads

1. There should be no resonance; that is, the natural frequency of the machine-foundation-soil system should not coincide with the operating frequency of the machine. In fact, a zone of resonance is generally defined and the natural frequency of the system must lie outside this zone (see Sec. 9.11).
2. The amplitudes of motion at operating frequencies should not exceed the limiting amplitude, which is generally specified by machine manufacturers. If the computed amplitude is within tolerable limits, but is at or close to resonance, it is important that this situation be avoided.
3. The vibrations must not be annoying to the persons working in the factory or be damaging to other precision machines. The nature of vibrations that are perceptible, annoying, or harmful depends upon the frequency of the vibrations and the amplitude of motion. Richart (1962) developed a plot for vibrations (Fig. 9.2) that gives various limits of frequency and amplitude for different purposes. The top two lines of damage and caution to structures apply to blasting effects on structures (Crandell, 1949). Also, limits for machines and machine foundations indicate the safety limits and not limits for satisfactory machine operation.

9.3 METHODS OF ANALYSIS

There are two principal methods of analysis of a machine foundation:

1. A method based on linear elastic weightless spring
2. A method based on linear theory of elasticity (elastic half space)

In the first method, soil is replaced by a spring. Damping may be introduced in the solution as a predetermined value, although damping does not apprecia-

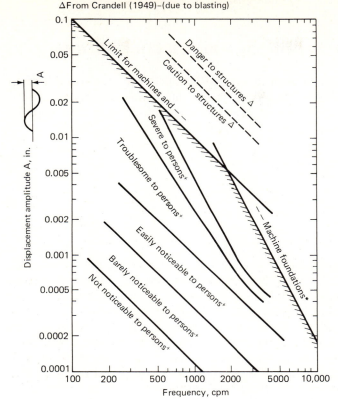

+ From Reiher and Meister (1931)-(steady-state vibrations)
* From Rausch (1943-(steady-state vibrations)
ΔFrom Crandell (1949)-(due to blasting)

Figure 9.2 Limiting amplitudes of vibrations for a particular frequency. (*After Richart, 1962.*)

bly affect the resonant frequency of the system. Damping does have a considerable effect on the resonant amplitudes. Since the zone of resonance is avoided in designing machine foundations, the effect of damping on amplitudes computed at operating frequency is also small as compared to that at resonance. In some cases, neglecting damping may result in rather conservative estimates.

The theory-of-elasticity approach is apparently more rational, but relatively more complicated. In simple cases, solution techniques have been perfected to a reasonable degree of simplicity in usage, as will be shown later. In more complicated cases, the solutions are still too involved for general use. In addition, the questions of depth of embedment, disturbance of soils during excavation and backfilling, soil mass participating in vibrations, and nonlinearity of soils complicate the solutions even more.

In the following sections, the analysis of block-type foundations will include the solution techniques and further comments on narrowing the gap between the two approaches. However, as far as the question of determining soil constants is concerned, the methods presented in Chap. 4 are not affected by the method adopted for machine foundation analysis.

9.4 DEGREES OF FREEDOM OF A BLOCK FOUNDATION

A block is regarded as rigid when compared with the soil over which it rests. Therefore, it shall be assumed that it undergoes only rigid-body displacements. Under the action of unbalanced forces, the rigid block may thus undergo displacements and oscillations as follows (Fig. 9.3):

1. translation along Z axis
2. translation along X axis
3. translation along Y axis
4. rotation about Z axis
5. rotation about X axis
6. rotation about Y axis

Any rigid-body displacement of the block can be resolved into these six independent displacements. Hence, the rigid block has six degrees of freedom and six natural frequencies.

Of six types of motion, translation along the Z axis and rotation about the Z axis can occur independently of any other motion. However, translation about the X axis (or Y axis) and rotation about the Y axis (or X axis) are coupled motions. Therefore, in the analysis of a block, we have to concern ourselves with four types of motions. Two motions are independent, and two are coupled. For determination of the natural frequencies in coupled modes, the natural frequencies of the system in pure translation and pure rocking need to be determined. Also, the states of stress below the block in all four modes of vibrations are quite different. Therefore, the corresponding soil-spring constants need to be defined before actual analysis of the foundations can be undertaken.

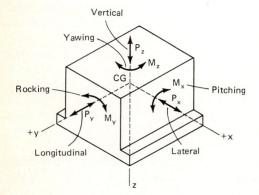

Figure 9.3 Degrees of freedom of a block foundation.

9.5 DEFINITION OF SOIL SPRING STIFFNESS

For all routine analysis and design, the soil behavior is considered to be linear and elastic. Figure 9.4 shows the block undergoing (*a*) vertical oscillations, (*b*) horizontal translation only, (*c*) rocking only, and (*d*) yawing. The stress below the block in each case, due to dynamic loading, is

1. uniform compression
2. uniform shear
3. nonuniform compression
4. nonuniform shear

    Therefore, the soil constant characterizing the stress below the block and the corresponding elastic deformation are different in each case. This concept is

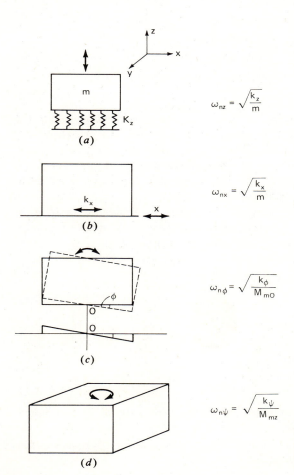

$$\omega_{nz} = \sqrt{\frac{k_z}{m}}$$

(*a*)

$$\omega_{nx} = \sqrt{\frac{k_x}{m}}$$

(*b*)

$$\omega_{n\phi} = \sqrt{\frac{k_\phi}{M_{mO}}}$$

(*c*)

$$\omega_{n\psi} = \sqrt{\frac{k_\psi}{M_{mz}}}$$

(*d*)

Figure 9.4 Vibrations of a block in decoupled modes. (*a*) Vertical vibrations. (*b*) Horizontal translation. (*c*) Rocking. (*d*) Yawing.

quite different from the theory of elasticity in which the shear modulus is G, whether the state of shear is uniform or nonuniform. Similarly, the modulus of elasticity is E, whether the compression is uniform or nonuniform.

The corresponding soil coefficients may then be defined as follows:

(1) Coefficient of elastic uniform compression (C_u):

$$= \frac{\text{uniform compression } (p)}{\text{elastic settlement } (s_e)} \tag{9.1a}$$

From definition, spring constant k_z

$$k_z = \frac{\text{load}}{\text{elastic deformation}} = \frac{pA}{s_e}$$

Therefore,

$$k_z = C_u A \tag{9.1b}$$

where A is area of the test plate.

(2) Coefficient of elastic uniform shear C_τ:

$$C_\tau = \frac{\text{uniform shear } \tau}{\text{elastic shear displacement } s_e'} \tag{9.2a}$$

As for the spring constant k_z, the corresponding spring constant k_x

$$k_x = C_\tau A \tag{9.2b}$$

(3, 4) Coefficient of elastic nonuniform compression C_ϕ, coefficient of elastic nonuniform shear C_ψ: Since the elastic deformation is not uniform over the base of the block as in cases 1 and 2 above, no simple definitions for C_ϕ and C_ψ can be given. However, precise definitions in terms of mathematical quantities and overall displacements (rotations) of the block and its geometry have been derived in Secs. 9.8 and 9.9, respectively.

Now C_u is considered to be analogous to E, and C_τ analogous to G, and there is a simple relationship between constants E and G. Barkan (1962) discussed the relationships between C_u, C_ϕ, and all other constants in detail. For analysis and design of machine foundations, he recommended that

$$C_u = 2C_\tau \tag{9.3}$$

$$C_\phi = 2C_u \tag{9.4}$$

$$C_\tau = 1.5 \, C_\psi \tag{9.5}$$

However, Indian Standard IS 5249 recommends that

$$C_u = 1.73 \, C_\tau \tag{9.6a}$$

$$C_\phi = 2C_u = 3.46 \, C_\tau \tag{9.6b}$$

The relationships for interpretation of C_ϕ and C_τ from the block resonance test [Eq. (4.13)] are based on Eq. (9.6) rather than on Eqs. (9.3) to (9.5).

Barkan (1962) recommended values for C_u for preliminary designs of machine foundations as shown in Table 9.1.

Table 9.1 Recommended design values for the coefficient of elastic uniform compression C_u for $A = 10$ m²*

Soil	Soil group	Permissible static load, kg/cm²	C_u, kg/cm³
1	2	3	4
I	Weak soils (clays and silty clays with sand, in a plastic state, clayey and silty sands, also soils of categories II and III with laminae of organic silt and of peat)	up to 1.5	up to 3
II	Soils of medium strength (clays and silty clays with sand, close to the plastic limit, sand)	1.5–3.5	3–5
III	Strong soils (clays and silty clays with sand, of hard consistency; gravels and gravelly sands; loess and loessial soils)	3.5–5.0	5–10
IV	Rocks	> 5.0	> 10

*After Barkan (1962).

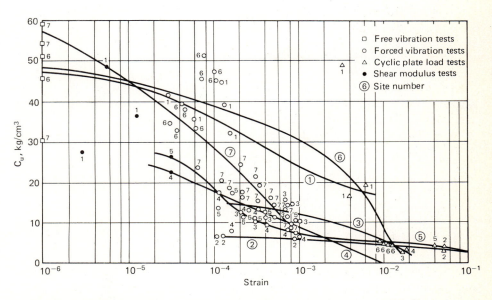

Figure 9.5 Coefficient of elastic uniform compression vs. shear strain for contact area = 1.5 × 0.75m². *(After Prakash and Puri, 1977.)*

It was shown in Chap. 4 that dynamic soil constants (C_u and G) depend upon strain level and confining pressure. Typical plots of C_u values for $A = 1.5 \times 0.75$ m^2 and for a mean confining pressure of 1 kg/cm^2 and at different strain levels are shown in Fig. 9.5 (Prakash and Puri, 1977).

9.6 VERTICAL VIBRATIONS OF A BLOCK

Let us consider a foundation of area A, placed at a depth of D_f below the ground level (Fig. 9.6a) and acted upon by a vertical unbalance force such that

$$P_z = P_0 \sin \omega t \tag{9.7}$$

For the sake of analysis, it shall be assumed that the block is placed at ground level (Fig. 9.6b), that is, $D_f = 0$. The amplitudes of vibrations are generally reduced due to the effect of embedment. Also, the soil is replaced by an equivalent spring k_z (Fig. 9.6c). Thus, the machine-foundation-soil system now becomes the equivalent spring-mass system shown in Fig. 9.6d. This system is similar to that shown in Fig. 2.5e.

If the unbalanced force acts through the center of gravity of the block, for the system in Fig. 9.6d, the equation of motion of this system, neglecting damping, is

$$m\ddot{z} + k_z z = P_0 \sin \omega t \tag{9.8}$$

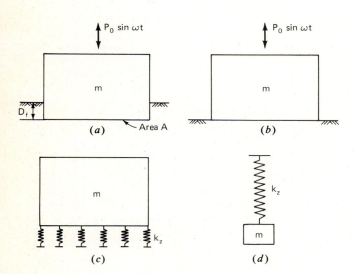

Figure 9.6 Block foundations under vertical vibrations. (a) Block resting at depth D_f. (b) Block resting on surface of ground. (c) Soil replaced by equivalent spring K_z. (d) Equivalent spring-mass system for analysis.

in which m= mass of machine and foundation

k_z = equivalent spring constant of the soil in vertical direction for base area A of the foundation = $C_u A$

C_u = coefficient of elastic uniform compression

Therefore, the natural frequency ω_{nz} of the system is

$$\omega_{nz} = \sqrt{\frac{C_u A}{m}} \qquad (9.9a)$$

The amplitude of motion A_z is given by

$$A_z = \frac{P_0 \sin \omega t}{C_u A - m\omega^2} \qquad (9.9b)$$

or

$$A_z = \frac{P_0 \sin \omega t}{m(\omega_{nz}^2 - \omega^2)} \qquad (9.9c)$$

Maximum amplitude of motion A_z is given by

$$A_z = \frac{P_0}{m(\omega_{nz}^2 - \omega^2)} \qquad (9.10)$$

The effect of a small value of damping on the natural frequency is negligible [Eq. (2.34)].

9.7 SLIDING VIBRATIONS OF A BLOCK

In practice, rocking and sliding occur simultaneously. But if the vibrations in rocking can be neglected, then only horizontal displacement of the foundation would occur under an exciting force $P_x \sin \omega t$ (Fig. 9.7) on the block of area A. The vibrations of the foundation in this case are analogous to vertical vibrations, with the constant $k_x = C_\tau A$ (Sec. 9.5).

The equation of motion of the block is:

$$m\ddot{x} + k_x x = P_x \sin \omega t \qquad (9.11)$$

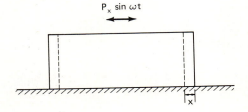

Figure 9.7 Block foundation under pure sliding vibrations.

which gives

$$\omega_{nx} = \sqrt{\frac{k_x}{m}} = \sqrt{\frac{C_\tau A}{m}} \tag{9.12a}$$

or

$$f_{nx} = \frac{1}{2\pi} \sqrt{\frac{k_x}{m}} = \frac{1}{2\pi} \sqrt{\frac{C_\tau A}{m}} \tag{9.12b}$$

$$\text{Maximum } A_x = \frac{P_x}{m(\omega_{nx}^2 - \omega^2)} \tag{9.12c}$$

where f_{nx} = natural frequency in pure sliding and A_x = maximum amplitude in pure sliding. All conclusions for vertical and sliding vibrations are similar.

9.8 ROCKING VIBRATIONS OF A BLOCK

Let us consider a block foundation of area A, resting on the ground surface and acted upon by a moment $M_y = M_0 \sin \omega t$ about the y axis in the xz plane (Fig. 9.8). It is assumed that the footing is symmetrical about the y axis and that the center of the mass of the machine and foundation and the centroid of the base area lie on a vertical line through O, the center of rocking vibrations.

We have learned that the rocking of a foundation is always accompanied by translation along the x axis. For the sake of simplicity, it will be assumed that resistance to sliding is so great that translation of the footing may be disregarded as a first approximation. In this case, the displaced position of the foundation is determined by only one independent variable ϕ, the rotation of the block about an axis passing through O and perpendicular to the plane of vibrations. Hence the system possesses only one degree of freedom.

The following moments act on the foundation, Fig. 9.8 (all moments would be considered about the center of rotation):

Moment due to soil reaction:

$$M_R = -\int_A dR \, dA \, 1$$

$$= -\int_A (C_\phi 1\phi \, dA)1 = -C_\phi \phi \int_A dA \, 1^2$$

$$= -C_\phi I\phi \tag{9.13}$$

and acts in an anticlockwise direction, where

dR = soil reaction acting over small area dA
1 = distance of dA from center of rotation
ϕ = angular displacement of block
I = moment of inertia of contact area about an axis passing through centroid of base contact area (center of rotation in this case and perpendicular to plane of vibrations)

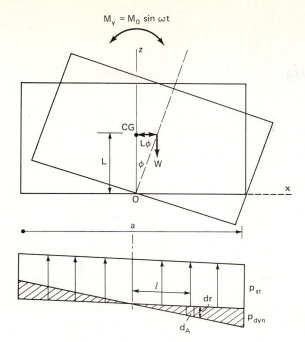

Figure 9.8 Block foundation under rocking vibrations.

It is assumed that soil reaction dR at any point is proportional to the displacement $l\phi$ at that point. The constant of proportionality is C_ϕ; therefore, $dR = C_\phi l\phi$.

Moment due to the displaced position of the center of gravity of the block:

$$M_w = WL\phi \qquad (9.14)$$

and acts in the clockwise direction.

Externally applied moment:

$$M_y = M_0 \sin \omega t \qquad (9.15a)$$

The equation of motion about the center of rotation may then be written in the following form:

$$M_{m0}\ddot{\phi} = \Sigma M \qquad (9.15b)$$

where M_{m0} = mass moment of inertia of the machine and foundation about the axis of rotation and $\ddot{\phi}$ = angular acceleration of the block. Therefore,

$$M_0 \sin \omega t - C_\phi I\phi + WL\phi = M_{m0}\ddot{\phi}$$

or

$$M_{m0}\ddot{\phi} + \phi(C_\phi I - WL) = M_{m0} \sin \omega t \qquad (9.16)$$

The natural frequency $\omega_{n\phi}$ of this system is given by

$$\omega_{n\phi} = \sqrt{\frac{C_\phi I - WL}{M_{m0}}} \tag{9.17}$$

and maximum displacement A_ϕ is given by

$$A_\phi = \frac{M_0}{M_{m0}(\omega_{n\phi}^2 - \omega^2)} \tag{9.18}$$

In practice, $C_\phi I$ is many times WL; hence Eq. (9.17) may be written:

$$\omega_{n\phi} = \sqrt{\frac{C_\phi I}{M_{m0}}} \tag{9.19a}$$

or

$$f_{n\phi} = \frac{1}{2\pi}\sqrt{\frac{C_\phi I}{M_{m0}}} \tag{9.19b}$$

If we compare Eq. (9.19a) with Eq. (9.9a), it will be seen that the spring constant in nonuniform compression k_ϕ is

$$k_\phi = C_\phi I \tag{9.19c}$$

Also, if the dimensions of the footing at the base are a and b in the x and y directions, respectively,

$$I = \frac{ba^3}{12} \tag{9.20}$$

$$f_{n\phi} = \frac{1}{2\pi}\sqrt{\frac{C_\phi}{M_{m0}}\frac{ba^3}{12}} \tag{9.21}$$

It is seen from Eq. (9.21) that the linear dimension of the contact area perpendicular to the axis of rotation exercises a considerably greater effect on the natural frequency of rocking vibrations than the other dimension. With a change in natural frequency, the maximum amplitude of motion [Eq. (9.18)] is also altered. This principle is sometimes used in proportioning the sides of a machine foundation undergoing predominantly rocking vibrations.

The amplitude of the vertical motion of the edge of the footing is

$$A = \frac{a}{2} \times A_\phi$$

$$= \frac{M_0 a/2}{M_{m0}(\omega_{n\phi}^2 - \omega^2)} \tag{9.22}$$

If the footing is undergoing vertical oscillations along with rocking, the total amplitude is

$$A_{total} = A + A_z \qquad (9.23)$$

where A_z is determined from Eq. (9.10).

Rocking vibrations occur mostly in machines that are mounted on high pedestals and that have unbalanced horizontal forces and exciting moments.

9.9 YAWING VIBRATIONS OF A BLOCK

If the footing is subjected to yawing under the influence of a torsional moment M_z in the plane on top of the block (Fig. 9.9) the equation of motion is

$$M_{mz}\ddot{\psi} + C_\psi J_z \psi = M_z \sin \omega t \qquad (9.24)$$

in which M_{mz}= mass moment of inertia of the machine and foundation about
the axis of rotation (z-axis)
J_z = polar moment of inertia of foundation base area
ψ = angle of torsion of foundation
C_ψ = coefficient of elastic nonuniform shear

The expressions for natural frequency and maximum angular displacements are as follows:

$$f_{n\psi} = \frac{1}{2\pi}\sqrt{\frac{C_\psi J_z}{M_{mz}}} \qquad (9.25a)$$

If we compare Eq. (9.25a) with Eq. (9.9a), it will be seen that the spring constant in nonuniform shear k_ψ

$$k_\psi = C_\psi J_z \qquad (9.25b)$$

$$\psi_{max} = \frac{M_z}{M_{mz}(\omega_{n\psi}^2 - \omega^2)} \qquad (9.26)$$

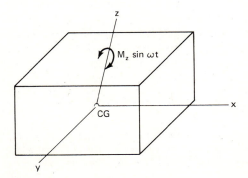

Figure 9.9 Block foundation undergoing yawing vibrations.

9.10 SIMULTANEOUS ROCKING, SLIDING, AND VERTICAL VIBRATIONS OF A BLOCK

In this section, a general case will be considered in which rocking, sliding, and vertical motions of a foundation occur simultaneously.

Figure 9.10 shows a foundation acted upon by the following oscillatory loads:

1. vertical force $P_z(t) = P_z \sin \omega t$
2. horizontal force $P_x(t) = P_x \sin \omega t$
3. moment $M(t) = M_y \sin \omega t$

All of these loads are acting at the combined center of gravity (CG) of the machine and the foundation. It will be assumed that the CG of the contact area and the CG of the machine and foundation mass lie on one vertical line. If the origin of coordinates is located at the center of gravity of the machine and foundation at O, the following displacements of the foundation have occurred (Fig. 9.10):

1. displacement in the vertical direction z
2. displacement in the horizontal direction x_0 at the base
3. rotation of the base ϕ

The equations of motions can be written as follows:

1. In the z direction:

$$m\ddot{z} = \Sigma F_z(t) \qquad (9.27)$$

2. In the x direction:

$$m\ddot{x} = \sum F_x(t) \qquad (9.28)$$

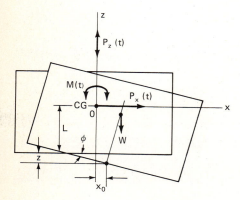

Figure 9.10 Block foundation under the action of simultaneous oscillatory vertical $[P_z(t)]$ and horizontal $[P_x(t)]$ forces and moment $[M(t)]$.

3. In the rotational mode:

$$M_m \ddot{\phi} = \sum M(t) \tag{9.29}$$

in which M_m = mass moment of inertia of the machine and foundation about an axis passing through the combined CG and in the direction of the y axis.

The loads and moments acting on the foundation in the displaced position will now be evaluated:

1. Due to vertical displacement Z of the foundation, upward reaction Z_1

$$Z_1 = -C_u A Z \tag{9.30}$$

Due to static weight W, the upward reaction is $C_u A Z_{\text{stat}}$, and the two forces balance numerically. But the displacement of the CG due to rotation of the block gives rise to a moment M_w about the y axis:

$$M_w = + WL \cdot \phi \tag{9.31}$$

in which L = distance of center of gravity of the machine and foundation from the base of the foundation.
This moment acts in the clockwise direction and is hence positive.

2. Horizontal reaction x_1, due to the elastic resistance of soil, acts opposite to the assumed positive direction of x_0; hence,

$$x_1 = -C_\tau A x_0 \tag{9.32}$$

If the displacement of the CG of the machine and foundation is x, then

$$x_0 = x - L\phi \tag{9.33a}$$

and

$$x_1 = -C_\tau A(x - L\phi) \tag{9.33b}$$

3. The moment of x_1 about the CG of the block is

$$M_x = C_\tau AL(x - L\phi) \tag{9.34}$$

and acts in the clockwise direction and is hence positive.

4. Resistance of soil induced by rotation of the foundation by Φ: The moment of soil reaction about the CG is from Eq. (9.13):

$$M_0 = -C_\phi \phi I \tag{9.35}$$

in which I = moment of inertia of foundation contact area with respect to the axis passing through the centroid of the area and perpendicular to the plane of vibrations.
Forces $P_z(t)$, $P_x(t)$ and moment $M(t)$ are all considered to be positive at this particular instant.

Substituting the relevant forces and moments in the equations of motion (9.27), (9.28), and (9.29), we get

$$m\ddot{Z} + C_u AZ\cdot = P_z \sin \omega t \qquad (9.36a)$$

$$m\ddot{x} + C_\tau Ax - C_\tau AL\phi = P_x \sin \omega t \qquad (9.36b)$$

$$M_m\ddot{\phi} + \phi(-WL + C_\tau AL^2 + C_\phi I) - C_\tau ALx = M_y \sin \omega t \qquad (9.36c)$$

Equation (9.36a) contains terms involving Z only. Hence, the motion in the Z direction is independent of any other motion. Equation (9.36b) and (9.36c) contain terms in both x and ϕ. Hence, motion in the x direction and about the y axis are interdependent. If a foundation is subjected to a horizontal force or a moment about its center of gravity, it will undergo both translation and rocking.

Since vertical vibrations can occur independently of any other vibrations, the treatment given in Sec. 9.6 for such vibrations holds. Simultaneous rocking and sliding are analyzed below:

Natural Frequencies

The system with motion represented by Eqs. (9.36b) and (9.36c) has two natural frequencies, which can be determined by making the right side equal to zero. Thus, we obtain

$$m\ddot{x} + C_\tau Ax - C_\tau AL\phi = 0 \qquad (9.37a)$$

$$M_m\ddot{\phi} + \phi(C_\tau AL^2 + C_\phi I - WL) - C_\tau ALx = 0 \qquad (9.37b)$$

Let

$$x = X \sin(\omega_n t + \alpha) \qquad (9.38a)$$

and

$$\phi = \Phi \sin(\omega_n t + \alpha) \qquad (9.38b)$$

be the solutions of Eq. (9.37), where X, Φ, and α are arbitrary constants characterized by the initial conditions of motion.

Substituting these solutions in Eq. (9.37), we get

$$-m\omega_n^2 X + C_\tau AX - C_\tau AL\Phi = 0$$

or $\qquad (9.39)$

$$X(C_\tau A - m\omega_n^2) - C_\tau AL\Phi = 0$$

and

$$-M_m\omega_n^2\Phi + \Phi(C_\tau AL^2 + C_\phi I - WL) - C_\tau ALX = 0$$

or $\qquad (9.40)$

$$-C_\tau ALX + \Phi(C_\tau AL^2 + C_\phi I - WL - M_m\omega_n^2) = 0$$

Equations (9.39) and (9.40) are homogeneous equations in X and Φ, and both of these constants can be eliminated. From Eq. (9.39), we obtain

$$X = \frac{C_\tau A L}{C_\tau A - m\omega_n^2} \Phi \tag{9.41}$$

and from Eq. (9.40), we obtain

$$X = \frac{C_\tau A L^2 + C_\phi I - WL - M_m \omega_n^2}{C_\tau A L} \Phi \tag{9.42}$$

From Eqs. (9.41) and (9.42), we get either

$$X = \Phi = 0$$

which is a trivial solution or

$$C_\tau^2 A^2 L^2 = (C_\tau A - m\omega_n^2)(C_\tau A L^2 + C_\phi I - WL - M_m \omega_n^2) \tag{9.43}$$

The above equation contains only ω_n as an unknown that can now be obtained. Eq. (9.43) is therefore the frequency equation. This may be rewritten as

$$C_\tau^2 A^2 L^2 = C_\tau A^2 L^2 + C_\tau A(C_\phi I - WL) - C_\tau A M_m \omega_n^2$$
$$- C_\tau A L^2 m\omega_n^2 - (C_\phi I - WL)m\omega_n^2 + M_m m\omega_n^4$$

Dividing by mM_m and rearranging, we obtain

$$\omega_n^4 - \omega_n^2 \left(\frac{C_\phi I - WL}{M_m} + \frac{C_\tau A}{m} \frac{M_m + mL^2}{M_m} \right) + \frac{C_\tau A}{m} \left(\frac{C_\phi I - WL}{M_m} \right) = 0 \tag{9.44}$$

If M_{m0} = mass moment of inertia of the foundation and machine about an axis passing through the centroid of the base area and perpendicular to the plane of vibrations, then

$$M_{m0} = M_m + mL^2$$

Letting

$$\frac{M_m}{M_{m0}} = \gamma(\gamma < 1)$$

Equation (9.44) can be rewritten as

$$\omega_n^4 - \frac{\omega_n^2}{\gamma} \left(\frac{C_\phi I - WL}{M_{m0}} + \frac{C_\tau A}{m} \right) + \frac{C_\tau A}{m} \frac{C_\phi I - WL}{\gamma M_{m0}} = 0$$

But according to Eqs. (9.12a) and (9.17):

$$\frac{C_\phi I - WL}{M_{m0}} = \omega_{n\phi}^2 \qquad \text{and} \qquad \frac{C_\tau A}{m} = \omega_{nx}^2$$

Therefore, the frequency equation becomes

$$\omega_n^4 - \frac{\omega_{n\phi}^2 + \omega_{nx}^2}{\gamma}\omega_n^2 + \frac{\omega_{n\phi}^2\omega_{nx}^2}{\gamma} = 0 \qquad (9.45)$$

This equation will have two positive roots ω_{n1} and ω_{n2} corresponding to the two natural frequencies of the system.

It can be shown that the smaller of the two natural frequencies ω_{n1} ($\omega_{n2} > \omega_{n1}$) is smaller than the smallest of the two limiting natural frequencies ω_{nx} and $\omega_{n\phi}$ and the larger natural frequency is always larger than ω_{nx} and $\omega_{n\phi}$. Now Eq. (9.45) will give two roots as follows:

$$\omega_{n1,2}^2 = \frac{1}{2\gamma}\left[\omega_{n\phi}^2 + \omega_{nx}^2 \pm \sqrt{\left(\omega_{n\phi}^2 + \omega_{nx}^2\right)^2 - 4\gamma\omega_{n\phi}^2\omega_{nx}^2}\right] \qquad (9.46)$$

or

$$\omega_{n1}^2 + \omega_{n2}^2 = \frac{\omega_{n\phi}^2 + \omega_{nx}^2}{\gamma} \qquad (9.47)$$

and

$$\omega_{n1}^2 \times \omega_{n2}^2 = \frac{\omega_{n\phi}^2\omega_{nx}^2}{\gamma} \qquad (9.48)$$

and

$$\omega_{n1}^2 - \omega_{n2}^2 = \frac{1}{\gamma}\sqrt{\left(\omega_{n\phi}^2 + \omega_{nx}^2 - 4\gamma\omega_{n\phi}^2\omega_{nx}^2\right)} \qquad (9.49)$$

Amplitudes of Motion

Having determined the natural frequencies of the system, we will next compute amplitudes of motion for several particular cases.

$P_x \sin \omega t$ only acting Equations (9.36b) and (9.36c) may then be rewritten as

$$m\ddot{x} + C_r A x - C_r A L\phi = P_x \sin \omega t \qquad (9.50)$$

$$M_m\ddot{\phi} + \phi\left(C_r A L^2 + C_\phi I - WL\right) - C_r A L x = 0 \qquad (9.51)$$

Let us assume that the solutions to these equations are

$$x = A_x \sin \omega t$$
$$\Phi = A_\phi \sin \omega t$$

where A_x and A_ϕ are the maximum sliding and rocking amplitudes. Substituting these solutions in the above equations, we obtain

$$A_x\left(C_r A - m\omega^2\right) - C_r A L A_\phi = P_x \qquad (9.52a)$$

$$- C_r A L A_x + A_\phi\left(C_r A L^2 + C_\phi I - WL - M_m\omega^2\right) = 0 \qquad (9.52b)$$

or

$$A_x = \frac{C_\tau A L^2 + C_\phi I - WL - M_m \omega^2}{C_\tau A L} A_\phi \qquad (9.52c)$$

Substituting for A_x from above in Eq. (9.52a), we get

$$\frac{(C_\tau A L^2 + C_\phi I - WL - M_m \omega^2)(C_\tau A - m\omega^2)}{C_\tau A L} A_\phi - C_\tau A L A_\phi = P_x$$

which gives

$$A_\phi = \frac{C_\tau A L}{m M_m \left\{ \dfrac{C_\tau A}{m} \dfrac{(C_\phi I - WL)}{M_m} - \omega^2 \left[\dfrac{C_\tau A}{m} \dfrac{(mL^2 + M_m)}{M_m} + \dfrac{(C_\phi I - WL)}{M_m} \right] + \omega^4 \right\}} P_x$$

$$= \frac{C_\tau A L}{m M_m \left[\dfrac{\omega_{nx}^2 \omega_{n\phi}^2}{\gamma} - \dfrac{\omega^2}{\gamma} (\omega_{nx}^2 + \omega_{n\phi}^2) + \omega^4 \right]} P_x$$

Substituting from Eqs. (9.47) and (9.48), we get

$$A_\phi = \frac{C_\tau A L}{m M_m \left[\omega_{n1}^2 \omega_{n2}^2 - \omega^2 (\omega_{n1}^2 + \omega_{n2}^2) + \omega^4 \right]} P_x$$

or

$$A_\phi = \frac{C_\tau A L}{m M_m (\omega_{n1}^2 - \omega^2)(\omega_{n2}^2 - \omega^2)} P_x \qquad (9.53)$$

Let $m M_m (\omega_{n1}^2 - \omega^2)(\omega_{n2} - \omega^2) = \Delta(\omega^2)$; we obtain

$$A_\phi = \frac{C_\tau A L}{\Delta(\omega^2)} \times P_x \qquad (9.54)$$

Substituting for A_ϕ in Eq. (9.52c), we get

$$A_x = \frac{C_\tau A L^2 + C_\phi I - WL - M_m \omega^2}{\Delta(\omega^2)} P_x \qquad (9.55)$$

$M_y \sin wt$ only acting If only $M_y \sin \omega t$ is acting, then Eqs. (9.36b) and (9.36c) may be rewritten as

$$m \ddot{x} + C_\tau A x - C_\tau A L \phi = 0 \qquad (9.56a)$$

$$M_m \ddot{\phi} + \phi (C_\tau A L^2 + C_\phi I - WL) - C_\tau A L x = M_y \sin \omega t \qquad (9.56b)$$

Assuming solutions as for Eqs. (9.50) and (9.51), it can be shown that the following expressions hold:

$$A_x = \frac{C_\tau AL}{\Delta(\omega^2)} M_y \qquad (9.57a)$$

$$A_\phi = \frac{C_\tau A - m\omega^2}{\Delta\omega^2} M_y \qquad (9.57b)$$

When both the unbalanced force P_x and moment M_y are acting, the amplitudes of motion are as follows:

$$A_x = \frac{(C_\tau AL^2 + C_\phi I - WL - M_m\omega^2)P_x + (C_\tau AL)M_y}{\Delta(\omega^2)} \qquad (9.58a)$$

and

$$A_\phi = \frac{(C_\tau AL)P_x + (C_\tau A - m\omega^2)M_y}{\Delta(\omega^2)} \qquad (9.58b)$$

If a foundation is subjected only to exciting moment M_y, from Eqs. (9.57), we obtain the ratio of two amplitudes as

$$\rho = \frac{A_x}{A_\phi} = \frac{C_\tau AL}{C_\tau A - m\omega^2} = \frac{\omega_{nx}^2}{\omega_{nx}^2 - \omega^2} L \qquad (9.58c)$$

If the frequency of excitation ω is small in comparison to ω_{nx}, $\rho \simeq L$; that is, then the axis of rotation lies along the central axis of the base area. The foundation undergoes only rocking, and sliding is absent.

As ω increases, the denominator decreases and ρ increases. The center of rotation shifts below the base of the footing and the foundation undergoes simultaneous rocking and sliding vibrations (Fig. 9.11a). The two motions are in phase with each other.

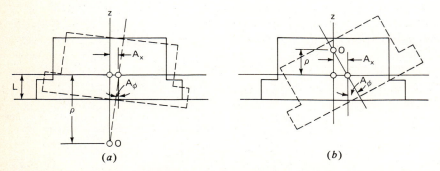

(a)   (b)

Figure 9.11 (a) Rocking and sliding in phase with each other. (b) Rocking and sliding in phase opposition.

If $\omega = \omega_{nx}$, $\rho \to \infty$; the foundation will undergo only sliding and rocking vibrations will be absent.

As ω becomes greater than ω_{nx}, ρ changes sign and sliding and rocking vibrations occur in phase opposition, as in Fig. 9.11b. If ω increases very much, $\rho \to 0$ and the axis of rotation lies at the center of gravity of the machine and foundation.

9.11 INDIAN STANDARD FOR DESIGN AND CONSTRUCTION OF FOUNDATIONS FOR RECIPROCATING MACHINES

No standards on the subject have been issued either by the U.S. Bureau of Standards or the ASTM. The Indian Standard Institution has issued several standards on the subject. These standards are based on the practices being followed in India and several European countries.

Indian Standard Institution issued IS 2974 (Part I) on this subject in 1964; it was revised in 1969. The salient provisions of this standard include:

Necessary data

1. The following information shall be obtained from the manufacturers of the machine for guidance in designing:
   (a) a detailed loading diagram comprising a plan, elevation, and section showing details of communication and the point of application of all loads on the foundation
   (b) the distance between the axis of the main shaft of the machine and the top of the foundation
   (c) capacity or rated output of the machine
   (d) operating speed of the machine
   (e) exciting forces of the machine and short-circuit moment of the motor, if any
2. The following subsurface soil should also be known:
   (a) soil profile and data (including soil characteristics) generally to a sufficient depth or hard stratum
   (b) soil investigation to the extent necessary in accordance with IS 1892-1962† and for the determination of dynamic properties of soil in accordance with IS 5249-1977
   (c) the relative positions of the water table below ground at different times of the year
3. The minimum distance to any important foundation in the vicinity of the machine foundation should be ascertained.

---

† Code of practice for site investigations for foundations, revised in 1977. Or ASTM D 420-69 (1975): "Investigating and Sampling Soil and Rock for Engineering Purposes."

Dimensional Criteria

Area of Block—The size of a foundation block (in plan) should be larger than the bed plate of the machine it supports, with a minimum all-round clearance of 150 mm.

Depth—In all cases, the foundation should be deep enough to rest on good bearing stratum and to ensure stability against rotations in the vertical plane.

Center of Gravity—The combined center of gravity of the machine and the block should be as far below the top of foundation as possible, but in no case shall it be above the top of foundations.

Eccentricity—The eccentricity should not exceed 5 percent of the least width in any horizontal direction.

Vibration Criteria

Wherever possible, the operating frequency should be smaller than the natural frequency of the foundation-soil system, and the frequency ratio should be less than 0.5. For unimportant machines, it may have a maximum value of 0.6. When the operating frequency is higher than the upper natural frequency of the foundation-soil system of the machine, the frequency ratio should be more than 2 for important machines and more than 1.5 for others.

Permissible Amplitude

In no case should the permissible amplitude exceed the limiting amplitude prescribed for the machine by the manufacturer.

In fixing the permissible amplitude, considerations should also be given to machines and structures in the neighborhood and the possibility of resonance or disturbance. From the data available so far, it appears that vibrations in neighboring structures will be negligible if the vibration amplitude of the foundation is less than 0.20 mm.

For machines generating translation and torsion, the combined amplitudes should be as estimated.

Several Machines on a Common Mat

A number of similar machines erected on individual pedestals may be mounted on a common raft. They should be placed symmetrically along the two axes so there is no rotation in the raft under dynamic forces.

The analyses for these machines should be made as though their foundations were independent of each other by breaking the raft into sections corresponding to separate foundations.

The design value for the permissible amplitude of vibrations may be increased by 30 percent.

Permissible Stresses†

The allowable stresses for concrete and steel specified in IS 456-1964‡ should be reduced to 40 percent for concrete and 55 percent for steel if the detailed designs for the foundation and its components are limited to the static load of the foundation and the machine. Considering temperature or shrinkage and all other loadings together, these assumed stresses may be exceeded by 33.33 percent.

Or

On the other hand, the full values of stresses for steel and concrete (as specified in IS:456-1964‡) may be allowed if the dynamic loads are separately considered in the detailed design, by applying suitable dynamic and fatigue factors.

The soil stress below the foundations should not exceed 80 percent of the allowable stress under static loading that is determined in accordance with IS 1904-1978.§

When seismic forces are considered, the allowable stresses on the soil may be increased as specified in IS: 1893-1975.¶

Construction

Concrete strength should be specified on the basis of 28 days strength. The concrete used should be grade M150-200.

It is desirable to concrete the entire block in one operation without construction joints.

The amount of reinforcement in the foundation should not be less than 25 kg/m^3. For machines that require special designs for their foundations, such as those that pump explosive gases, the reinforcement may be increased.

Around all openings, and so forth, steel reinforcements in the form of a cage and equal to 0.50 to 0.75 percent of a cross section of the opening should be provided.

The minimum diameter of the bars should be 12 mm and the maximum spacing should be 200 mm in order to take care of any shrinkage in the concrete. A minimum cover of 75 mm at the bottom and 50 mm on the sides and top should be provided.

Foundation bolts should be properly anchored.

---

† For permissible stresses in steel and concrete and on soil, the corresponding stresses under static conditions may also be adopted from codes.

‡ Code of practice for plain and reinforced concrete, 2d rev.

§ Code of practice for structural safety of buildings: Foundations, 2d rev.

¶ Criteria for earthquake resistant design of structure, 3d rev.

9.12 DESIGN PROCEDURE FOR A BLOCK FOUNDATION

Having studied the analysis of a block and provisions of a code on the design and construction of a foundation, a step-by-step listing of design procedure follows.

Design Data

Check to ensure that all design data listed in Sec. 9.11 have been supplied. Many times, manufacturers may not supply all of the information initially. Therefore, this information must be obtained even if repeated requests have to be made.

Selecting Soil Constants

For a preliminary design, the soil constants may be adopted from the values given in this chapter as well as in Chap. 4. For all important jobs, it is recommended that dynamic soil properties be determined in the laboratory and in the field for at least three different strain levels. A particular value may be picked for an anticipated strain level in a given design problem. A correction for confining pressure must be applied before proceeding with a design.

Often it may be desirable to pick a range of soil constants and to work out limiting values of the natural frequencies and motion amplitudes for the range of soil constant values selected.

Design Diagram of a Foundation

From dimensional criteria listed in Sec. 9.11, select trial dimensions for the foundation. To simplify computations, it is advisable to select a simple shape in plan. Any grooves, projections, and asymmetry should be avoided as far as possible.

Centering the Foundation Area in Contact With Soil and Determining Soil Pressures

Determine the combined center of gravity* for the machine and the foundations in x, y, and z plane and check to see that the eccentricity along x or y axis is not over 5 percent. This is the upper limit for this type of analysis. If eccentricity exceeds 5 percent, the additional rocking due to vertical eccentric loading must be considered in the analysis (Barkan, 1962).

The static pressure should be checked; it should be less than 80 percent of the allowable soil pressure under static conditions. This condition is met in most practical foundations.

---

* This is better determined in a tabular form as shown in Table 9.2.

Table 9.2 Determination of CG of the system

Element of system	Dimensions			Weight of element	Mass of element	Coordinate CG of the element			Static moments of mass of elements		
	a_x	a_y	a_z			x_i	y_i	z_i	$m_i x_i$	$m_i y_i$	$m_i z_i$
1											
2											
3											
Total					Total		Total				

Design Values for Exciting Loads and Possible Forms of Foundation Vibrations

The final values of forces and resulting moments may now be redetermined with respect to the combined center of gravity of the system. If the vertical unbalanced force acts at some eccentricity, it would give rise to a moment. Similarly, the horizontal unbalanced force acts at a certain distance above the top of a block foundation. The magnitude of the moment due to horizontal force equals the product of the horizontal force and the sum of the distance between the bearing level of the machine and the top of the block, plus the distance between the top of the block and the center of gravity of the combined system.

The relative magnitudes of the unbalanced forces and moments should help determine the nature of vibrations in the block foundation.

Determining Moments of Inertia and Mass Moments of Inertia

The following moments of inertia and mass moments of inertia need be determined.

I = Moment of inertia of the base area about an axis passing through the centroid of the base contact area and perpendicular to the plane of vibrations. It equals $b \cdot a^3 / 12$, where a is the dimension of the rectangular area in the plane of vibration and b is the dimension perpendicular to this plane.

M_{m0} = Mass moment of inertia of the whole system about the above axis.

M_m = Mass moment of inertia of the system about an axis passing through the combined center of gravity and perpendicular to the plane of vibrations.

$$M_m = M_{m0} - mL^2$$

in which L = height of the combined center of gravity above the base.

Then
$$\frac{M_m}{M_{m0}} = \gamma$$

If a moment in the plan of the top of the block is also acting, then the following moment of inertia and mass moment of inertia also are determined:

$J_z =$ Polar moment of foundation base area about the vertical axis of rotation passing through CG of the contact area.

$M_{mz} =$ Mass moment of inertia of the block and foundation about the axis of rotation.

Computation of Natural Frequencies and Amplitudes of Motion

Decoupled modes Vertical oscillations and torsional vibrations can occur independently of any other vibrations. Thus the natural frequencies and corresponding amplitudes can be determined with the help of the following equations:

$$\omega_{nz} = \sqrt{\frac{C_u A}{m}} \tag{9.9a}$$

$$A_z = \frac{P_0}{m(\omega_{nz}^2 - \omega^2)} \tag{9.10}$$

$$\omega_{n\psi} = \sqrt{\frac{C_\phi \cdot J_z}{M_{mz}}} \tag{9.25a}$$

$$\psi_{max} = \frac{M_z}{M_{mz}(\omega_{n\psi}^2 - \omega^2)} \tag{9.26}$$

Coupled modes Sliding and rocking are coupled modes of vibrations. The following natural frequencies are determined:

$$\omega_{nx} = \sqrt{\frac{C_\tau \cdot A}{m}} \tag{9.12a}$$

$$\omega_{n\phi} = \sqrt{\frac{C_\phi \cdot I}{M_{mo}}} \tag{9.19a}$$

and

$$\omega_{n1,2}^2 = \frac{1}{2\gamma}\left[(\omega_{n\phi}^2 - \omega_{nx}^2) \pm \sqrt{(\omega_{n\phi}^2 + \omega_{nx}^2)^2 - 4\gamma\omega_{n\phi}^2 \cdot \omega_{nx}^2}\right] \tag{9.46}$$

Now amplitudes of forced vibrations can be computed with the help of the following equations:

$$A_x = \frac{\left(C_\tau AL^2 + C_\phi I - WL - M_m \omega^2 \right) P_x + \left(C_\tau AL \right) M_y}{\Delta(\omega^2)} \quad (9.58a)$$

$$A_\phi = \frac{\left(C_\tau AL \right) P_x + \left(C_\tau A - m\omega^2 \right) M_y}{\Delta(\omega^2)} \quad (9.58b)$$

in which A_x = linear horizontal amplitude of the combined center of gravity and A_ϕ = rotational amplitude in radians about the combined center of gravity.

Now the amplitude of the block should be determined at the bearing level of the foundation. It is this amplitude that needs to be compared with the permissible amplitude of motion.

9.13 VERTICAL VIBRATIONS ACCORDING TO THE ELASTIC-HALF-SPACE THEORY

The soil is assumed to be homogeneous, isotropic, and elastic, and characterized by shear modulus G and Poisson's ratio v.

Reissner (1936, 1937) established the theoretical basis for studying the response of a footing supported by an elastic half space. The pressure distribution below the base of the circular footing was considered to be uniform for vertical vibrations. The effects of variation in the contact pressure beneath a footing oscillating vertically were studied by Sung (1953) and Quinlan (1953). Bycroft (1956) gave solutions for vibrations of a thin, rigid, circular disc in all of the four modes. The use of elastic-half-space theories for analysis and design of vibrating footings has been described by Richart (1962), Richart and Whitman (1967), Whitman and Richart (1967), and Richart, Hall, and Woods (1970). A brief description of the analysis will be presented.

Vertical Vibrations

The footing is generally assumed to be circular with a radius r_0 and mass m. Reissner (1936, 1937) established two dimensionless parameters to define the motion of this footing. These are:

Dimensionless frequency factor

$$a_0 = \omega r_0 \sqrt{\frac{\rho}{G}} = \frac{2\pi f r_0}{v_s} \quad (9.59)$$

in which ω = circular frequency of vibrations
$\qquad r_0$ = radius of the footing
$\qquad \rho = \gamma/g$, mass density of the elastic body
$\qquad G$ = shear modulus
$\qquad f$ = frequency of vibrations
$\qquad v_s = \sqrt{G/\rho}$ velocity of propagation of shear wave in elastic body

Mass ratio b and B_z (Lysmer and Richart, 1966)

$$b = \frac{m}{\rho r_0^3} = \frac{W}{\rho r_0^3 \cdot g} \qquad (9.60a)$$

and

$$B_z = \frac{1 - \nu}{4} \frac{m}{\rho r_0^3} \qquad (9.60b)$$

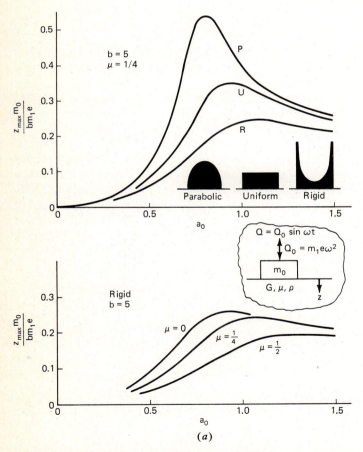

Figure 9.12a Effect by pressure distribution and Poisson's ratio on theoretical response for vertical footing vibrations. *(After Richart and Whitman, 1967.)*

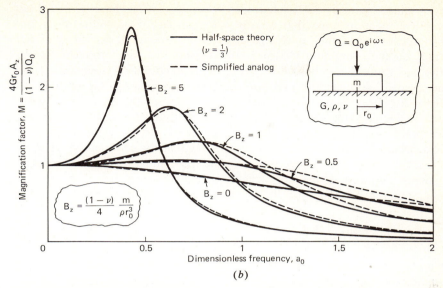

Figure 9.12b Response of rigid circular footing to vertical force developed by constant force excitation. *(After Lysmer and Richart, 1966.)*

Figure 9.12*a* shows typical response curves for three types of pressure distributions for $b = 5$ and $\mu = \frac{1}{4}$ for frequency-dependent excitation. The effect of Poisson's ratio on the response is as shown in Fig. 9.12*a*.

The shapes of the curves in Fig. 9.12 are similar to those in Fig. 2.15*a*. Theoretically, damping is zero in an elastic body. However, the effect of damping is introduced throughout the semi-infinite body by the loss of energy radiated from the footing. Curves in Fig. 9.12 show a distinct finite peak, as for a damped case (Richart and Whitman, 1967).

The shapes of the response curves are mainly related to parameter *b*. An increase in *b* leads to sharper peaks with greater maximum motions. Figure 9.12*a* also shows the influence of changes in pressure distribution on these theoretical response curves. A change from a pressure distribution corresponding to a rigid base (where most of the reaction is concentrated near the periphery) to a distribution where the load is carried nearer the center increases the amplitude of oscillation and reduces the frequency at which maximum amplitude occurs. Thus, for a given footing-soil system, the shape and position of the response curve can be changed if the pressure distribution on the base of the footing is a function of frequency and amplitude of motion.

Figure 9.12*b* shows the influence of a change in Poisson's ratio on the response of the footing.

In the theory of elastic spring, the pressure distribution did not affect the response.

Throughout the past several decades there have been numerous attempts to fit theoretical curves to test data from vibrating footing tests by appropriate choices of lumped parameters (Richart and Whitman, 1967). Hertwig, Früh, and Lorenz (1933) demonstrated that this fit was possible for individual tests, but that different values of the lumped parameters were required for different test conditions on the same soil. Reissner (1936) compared his theoretical results from the half-space theory with those from the lumped-mass system and found that the lumped parameters should be dependent on frequency for good agreement between these two methods. Hsieh (1962) described this frequency dependence of the lumped parameters in more detail. Lysmer and Richart (1966) showed that a lumped-system analogue can be developed for vertical vibration of a rigid circular footing, which provides close agreement between the response curves from the elastic-half-space theory in the frequency range near resonance where significant amplitudes are developed. The motion equation for this lumped-system representation of the vertical motion of the rigid circular footing is

$$m\ddot{z} + \frac{3.4}{1 - \nu} r_0^2 \sqrt{G\rho}\, \dot{z} + \frac{4Gr_0}{1 - \nu} z = P_0(t) \tag{9.61}$$

in which z is the vertical displacement, $\dot{z}$ the velocity, and $\ddot{z}$ the acceleration, and $P_0(t)$ is the time-dependent exciting force. Figure 9.12b shows a comparison of the response of a vertically vibrating footing by the exact solution and the analogue. Equation 9.61 is similar to Equation 2.37a with

$$c = \frac{3\cdot4}{1 - \nu} r_0^2 \sqrt{G\rho} \tag{9.62}$$

and

$$k = \frac{4Gr_0}{1 - \nu} \tag{9.63}$$

Now the critical damping c_c is

$$c_c = 2\sqrt{km} = 2\sqrt{\frac{4Gr_0}{1 - \nu} m} \tag{9.64}$$

and

$$\xi = \frac{c}{c_c} = \frac{0.85}{\sqrt{1 - \nu}} \frac{1}{\sqrt{b}} \tag{9.65}$$

It should be noticed that damping automatically enters into the solution by elastic-half-space theory, while damping had been neglected in the linear spring theory. As pointed out earlier, the effect of neglecting small damping is to make the foundation design overly conservative in many cases.

The above analysis was considered for a circular footing. If the footing is rectangular in plan, with dimensions of $a \times b$, the equivalent radius may be determined from the following relationship:

$$r_0 = \sqrt{\frac{a \times b}{\pi}} \tag{9.66}$$

Chae's (1969) experimental data, however, showed that use of the equivalent radius r_0 is reasonable for determining resonant frequency, but that the amplitude of vibration is smaller than that for an equivalent circular foundation. Thus, the use of Eq. (9.66) may lead to somewhat conservative results.

9.14 SLIDING VIBRATIONS ACCORDING TO THE ELASTIC-HALF-SPACE THEORY

Bycroft (1956) gave a solution for the motion of a rigid circular plate on the surface of an elastic half space. For sliding motion, the solution is valid for all values of Poisson's ratio ν. Hall (1967) developed an analogue between the above solution and the one based on elastic linear weightless springs. The expressions for equivalent spring and damping are as follows:

$$k_x = \frac{32(1 - \nu)}{7 - 8\nu} Gr_0 \tag{9.67}$$

and

$$c = \frac{18.4(1 - \nu)}{7 - 8\nu} r_0^2 \sqrt{\rho G} \tag{9.68}$$

The corresponding mass ratio (B_x) and the dimensionless frequency factor are defined as follows:

$$B_x = \frac{7 - 8\nu}{32(1 - \nu)} \frac{m}{\rho r_0^3} \tag{9.69}$$

and

$$a_0 = \omega r_0 \sqrt{\frac{\rho}{G}} \tag{9.59}$$

Critical damping c_c is given by

$$c_c = 2\sqrt{mk}$$

or

$$c_c = 2\sqrt{\frac{m32(1 - \nu)}{(7 - 8\nu)} Gr_0} \tag{9.70}$$

and

$$\xi = \frac{c}{c_c}$$

$$\xi = \frac{0.2875}{\sqrt{B_x}} \tag{9.71}$$

Figure 9.13 shows a comparison of the magnification factor† versus the nondimensional frequency factor by the exact solution and the analogue solution. For all practical purposes, the two solutions are identical.

† Defined as ratio of dynamic displacement to static displacement.

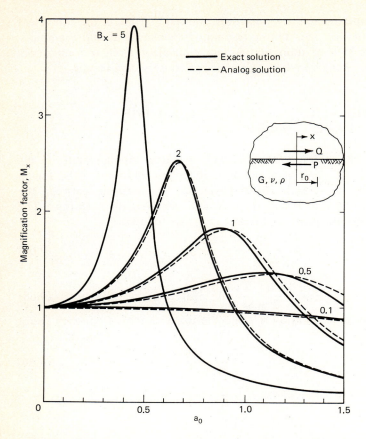

Figure 9.13 Response of a rigid circular footing on elastic half space in pure sliding. (*After Hall, 1967.*)

If the footing is not circular, the equivalent radius r_0 can be determined from Eq. (9.66):

$$r_0 = \sqrt{\frac{ab}{\pi}} \qquad (9.66)$$

9.15 ROCKING VIBRATIONS ACCORDING TO THE ELASTIC-HALF-SPACE THEORY

Bycroft (1956) gave solutions for pure rocking of a circular rigid footing resting on the surface of an elastic half space for $\nu = 0$. Hall (1967) defined a spring constant and damping for the analogue to reproduce the exact solution, as for pure sliding, as follows:

$$k_\phi = \frac{8Gr_0^3}{3(1 - \nu)}$$ (9.72)

and

$$c = \frac{0.80r_0^4\sqrt{G\rho}}{(1 - \nu)(1 + B_\phi)}$$ (9.73)

The corresponding inertia ratio B_ϕ† and nondimensional frequency factors are defined as follows:

$$B_\phi = \frac{3(1 - \nu)}{8}\frac{M_{m0}}{\rho r_0^5}$$ (9.74)

and

$$a_0 = \omega r_0\sqrt{\rho/G}$$ (9.59)

Critical damping c_c is given by

$$c_c = 2\sqrt{k_\phi M_{m0}}$$

$$c_c = 2\sqrt{\frac{8Gr_0^3}{3(1 - \nu)} \times M_{m0}}$$ (9.75)

and

$$\xi = \frac{c}{c_c}$$

or

$$\xi = \frac{0.15}{(1 + B_\phi)\sqrt{B\phi}}$$ (9.76)

Figure 9.14 shows a comparison of the magnification factor versus the nondimensional frequency factor by the exact solution and the analogue solution. For all practical purposes, the two solutions are similar.

If the footing is not circular, the equivalent radius r_0 may be determined from Eq. (9.77):

$$r_0 = \sqrt[4]{\frac{a \times b^3}{3\pi}}$$ (9.77)

† Analogous to mass ratio in translation.

9.16 TORSIONAL VIBRATIONS ACCORDING TO THE ELASTIC-HALF-SPACE THEORY

Reissner (1937) and Reissner and Sagoci (1944) presented analytical solutions for the torsion oscillations of a circular footing resting on the surface of an elastic half space. Again, the solutions depend on the dimensionless frequency factor a_0 [Eq. (9.59)] and mass ratio B_ψ, defined as

$$B_\psi = \frac{J_\psi}{\rho r_0^5} \tag{9.78}$$

where J_ψ = polar mass moment of inertia of the footing about the vertical axis of rotation.

Richart, Hall, and Woods (1970) defined the spring constant K_ψ and damping factor ξ for torsion vibrations as follows:

$$K_\psi = \frac{16}{3} G r_0^3 \tag{9.79}$$

$$\xi = \frac{0.5}{1 + 2B_\psi} \tag{9.80}$$

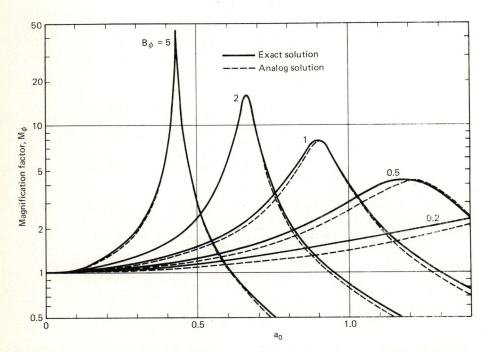

Figure 9.14 Response of a rigid footing in elastic half space in pure rocking. (*After Hall, 1967.*)

If the footing is rectangular $(a \times b)$ the equivalent radius r_0 may be determined from Eq. (9.81):

$$r_0 = \sqrt[4]{\frac{ab(a^2 + b^2)}{6\pi}} \qquad (9.81)$$

9.17 FOUNDATIONS FOR IMPACT MACHINES

As the name suggests, these machines produce an impact on the foundation. Therefore, the problem of energy dissipation and absorption would require additional consideration in this case.

Figure 9.15 shows a typical foundation for a hammer with its frame mounted on an anvil, as well as one with an A frame mounted on the foundation.

An anvil is a massive steel block on which material is forged into desired shapes by repeated blows of a falling tup. The frame supporting the tup may be mounted on the anvil or on the foundation. An elastic pad is introduced between the anvil and the foundation to absorb the energy of the impact of the tup on the anvil.

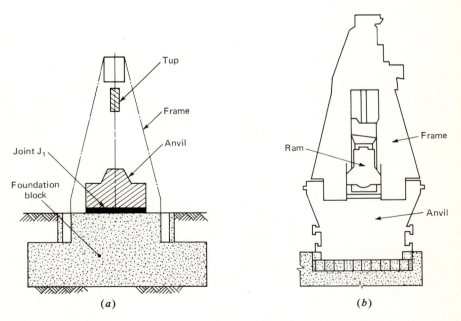

Figure 9.15 Typical arrangement of a hammer foundation resting on soil with (a) A frame mounted on foundation; (b) A frame mounted on the anvil.

Dynamic Analysis

The anvil, pad, foundation, and soil constitute a two-degree freedom system as shown in Fig. 9.16. The anvil and the block foundation are assumed to be rigid and the pad and soil to be equivalent elastic springs without mass. If

m_1 = mass of foundation and frame if the latter is mounted on the foundation, as in Fig. 9.15a

m_2 = mass of anvil (with frame if the latter is mounted on the anvil as in Fig. 9.15b)

$K_1 = C_u'A$ = coefficient of rigidity (equivalent spring constant) of soil under consideration

$Cu' = \lambda C_u$ = modified coefficient of elastic uniform compression, a multiplying factor that governs the relationship between C_u and C_u', usually 1–2, for impact depending upon the soil type

$k_2 = (E/b) \times A_2$ = coefficient of rigidity (equivalent spring constant) of the pad under the anvil

E = Young's modulus of the pad material

b = thickness of the pad

A_2 = area of the pad

Z_1 = displacement of foundation from the equilibrium position

Z_2 = displacement of anvil from the equilibrium position

ω_{na} = circular natural frequency of the foundation of the anvil on the pad

$$\omega_{na} = \sqrt{\frac{k_2}{m_2}} \tag{9.82}$$

ω_{nl} = limiting natural frequency of the foundation and anvil on soil

$$\omega_{nl} = \sqrt{\frac{k_1}{m_1 + m_2}} \tag{9.83}$$

$$\mu = \frac{m_2}{m_1}$$

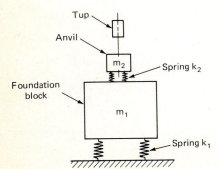

Figure 9.16 Two-mass-spring analogy for hammer foundation.

The equation of motion in free vibration may then be written as follows:

$$m_1\ddot{z}_1 + k_1 z_1 + k_2(z_1 - z_2) = 0 \qquad (9.84a)$$

$$m_2\ddot{z}_2 + K_2(z_2 - z_1) = 0 \qquad (9.84b)$$

The frequency equation can be determined by particular solutions of the motion equation.

Let

$$z_1 = A \sin \omega_n t \qquad \text{and} \qquad z_2 = B \sin \omega_n t \qquad (9.85)$$

be the solutions of Eqs. (9.84a) and (9.84b), respectively, then substituting these solutions in the motion equation gives

$$\frac{B}{A} = \frac{k_2 + k_1 - m_1\omega_n^2}{k_2} \qquad (9.86a)$$

and

$$\frac{B}{A} = \frac{k_2}{k_2 - m_2\omega_n^2} \qquad (9.86b)$$

which gives

$$k_2^2 = (k_1 + k_2)k_2 - m_1\omega_n^2 k_2 - (k_1 + k_2)m_2\omega_n^2 + m_1 m_2\omega_n^4$$

or

$$\omega_n^4 - \left(\frac{k_2(m_1 + m_2)}{m_1 m_2} + \frac{k_1}{m_1}\right)\omega_n^2 + \frac{k_1 k_2}{m_1 m_2} = 0$$

or

$$\omega_n^4 - \left(1 + \frac{m_2}{m_1}\right)\left(\frac{k_2}{m_2} + \frac{k_1}{m_1 + m_2}\right)\omega_n^2 + \frac{k_2}{m_2}\frac{k_1}{m_1 + m_2}\left(1 + \frac{m_2}{m_1}\right) = 0$$

or

$$\omega_n^4 - (1 + \mu)\left(\omega_{na}^2 + \omega_{nl}^2\right)\omega_n^2 + (1 + \mu)\omega_{nl}^2\omega_{na}^2 = 0$$

or

$$\omega_{n1,2}^2 = \tfrac{1}{2}\left[(1 + \mu)\left(\omega_{na}^2 + \omega_{nl}^2\right)\right]$$

$$\pm \sqrt{\left[(1 + \mu)\left(\omega_{na}^2 + \omega_{nl}^2\right)\right]^2 - 4(1 + \mu) \times \left(\omega_{nl}^2\omega_{na}^2\right)} \qquad (9.87)$$

The two natural frequencies of the hammer foundation may be determined by solving this frequency equation.

To solve the motion amplitudes of the anvil and hammer, proceed as follows:

Substituting ω_{n1} and ω_{n2} in Eq. (9.86b) gives

$$\left(\frac{B}{A}\right) = a_1(\text{say}) = \frac{k_2}{k_2 - m_2\omega_{n1}^2} = \frac{\omega_{na}^2}{\omega_{na}^2 - \omega_{n1}^2}$$

if $\omega_n = \omega_{n1}$ and

$$\left(\frac{B}{A}\right) = a_2(\text{say}) = \frac{\omega_{na}^2}{\omega_{na}^2 - \omega_{n2}^2}$$

if $\omega_n = \omega_{n2}$.

The general solution of differential (Eq. 9.84a and 9.84b) is given by

$$z_1 = A_1 \sin \omega_{n1}t + A_2 \cos \omega_{n1}t + B_1 \sin \omega_{n2}t + B_2 \cos \omega_{n2}t \tag{9.88a}$$

$$z_2 = a_1 A_1 \sin \omega_{n1}t + a_1 A_2 \cos \omega_{n1}t + a_2 B_1 \sin \omega_{n2}t + a_2 B_2 \cos \omega_{n2}t \tag{9.88b}$$

where A_1, A_2, B_1, and B_2 are arbitrary constants that depend upon the initial conditions of motion (to be defined later for a hammer foundation), and a_1 and a_2 correlate the motion of the anvil and the foundation. Letting

$$A_1 = \left(\omega_{na}^2 - \omega_{n1}^2\right)c^{(1)} \qquad A_2 = \left(\omega_{na}^2 - \omega_{n1}^2\right)c^{(2)}$$

$$B_1 = \left(\omega_{na}^2 - \omega_{n2}^2\right)c^{(3)} \qquad B_2 = \left(\omega_{na}^2 - \omega_{n2}^2\right)c^{(4)}$$

$$a_1 A_1 = \omega_{na}^2 c^{(1)} \qquad a_2 B_1 = \omega_{na}^2 c^{(3)}$$

$$a_1 A_2 = \omega_{na}^2 c^{(2)} \qquad a_2 B_2 = \omega_{na}^2 c^{(4)}$$

Substituting these values in Eq. (9.87a and b) gives

$$z_1 = \left(\omega_{na}^2 - \omega_{n1}^2\right)c^{(1)} \sin \omega_{n1}t + \left(\omega_{na}^2 - \omega_{n1}^2\right)c^{(2)} \cos \omega_{n1}t$$
$$+ \left(\omega_{na}^2 - \omega_{n2}^2\right)c^{(3)} \sin \omega_{n2}t + \left(\omega_{na}^2 - \omega_{n2}^2\right)c^{(4)} \cos \omega_{n2}t \tag{9.89}$$

$$z_2 = \omega_{na}^2 c^{(1)} \sin \omega_{n1}t + \omega_{na}^2 c^{(2)} \cos \omega_{n1}t + \omega_{na}^2 c^{(3)} \sin \omega_{n2}t$$
$$+ \omega_{na}^2 c^{(4)} \cos \omega_{n2}t \tag{9.90}$$

The initial conditions of motion are:

At $t = 0$, $\qquad z_1 = z_2 = 0 \qquad \dot{z}_1 = 0 \qquad \dot{z}_2 = v_a$

Substituting this condition in Eqs. (9.89) and (9.90) gives

$$0 = \left(\omega_{na}^2 - \omega_{n1}^2\right)c^{(2)} + \left(\omega_{na}^2 - \omega_{n2}^2\right)c^{(4)} \tag{9.91a}$$

and

$$0 = c^{(2)}\omega_{na}^2 + c^{(4)}\omega_{na}^2 \tag{9.91b}$$

$$0 = c^{(1)}\omega_{n1}\left(\omega_{na}^2 - \omega_{n1}^2\right) + c^{(3)}\omega_{n2}\left(\omega_{na}^2 - \omega_{n2}^2\right) \tag{9.91c}$$

$$v_a = c^{(1)}\omega_{n1}\omega_{na}^2 + c^{(3)}\omega_{n2}\omega_{na}^2 \tag{9.91d}$$

Equation (9.91b) gives

$$c^{(2)} = -c^{(4)}$$

Substitute for $c^{(2)}$ in Eq. (9.91a):

$$c^{(4)}\left(-\omega_{na}^2 + \omega_{n1}^2 + \omega_{na}^2 - \omega_{n2}^2\right) = 0$$

or

$$c^4\left(\omega_{n1}^2 - \omega_{n2}^2\right) = 0$$

Since

$$\omega_{n1}^2 \neq 0 \qquad \omega_{n2} \neq 0 \qquad \omega_{n1} \neq \omega_{n2}$$

$$c^{(4)} \neq 0 \tag{9.92}$$

Multiply Eq. (9.91c) by ω_{na}^2 and (9.91d) by $(\omega_{na}^2 - \omega_{n1}^2)$

$$0 = c^{(1)}\omega_{n1}(\omega_{n1}^2 - \omega_{n1}^2)\omega_{na}^2 + c^{(3)}\omega_{n2}(\omega_{na}^2 - \omega_{n2}^2)\omega_{na}^2$$

and

$$V_a(\omega_{na}^2 - \omega_{n1}^2) = c^{(1)}\omega_{n1}\omega_{na}^2(\omega_{na}^2 - \omega_{n1}^2) + c^{(3)}\omega_{n2}\omega_{na}^2(\omega_{na}^2 - \omega_{n1}^2)$$

Subtraction gives

$$V_a(\omega_{na}^2 - \omega_{n1}^2) = c^{(3)}\omega_{n2}\omega_{na}^2(\omega_{n2}^2 - \omega_{n1}^2)$$

or

$$c^{(3)} = \frac{\omega_{n1}^2 - \omega_{na}^2}{\omega_{n2}\omega_{na}^2(\omega_{n1}^2 - \omega_{n2}^2)}v_a$$

Substitute for $c^{(3)}$ in Eq. (9.91d):

$$V_a = c^{(1)}\omega_{n1}\omega_{na}^2 + \frac{v_a(\omega_{n1}^2 - \omega_{na}^2)}{\omega_{n2}\omega_{na}^2(\omega_{n1}^2 - \omega_{n2}^2)}\omega_{n2}\omega_{na}^2$$

or

$$c^{(1)} = \frac{v_a}{\omega_{n1}\omega_{na}^2}\frac{\omega_{na}^2 - \omega_{n2}^2}{\omega_{n1}^2 - \omega_{n2}^2}$$

Substituting for $c^{(1)}$, $c^{(2)}$, $c^{(3)}$, and $c^{(4)}$ in Eqs. (9.89) and (9.90) gives

$$z_1 = \frac{v_a(\omega_{na}^2 - \omega_{n2}^2)(\omega_{na}^2 - \omega_{n1}^2)}{\omega_{n1}\omega_{na}^2(\omega_{n1}^2 - \omega_{n2}^2)}\sin\omega_{n1}t$$

$$+ \frac{v_a(\omega_{n1}^2 - \omega_{na}^2)(\omega_{na}^2 - \omega_{n2}^2)}{\omega_{n2}\omega_{na}^2(\omega_{n1}^2 - \omega_{n2}^2)}\sin\omega_{n2}t$$

or

$$z_1 = \frac{(\omega_{na}^2 - \omega_{n1}^2)(\omega_{na}^2 - \omega_{n2}^2)}{\omega_{na}^2(\omega_{n1}^2 - \omega_{n2}^2)}\left(\frac{\sin\omega_{n1}t}{\omega_{n1}} - \frac{\sin\omega_{n2}t}{\omega_{n2}}\right)V_a \qquad (9.93a)$$

and

$$z_2 = \frac{v_a}{\omega_{n1}^2 - \omega_{n2}^2}\left[\frac{(\omega_{na}^2 - \omega_{n2}^2)\sin\omega_{n1}t}{\omega_{n1}} - \frac{(\omega_{na}^2 - \omega_{n1}^2)\sin\omega_{n2}t}{\omega_{n2}}\right] \qquad (9.93b)$$

Maximum stress in pad

$$\sigma_2 = k_2\frac{z_1 + z_2}{A_2} \qquad (9.94)$$

Field observations of the amplitudes of the anvil and the foundation (Barkan, 1962) showed that the vibrations occurred at the lower frequency only. Therefore, for all practical purposes, it may be assumed that the amplitude of motion for $\sin \omega_{n1} t$ (where $\omega_{n1} > \omega_{n2}$) equals zero. The approximate expressions for maximum displacement of the foundation and anvil then become

$$z_1 = \frac{(\omega_{na}^2 - \omega_{n1}^2)(\omega_{na}^2 - \omega_{n2}^2)}{\omega_{na}^2(\omega_{n1}^2 - \omega_{n2}^2)\omega_{n2}} V_a \qquad (9.95)$$

and

$$z_2 = \frac{(\omega_{na}^2 - \omega_{n1}^2)V_a}{(\omega_{n1}^2 - \omega_{n2}^2)\omega_{n2}} \qquad (9.96)$$

(The maximum values of z_1 and z_2 occur when $\sin \omega_{n2} t = 1$.)

Determination of V_a The initial velocity of the anvil is computed from considerations of the impact of the tup and the anvil.

If h = drop of the tup in m
 g = acceleration due to gravity
 V_{Ti} = initial velocity of the tup, m/s
 η = efficiency of drop

then

$$V_{Ti} = \sqrt{2gh} \cdot \eta \qquad (9.97a)$$

However, if the tup is operated by pneumatic pressure p kg/cm^2 and the area of the cylinder is $A_c (m^2)$ and W_0 is weight of tup, then

$$V_{Ti} = \sqrt{\frac{2g(W_0 + pAc)h}{W_0}} \cdot \eta \qquad (9.97b)$$

Actual field measurements on the tups of double-acting hammers by Barkan showed that η ranged between 0.45 and 0.80. Therefore, the average may be taken as 0.65.

The height of the drop of a ram and the steam or air pressure vary within comparatively narrow ranges. Therefore, the design velocity values do not vary much in many cases. For double-acting die-stamping hammers, these equal from 6 to 6.5 m/s. In the example given on page 401, this equals 7.13 m/s.

The principle of impact between the tup and the anvil is that the momentum of the colliding bodies, before and after impact, is constant.

The momentum of tup and anvil before impact = $(W_0/g)V_{Ti}$. Since the anvil is stationary before impact, the momentum of tup and anvil after impact

$$= \frac{W_0}{g} V_{Ta} + \frac{W_2}{g} V_a$$

where W_2 = weight of anvil (including frame if it is mounted on the anvil)
 V_a = velocity of anvil after impact
 V_{Ta} = velocity of tup after impact

$$\frac{W_0}{g} V_{Ti} = \frac{W_0}{g} V_{Ta} + \frac{W_2}{g} V_a$$

or

$$W_0 V_{Ti} = W_0 V_{Ta} + W_2 V_a \tag{9.98}$$

There are two unknowns (V_{Ta} and V_a) that cannot be solved with one equation. To obtain another relationship between velocities, use the coefficient of elastic restitution e, defined as

$$e = \frac{\text{relative velocity after impact}}{\text{relative velocity before impact}} \tag{9.99a}$$

or

$$e = \frac{V_a - V_{Ta}}{V_{Ti}} \tag{9.99b}$$

Substituting V_{Ta} from Eq. (9.99b) in Eq. (9.98) gives

$$V_a = V_{Ti} \frac{(1 + e)}{1 + \dfrac{W_2}{W_0}} \tag{9.100}$$

The coefficient of elastic restitution between two bodies depends only on the material of the bodies undergoing impact.

Since V_a depends on e and motion amplitudes of the foundation z_1 and z_2 depend on V_a directly, the effect of e on z_1 and z_2 is established. For real bodies, $0 < e < 1$. In forge hammers, e depends on the temperature of the forged piece and the elastic properties of the materials in the ram, head, and anvil. Barkan's field measurement showed that, when the temperature of the forged piece was high, the value of e was small (0.1 in a particular case). With subsequent blows, as the temperature of the forged piece decreased, it became stiffer and e increased to approximately 0.5. For cold forgings, the value did not increase beyond 0.5. Since a larger e gives larger amplitudes of motion, e should be taken as 0.5 in designing hammer foundations.

9.18 INDIAN STANDARD FOR DESIGN AND CONSTRUCTION OF FOUNDATIONS FOR IMPACT MACHINES

The Indian Standards Institution prepared a standard on the above subject for use by practicing engineers. This standard was first issued in 1966, when the subject of designing machine foundations was in its infancy in that country. The standard has been under revision for several years, and the revised standard will be adopted by the ISI shortly. Until such time as it is adopted, the standard already in use is referred to in the design. Salient provisions of this standard will be described.

Necessary Information

All data regarding the size and the weight of the various components of the hammer, the resilient properties of the media at the joints, the rate of striking, and the maximum fall of the tup should be given.

For hammers of up to 1-t capacity, soil data should generally be collected to a 6-m depth. For heavier hammers, it is preferable to investigate soil conditions to a 12-m depth, or to hard strata. If piles are to be used, the investigation should be done to a suitable depth.

General Considerations

The hammer foundation should satisfy the following requirements:

1. The stresses produced in the foundation base (soil, timber sleepers, cork, spring elements, or piles) at the time of impact should be within 0.8 times the allowable static stress.
2. The design of the entire foundation system should be such that the centers of gravity of the anvil, the foundation block, and the elastic pad coincide with the line of the hammer tup fall.
3. The design should be such that the natural frequency of the foundation system will not be a whole-number multiple of the maximum operating frequency of impact. A natural frequency of the foundation system that is two and one-half times the frequency of impact may be considered satisfactory. When the natural frequency is designed to be less than the frequency of impact, it should be at least 30 percent less.

Permissible Amplitudes

For the foundation block—The maximum vertical vibration amplitude for the foundation should not exceed 1.2 mm. In cases where foundations are on sand below the ground-water table, the maximum permissible amplitude is 0.8 mm.

For the anvil—The permissible amplitudes, which depend on the weight of the tup, are as follows:

	Weight of tup		
	Up to 1 T	2 T	More than 3 T
Maximum permissible amplitude	1 mm	2 mm	3–4 mm

In case an important structure exists near the foundation, the foundation amplitude should be adjusted so that the velocity of the vibrations at the structure do not exceed 0.3 cm/s. This condition may generally be met in cases where the foundation rests directly on the soil and where the following distances† are maintained between the foundation and the structure:

35 m in the case of hammers up to 2 T·m of impact energy
50 m in the case of hammers up to 12 T·m of impact energy
80 m in the case of hammers up to 12 to 22 T·m of impact energy

Dimensional Criteria

Area The area at the base of the foundation block should be such that the safe loading intensity of the soil is never exceeded while the hammer is operating.

Depth The depth of the foundation block should be designed so that the block is safe in punching shear and in bending. The inertia forces that develop should also be included in the calculations. However, the following minimum thickness should be provided for a foundation block:

Weight of tup, T	Minimum thickness (depth) of foundation block, m
Up to 1.0	1.00
1.0–2.0	1.25
2.0–4.0	1.75
4.0–6.0	2.25
Over 6.0	2.50

Weight The weight of the anvil may generally be kept at 20 times the weight of the tup. The weight of the foundation block W_{1f} generally varies from 66 to 120 times the weight of the tup.

Where the foundation is supported on piles, the weight of the block should be at least 66 times the weight of the tup.

For foundations resting on stiff clays or compact sandy deposits, the weight should be from 75 to 90 times the weight of the tup.

For moderately firm to soft clays and for medium-dense to loose sandy deposits, the weight of the block should be from 90 to 120 times the weight of the tup.

---

† When foundations have an elastic support or rest on piles reduced distances may be taken.

Construction

The foundation block should be made of reinforced concrete. Grade M 150 concrete should be used. The recommended maximum sizes of aggregate are 20 mm in the top 15 cm of the foundation block, and 25 mm in the rest of the block.

It is desirable to cast the entire foundation block in one operation. If a construction joint cannot be avoided, the joint plane should be horizontal, and measures should be taken to provide a proper joint. The following measures are recommended.

Dowels 12 to 16 mm in diameter, at 60-mm centers, should be embedded at least 30 cm deep on both sides of the joint. Before placing a new layer of concrete, the previously laid surface should be roughened, thoroughly cleaned, washed by a jet of water, and then covered with a 2-cm-thick layer of rich 1 : 2 cement grout. The concrete should be poured within 2 h after the grout is laid, and it should be reinforced along the three axes and also diagonally to prevent shear. The top of the foundation block should have more reinforcement than the sides. Reinforcement at the top may be provided by layers of grills, made of 16-mm-diameter bars and suitably spaced to allow concrete to be easily poured. The top reinforcement layer should have a 5-cm cover, at least. The reinforcement should be at least 25 kg/m^3 of concrete.

9.19 DESIGN PROCEDURE FOR A FOUNDATION FOR AN IMPACT MACHINE

Having studied the analysis of a foundation for an impact machine, and the provisions of the code, a step-by-step design procedure can be outlined for this foundation.

Design Data

Check to ensure that design data listed in Sec. 9.18 have been supplied by the manufacturer.

Selecting Soil Constants

For a preliminary design, soil constants may be adopted from the values given in this chapter and in Chap. 4. For a hammer foundation design, it is recommended that the dynamic soil properties be determined at three different strain levels and that the constant be picked at the anticipated strain level of the actual foundation.

Selecting Data for Assumed Quantities

Select the trial dimensions of the block, choose the size and thickness of the timber pad, and adopt the elastic properties of the timber from a relevant code. Adopt $C'_u = \lambda C_u$ where λ varies between 1 and 2 and $e = 0.6$ (IS 2974) Part II.

Foundation-Soil Contact Areas and Weight

The weight of any soil backfill is added to the weight of the block.

Natural Frequencies of the Soil-Foundation-Hammer System

Compute

$$\omega_{na} = \sqrt{\frac{k_2}{m_2}} \tag{9.82}$$

and

$$\omega_{n\ell} = \sqrt{\frac{k_1}{m_1 + m_2}} \tag{9.83}$$

in which $k_2 = \dfrac{E}{b} \cdot A_2$

E = Young's modulus of pad material
b = thickness of the pad
A_2 = area of the pad
$k_1 = C'_u A = 2C_u A$

Natural frequencies of the combined system are given by Eq. (9.87):

$$\omega_{n1,2}^2 = \tfrac{1}{2}\Big[(1 + \mu)(\omega_{na}^2 + \omega_{n\ell}^2)$$

$$\pm \sqrt{\big[(1 + \mu)(\omega_{na}^2 + \omega_{n\ell}^2)\big]^2 - 4(1 + \mu)(\omega_{na}^2 \omega_{n\ell}^2)} \tag{9.87}$$

Velocity of Dropping Parts to Anvil

Compute the velocity V_{Ti} of the tup before impact [Equation (9.97b)]:

$$V_{Ti} = \eta \sqrt{\frac{2g(W_0 + pA_c)h}{W_0}} \tag{9.97b}$$

in which W_0 = weight of tup
p = steam or air pressure
A_c = area of the piston
h = drop of the tup
η = efficiency of drop, usually 0.65

Compute the velocity of the anvil V_a after impact by Eq. (9.100):

$$V_a = \frac{1 + e}{1 + \dfrac{W_2}{W_0}} V_{Ti} \tag{9.100}$$

in which e = coefficient of elastic restitution. The value of e may be adopted as 0.6.

Motion Amplitudes of the Foundation and Anvil

Compute the maximum foundation and anvil amplitudes with Eqs. (9.95) and (9.96), respectively, as

$$z_1 = \frac{\left(\omega_{na}^2 - \omega_{n1}^2\right)\left(\omega_{na}^2 - \omega_{n2}^2\right)}{\omega_{na}^2\left(\omega_{n1}^2 - \omega_{n2}^2\right)\omega_{n2}} V_a \tag{9.95}$$

$$z_2 = \frac{\omega_{na}^2 - \omega_{n1}^2}{\left(\omega_{n1}^2 - \omega_{n2}^2\right) \times \omega_{n2}} V_a \tag{9.96}$$

where ω_{n2} is the smaller natural frequency.

Dynamic Stress in Pad σ_2

Compute dynamic stress in the pad by Eq. (9.94):

$$\sigma_2 = \frac{k_2(Z_1 - Z_2)}{A_2} \tag{9.94}$$

Computed values of natural frequencies should satisfy the criteria for the frequency of operation of the hammer. Also, motion amplitudes should be smaller than permissible values, and the stress in the elastic pad should be smaller than permissible values in the pad material.

9.20 EXAMPLES

Example 9.1
(a) At the proposed site of 2-cylinder vertical compressor, the following tests were performed as per IS 5249:

(i) Cyclic-plate-load test on a 60-cm-square plate. The pit was 3m × 3m × 3.75 m deep. Cyclic-plate-load test data are plotted in Fig. 9.17.
(ii) Vertical block-resonance test. Resonance curves are plotted in Figs. 9.18 and 9.19.

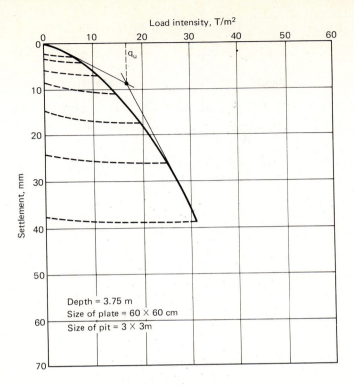

Load intensity, T/m²

Figure 9.17 Cyclic-plate-load test (Example 9.1).

(*iii*) Surface-wave propagation test. The shear wave velocity was found to be 314 m/s.

The soils at site are SM, SC (Fig. 9.20).

Determine the plot of C_u versus strain level at a confining pressure of 1 kg/cm² and select a suitable value for design of the compressor in question.

(*b*) The two-cylinder vertical compressor weighs 10 T and is driven with an electric motor weighing 3.5 T. The operational speed of the compressor is 600 r/min.

The exciting forces generated by the moving parts are

$$P_z = 3\sin(2\pi \times 10) \text{ T}$$

in tons in the direction of motion. The two cylinders move out of phase by 90°. The distance between the cylinders is 1.2 m. Prepare a design for an amplitude of 0.25 m as specified by the manufacturer.

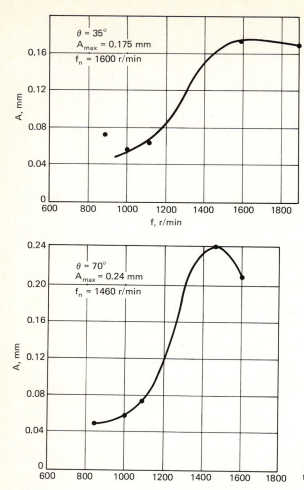

Figure 9.18 Vertical-resonance test $\theta = 35°, 70°$ (Example 9.1).

SOLUTION

(*a*) (*i*) *Cyclic-plate-load test* The elastic part of the settlements is determined at each stress level and the following values are obtained:

S. no.	Load per unit area p, T/m^2	S_e, mm
1	5	0.70
2	8	0.80
3	12	1.30
4	15.5	2.25
5	19.5	2.40

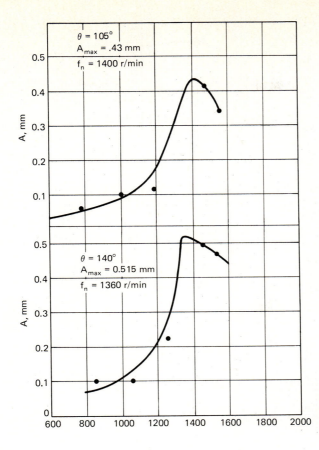

Figure 9.19 Vertical-resonance test $\theta = 105°$, $140°$ (Example 9.1).

A plot of p and S_e is shown in Fig. 9.21.
The value of $C_u = 7.6$ kg/cm³,

$$A = 0.36 \text{ m}^2$$

$C_{u'}$ corrected for area $(A = 10 \text{ m}^2) = 7.6\sqrt{\dfrac{0.36}{10}} = 1.44$ kg/cm²

For $p = 15$ T/m²,

$$z = 0.30 \text{ m} \qquad nz = mz = 0.30 \text{ m} \qquad m = 1 \qquad n = 1$$

From Fig. 9.22,

$$I = 0.177$$

$$\sigma_v = (1.8 \times 0.3) + (4 \times 0.177 \times 15) = 11.16 \text{ T/m}^2$$

C_u'' corrected for a vertical pressure 10 T/m²,

$$C_{u''} = 1.44\sqrt{\dfrac{10}{11.16}} = 1.36 \text{ kg/cm}^2$$

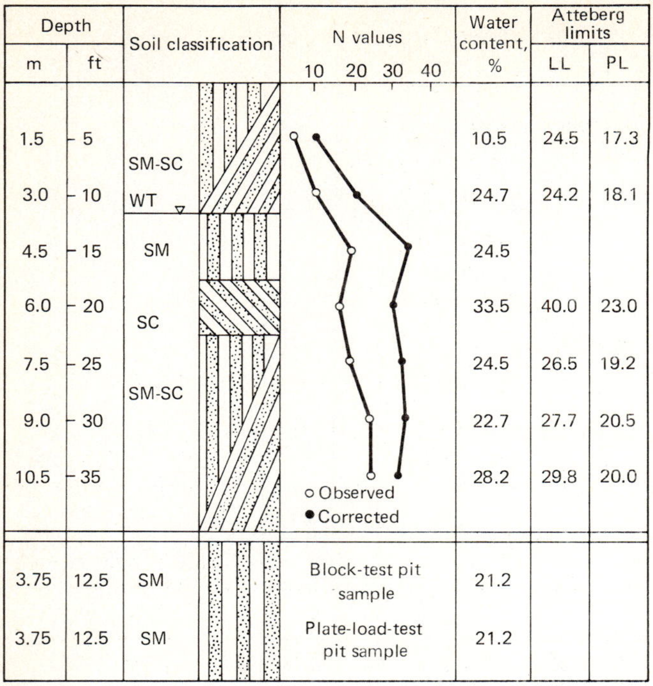

Depth		Soil classification	N values	Water content, %	Atteberg limits	
m	ft		10 20 30 40		LL	PL
1.5	5	SM-SC		10.5	24.5	17.3
3.0	10	WT ▽		24.7	24.2	18.1
4.5	15	SM		24.5		
6.0	20	SC		33.5	40.0	23.0
7.5	25			24.5	26.5	19.2
9.0	30	SM-SC		22.7	27.7	20.5
10.5	35		○ Observed ● Corrected	28.2	29.8	20.0
3.75	12.5	SM	Block-test pit sample	21.2		
3.75	12.5	SM	Plate-load-test pit sample	21.2		

Figure 9.20 Soil profile (Example 9.1).

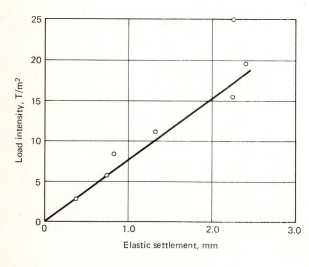

Figure 9.21 Load intensity vs. elastic settlement (Example 9.1).

$$\text{Vertical strain under the plate} = \frac{2}{600} = 3.3 \times 10^{-3}$$

(*ii*) *Vertical block-resonance test*

$$z = 0.375 \text{ m}$$
$$mz = 0.375 \text{ m}$$

Therefore,
$$m = 1$$
$$nz = 0.75 \text{ m}$$

Therefore,
$$n = 2$$

From Fig. 9.22, $I = 0.99$

$$\sigma_V = (1.8 \times 0.375) + (4 \times 0.199 \times 1.68) = 2 \text{ T/m}^2$$

The computations are done in a tabular form.

S. no.	Eccen-tricity	fn, r/min	C_u, kg/cm² $A = 1.125$ m²	$C_{u'}$ for $A = 10$ m²	$C_{u''}$ for $A = 10$ m² $\sigma_v = 10$ T/m²	A_z mm	$\varepsilon_v \times 10^{-4}$
1	2	3	4	5	6	7	8
1	35°	1,600	4.80	1.61	3.60	0.175	2.33
2	70°	1,460	3.98	1.33	2.97	0.240	3.20
3	105°	1,400	3.66	1.23	2.75	0.430	5.73
4	140°	1,360	3.47	1.16	2.59	0.515	8.86

$$C_u' = C_u \sqrt{\frac{1.125}{10}} \qquad C_u'' = C_u' \sqrt{\frac{10}{\sigma_v}} \qquad \text{Strain} = \frac{A_z}{750}$$

(*iii*) *Wave velocity*

$$v_s = 314 \text{ m/s}$$

Therefore,
$$\sqrt{\frac{G}{\rho}} = v_s$$

Therefore,
$$G = \rho v_s^2$$

Let $\gamma = 1.8 \text{ T/m}^3$

Therefore
$$G = \frac{1.8}{9.81} \times (314)^2 = 18,091 \text{ T/m}^2$$

The effective depth of the R Wave has been empirically related to one-half λ_R (Woods, 1978).

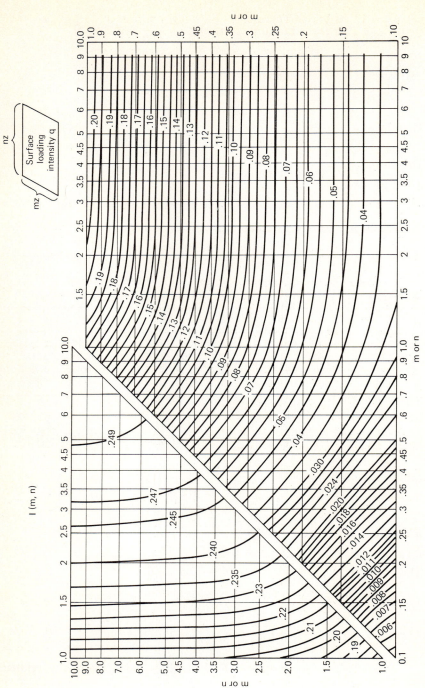

Figure 9.22 Chart for determining vertical stresses below corners of loaded rectangular areas. *(After Taylor, 1948. Reproduced by permission of John Wiley and Sons.)*

Let $\lambda_R = 12$ m (say). Therefore, confining pressure at depth equal to $\frac{1}{4}$ wavelength $= 1.8 \times 3 = 5.4$ T/m^2.

$$E = 2G(1 + \nu) \qquad \text{Let } \nu = 0.3$$

$$= 2 \times 18{,}091 \times 1.3 = 47{,}036 \text{ T/m}^2$$

$$C'_u = \frac{1.13E}{(1 - \nu^2)\sqrt{A}} = \frac{1.13 \times 47{,}036}{(1 - 0.09)}\sqrt{10}$$

$$= 18{,}470 \text{ T/m}^3$$

$$C''_u = 18{,}470 \times \sqrt{\frac{10}{5.4}} = 25{,}134 \text{ T/m}^3$$

$$\varepsilon_v = 10^{-6}$$

All the values of C_u versus strain level are now tabulated below:

C_u, kg/cm^3	ε_v	Test
1.36	3.33×10^{-3}	Plate-load test
3.60	2.33×10^{-4}	Vertical-vibration
2.97	3.20×10^{-4}	Vertical-vibration
2.25	5.73×10^{-4}	Vertical-vibration
2.59	6.86×10^{-4}	Vertical-vibration
25.13	10^{-6}	Wave Velocity

These values have been plotted in Fig. 9.23.

Selection of value for the problem:

Assume allowable soil pressure $= 6$ T/m^2

Water table at ground level $\gamma_b = 1$ g/cm$^3 = 1$ T/m^3

Let $a \times b = 6.6$ m $\times$ 4 m

$$z = 2 \text{ m} \qquad mz = 2 \text{ m},$$

Therefore, $\qquad m = 1.$

$$nz = 3.3 \text{ m}$$

Therefore, $\qquad n = 1.65$

$$I = 0.196$$

$$\sigma_v = (1 \times 1.5) + (4 \times 0.196 \times 6)$$

$$= 6.2 \text{ T/m}^2$$

$$\varepsilon_v = \frac{0.25}{4 \times 1000} = 6.25 \times 10^{-5}$$

$$C''_u = 5.8 \times \sqrt{\frac{6.2}{10}} = 4.0 \times 10^3 \text{ T/m}^2$$

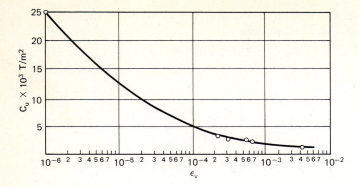

Figure 9.23 C_u vs. strain (Example 9.1).

(*b*) Design of Compressor Foundation—*Design Steps*

Step 1—design data   As shown in Fig. 9.24.
   Weight of compressor = 10^T (static)
   Weight of motor = 3.5^T (static)
   Dynamic load amplitude of the two cylinders = 3.0^T each
   Frequency = 20π rad/s.
   Phase difference between two cylinders = $\frac{\pi}{2}$
   Distance (*c/c*) between the two cylinders = 1.2 m
   Distance (*c/c*) between motor and compressor = 2.2 m
   Working load level of both motor and compressor = 0.75 m (from the
top surface of the foundation)

Step 2—selection of soil constants   The following values of soil constants
shall be adopted for design:

$$C_u = 4.0 \times 10^3 \text{ T/m}^3$$
$$C_\tau = 2.0 \times 10^3 \text{ T/m}^3$$
$$C_\phi = 8.0 \times 10^3 \text{ T/m}^3$$

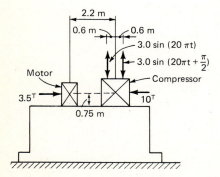

Figure 9.24 Loading diagram (Example 9.1).

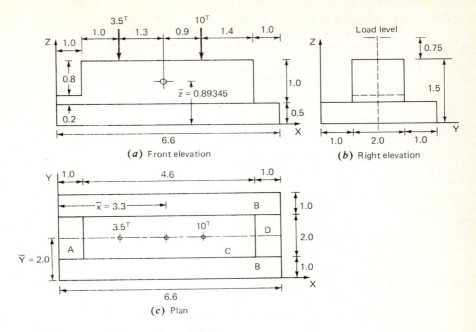

Figure 9.25 Design diagram (Example 9.1).

Allowable soil pressure $\qquad q = 8\ \mathrm{T/m^2}$

Step 3—design diagram of foundation The design diagram of the foundation is shown in Fig. 9.25.

Step 4—centering foundation contact area and determination of soil (static) pressure The CG of the foundation in Fig. 9.25 is determined using Table 9.3.

Coordinates of the center of gravity:

$$\bar{x} = \frac{\Sigma m_i x_i}{\Sigma m_i} = \frac{23.128}{6.954} = 3.3258\ \mathrm{m}$$

Eccentricity $\epsilon_x = \dfrac{3.3258 - 3.3}{3.3} \times 100 = 0.78\%$, which is small and may be neglected.

$$\bar{y} = \frac{\Sigma m_i y_i}{\Sigma m_i} = \frac{13.908}{6.954} = 2.0\ \mathrm{m}$$

$$\bar{z} = \frac{\Sigma m_i z_i}{\Sigma m_i} = \frac{6.2131}{6.954} = 0.89345\ \mathrm{m}$$

Table 9.3 Determination of CG of system

Elements of system	Dimensions of elements, m			Weight of element, T	Mass of element, $T \cdot s^2/m$	Coordinates of CG of element, m			Static moments of mass elements $T \cdot s^2$		
	a_x	a_y	a_z			x_i	y_i	z_i	$m_i x_i$	$m_i y_i$	$m_i z_i$
Foundation slab											
Part A	1.0	2.0	0.7	3.36	0.3425	0.5	2.0	0.35	0.1713	0.6850	0.1199
Part B	6.6	2×1.0	0.5	15.84	1.6147	3.3	2.0	0.25	5.3244	3.2294	0.4037
Part C	4.6	2.0	1.5	33.12	3.3762	3.3	2.0	0.75	11.1413	6.7523	2.5321
Part D	1.0	2.0	0.5	2.4	0.2447	6.1	2.0	0.25	1.4924	0.4893	0.0612
Compressor	—	—	—	10.0	1.0194	4.2	2.0	2.25	4.2814	2.0387	2.2938
Motor	—	—	—	3.5	0.3568	2.0	2.0	2.25	0.7136	0.7136	0.8028
Total				68.22	6.954				23.128	13.908	6.2131

Static soil pressure check:

$$p_{stat} = \frac{W}{A} = \frac{68.22}{26.4} = 2.584 \frac{t}{m^2} < q = 6 \frac{T}{m^2}$$

$$A = \text{Area (contact)} = 6.6 \times 4 = 26.4 \text{ m}^2$$

$$W = \text{Total weight} = 68.22 \text{ T}$$

Step 5—design values of exciting loads and possible forms of foundation vibrations

(*i*) Resultant vertical unbalanced force:

$$P_z = P_{z1} \sin \omega t + P_{z2} \sin\left(\omega t + \tfrac{\pi}{2}\right)$$

$$= 3.0 \sin(\omega t) + 3.0 \sin\left(\omega t + \tfrac{\pi}{2}\right)$$

$$\omega = 20\pi \text{ rad/s}$$

Hence from the vector diagram (Fig. 9.26):

$$P_z = 3\sqrt{2} \sin\left(\omega t + \tfrac{\pi}{4}\right)$$

or

$$P_z = 4.2426 \sin\left(20\pi t + \tfrac{\pi}{4}\right)$$

Therefore,

$$P_z(\text{max}) = 4.2426^T$$

(*ii*) *Resultant horizontal unbalanced force*: Because of symmetry, this force is assumed to be zero.

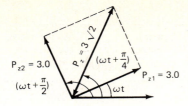

Figure **9.26** Vector diagram (Example 9.1).

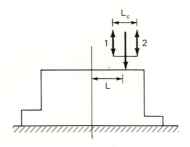

Figure **9.27** Unbalanced moment (Example 9.1).

(*iii*) *Resultant unbalanced moment due to asymmetric position of the compressor about the y axis.* From Fig. 9.27,

L = distance (c/c) between CG of foundation and CG of compressor

   = 0.9 m

L_c = distance (c/c) between cylinders 1 and 2 of the compressor

   = 1.2 m

$$M_y = P_{z1}\left(L - \frac{Lc}{2}\right)\sin \omega t + P_{z2}\left(L + \frac{Lc}{2}\right)\sin\left(\omega t + \frac{\pi}{2}\right)$$

$$= 3.0(0.9 - 0.6)\sin \omega t + 3.0(0.9 + 0.6)\sin\left(\omega t + \frac{\pi}{2}\right)$$

$$= 0.9 \sin \omega t + 4.5 \sin\left(\omega t + \frac{\pi}{2}\right)$$

or (from Fig. 9.28)

$$M_y = 4.589 \sin(\omega t + \phi)$$

where

$$\phi = \tan^{-1}\frac{4.5}{0.9} = 78.69°$$

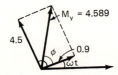

Figure **9.28** Computation of maximum unbalanced moment (Example 9.1).

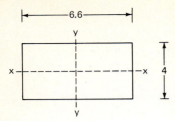

Figure 9.29 Contact area (Example 9.1).

Step 6—determination of moments of inertia

(*i*) $I_{\text{base}} = \dfrac{ba^3}{12} = \dfrac{4 \times 6.6^3}{12} = 95.832$ m^4 (see Fig. 9.29)

(*ii*) Mass moment of inertia about *y* axis

From Fig. 9.30*a* and using Table 9.3,

$$M_{m0}^A = m_A\left(\frac{a_{xa}^2 + a_{za}^2}{12}\right) + m_A(0.35)^2 + m_A(2.8)^2$$

$$= 0.3425\left(\frac{1^2 + 0.7^2}{12} + 0.35^2 + 2.8^2\right)$$

$$= 2.769683 \text{ Tms}^2$$

From Fig. 9.30*b*,

$$M_{m0}^B = 1.614679\left(\frac{0.5^2 + 6.6^2}{12} + 0.25^2\right)$$

$$= 5.99584 \text{ Tms}^2$$

From Fig. 9.30*c*,

$$M_{m0}^C = 3.376147\left(\frac{1.5^2 + 4.6^2}{12} + 0.75^2\right)$$

$$= 8.485383 \text{ Tms}^2$$

From Fig. 9.30*a*,

$$M_{m0}^D = 0.244648\left(\frac{1^2 + 0.5^2}{12} + 0.25^2 + 2.8^2\right)$$

$$= 1.958815 \text{ Tms}^2$$

From Fig. 9.25 (compressor),

$$M_{m0}^{(\text{compressor})} = 1.019368(0.9^2 + 2.25^2) = 5.9862386 \text{ Tms}^2$$

$$M_{m0}^{(\text{motor})} = 0.3567788(1.3^2 + 2.25^2) = 2.4091488 \text{ Tms}^2$$

Therefore,

$$M_{m0} = M_{m0}^A + M_{m0}^B + M_{m0}^C + M_{m0}^D + M_{m0}^{(\text{comp})} + M_{m0}^{(\text{motor})}$$

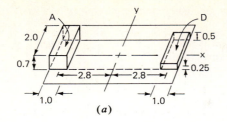

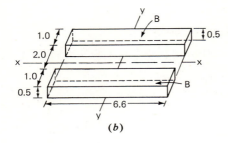

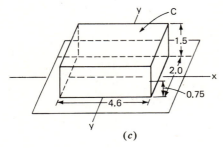

Figure 9.30 Mass moment of inertia (Example 9.1).

or

$$M_{m0} = 27.605 \text{ Tms}^2$$

M_m = mass moment of inertia of the system about the y axis passing through the CG of the system

Therefore,

$$M_m = M_{m0} - m(\bar{z})^2$$

$$= 27.605 - 6.954 \times 0.89345^2 \qquad \text{or} \qquad M_m = 22.054 \text{ Tms}^2$$

$$\frac{M_m}{M_{m0}} = \gamma = \frac{22.054}{27.605} = 0.7989$$

Step 7—computation of natural frequency and amplitude of motion:
    Assume

1. Unbalanced force along x direction $= P_x = 0$.
2. Unbalanced force along y direction $= P_y = 0$.
3. Torsional moment is negligible.
4. Damping $= 0$.

For decoupled modes:

$A = 26.4 \text{ m}^2$ $C_u = 4.0 \times 10^3 \text{ T/m}^3$ $C_\phi = 8.0 \times 10^3 \text{ T/m}^3$

$C_\tau = 2.0 \times 10^3 \text{ T/m}^3$ $\omega_z = 20\pi \text{ rad/s}$ $m = 6.954 \text{ T s}^2\text{m}^{-1}$

$P_z = 4.2426^T$ $M_y = 4.589 \text{ T} \cdot \text{m}$

(*i*) Vertical:

$$\omega_{nz} = \sqrt{\frac{C_u A}{m}} = \sqrt{\frac{4000 \times 26.4}{6.954}} = 123.2312 \text{ rad/s}$$

$$A_z = \frac{4.2426}{m(\omega_{nz}^2 - \omega^2)} = \frac{4.2426}{6.954\left[(123.2312)^2 - (20\pi)^2\right]} = 0.0000543 \text{ m}$$

Check

$$A_z = 0.0543 \text{ mm} < 0.25 \text{ mm} \qquad \text{(O.K.)}$$

Check

$$\frac{\omega}{\omega_{nz}} = \frac{20\pi}{123.2312} = 0.5096 \simeq 0.50 \qquad \text{(O.K.)}$$

(*ii*) Horizontal:

$$\omega_{nx} = \sqrt{\frac{C_\tau A}{m}} = \frac{2000 \times 26.4}{6.954} = 87.1364 \text{ rad/s}$$

(*iii*) Rotational:

$$\omega_{n\phi} = \sqrt{\frac{C_\phi \cdot I - W\bar{z}}{M_{m0}}} = \frac{8000 \times 95.832 - 68.22 \times 0.89345}{27.605}$$

or

$$\omega_{n\phi} = 166.64379 \text{ rad/s}$$

For coupled modes:

(*i*)

$$(\omega_{n1,n2})^2 = \frac{1}{2\gamma}\left[\omega_{n\phi}^2 + \omega_{nx}^2 \pm \sqrt{\left(\omega_{n\phi}^2 + \omega_{nx}^2\right)^2 - 4\gamma\left(\omega_{n\phi}^2 \cdot \omega_{nx}^2\right)}\right]$$

$$= \frac{1}{2 \times 0.7989}\left[166.644^2 + 87.136^2\right.$$

$$\left.\pm \sqrt{(166.644^2 + 87.136^2)^2 - 4 \times .7989(166.644 \times 87.136)^2}\right]$$

$$= 37,162.5, 7101.991$$

Therefore,

$$\omega_{n1,n2} = 192.778, 84.273 \text{ rad/s}$$

(*ii*) $\quad \Delta(\omega^2) = mM_m(\omega_{n1}^2 - \omega^2)(\omega_{n2}^2 - \omega^2)$

$$= 6.954 \times 22.054(37162.5 - 3947.84)(7101.99 - 3947.84)$$

$$= 1.606698 \times 10^{10}$$

(*iii*) $\qquad A_x = \dfrac{C_\tau A\bar{z}}{\Delta(\omega^2)}M_y = \dfrac{2000 \times 26.4 \times 0.89345}{1.606698 \times 10^{10}} \times 4.589$

$$= 1.3474 \times 10^{-5}\text{m}$$

$$= 0.01347 \text{ mm}$$

(*iv*) $\quad A_\phi = \dfrac{C_\tau A - m\omega^2}{\Delta(\omega^2)}M_y = \dfrac{2000 \times 26.4 - 6.954 \times 3947.84}{1.606698 \times 10^{10}} \times 4.589$

$$= 7.23945 \times 10^{-6} \text{ rad}$$

(*v*) Combined final amplitudes of vibrations from Fig. 9.31:
Horizontal

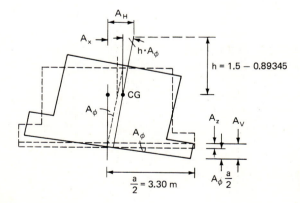

Figure 9.31 Combined dynamic displacements (Example 9.1).

$$A_H = A_x + hA_\phi$$

$$= (0.01347 + 7.2395 \times 10^{-6} \times 1.35655 \times 10^3) \text{ mm}$$

$$= 0.02329 \text{ mm} < 0.25 \text{ mm}$$

Vertical

$$A_V = A_z + A_\phi \frac{a}{2} \text{ (Fig. 9.31)}$$

$$= (0.0543 + 7.2395 \times 10^{-6} \times 3.3 \times 10^3) \text{ mm}$$

$$= 0.0782 \text{ mm} < 0.25 \text{ mm}$$

Example 9.2 Forgings Private Limited, Faridabad, propose to install a 1.55-T forging hammer for the manufacture of leaf springs. Soil at site consists of silty clay of medium plasticity mixed with Kankar and intermittent layers of fine, silty sand of medium relative density. The water table is at a depth of about 5.65 m below ground level. The coefficient of elastic uniform compression of soil C_u is equal to 1.1325×10^3 T/m^3 for an area of 10 m^2 as determined by tests at site (Prakash and Gupta, 1968).

The hammer has the following specifications:

tup weight without die: 1150 kg
maximum tup stroke, h: 900 mm
supply steam pressure, p: 100 lb/in^2 = 70 T/m^2
anvil block weight: 22.5 T
total weight of hammer: 34.3 T
bearing area of anvil: $2.1 \times 1.3 = 2.73$ m^2
weight of half die = 400 Kg
area of piston = 0.129 m^2

DATA ASSUMED For design purposes, the following data were assumed:

material of pad below anvil—teak heart wood
modulus of elasticity of pad—5×10^4 T/m^2
thickness of pad below anvil—0.61 m
dimensions of the foundation block—6.50 m × 5.70 m × 1.75 m
dimensions of RCC walls—0.50 × 1.34 m all around anvil as shown in Figs.
    9.32 and 9.33
unit weight of RCC = 2.4 T/m^3
unit weight of backfill = 1.76 T/m^3
modified coefficient of elastic uniform compression for impact loading
    $C_u' = 2C_u$
coefficient of elastic restitution $e = 0.5$
coefficient η that takes into account counterpressure and frictional forces =
    0.65

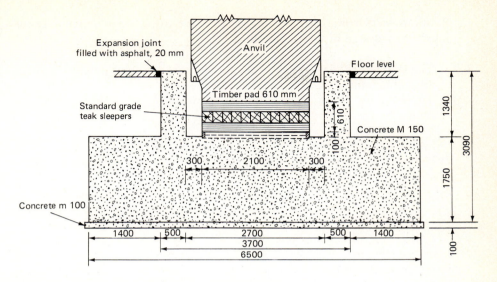

Figure 9.32 Section of hammer foundation (Example 9.2).

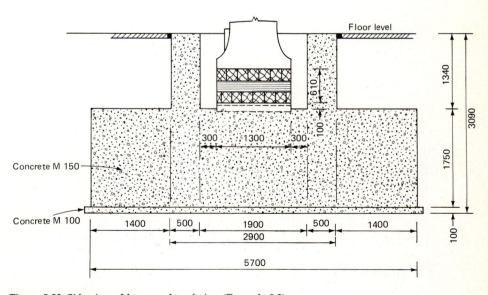

Figure 9.33 Side view of hammer foundation (Example 9.2).

REQUIREMENTS FOR DESIGN The following are the main requirements for satisfactory design of the foundation:

1. The amplitudes of vibration of the foundation and anvil should be within allowable limits.
2. The dynamic stress on the soil and pad should be within permissible limits.

According to Barkan (1962) and Indian Standard Code of Practice IS 2974-1966, the following are the permissible limits for amplitudes of vibration:

$$Z_1 = A_{\text{foundation}} = 1.0 \text{ to } 1.2 \text{ mm}$$
$$Z_2 = A_{\text{anvil}} = 1.0 \text{ mm for 1-T hammer and}$$
$$= 2.0 \text{ mm for 2-T hammer}$$

According to Indian Standard Code IS 883-1961, the allowable limit for stress on teak heart wood loaded perpendicular to grains is as follows: σ allowable $= 400 \text{ T/m}^2$ in compression.

COMPUTATIONS

1. *Soil contact area and weight of foundation* Figures 9.32 and 9.33 show the assumed dimension of the foundation.
   Foundation area in contact with soil $= 6.50 \times 5.70 = 37.05 \text{ m}^2$
   Weight of foundation and backfill:
   Volume of the block $= 6.50 \times 5.70 \times 1.75 \quad = 64.8375 \text{ m}^3$
   Walls $= 2 \times 3.70 \times 0.50 \times 1.34 = 4.958 \text{ m}^3$
   $\quad\quad 2 \times 1.90 \times 0.50 \times 1.34 = \underline{2.546 \text{ m}^3}$
   $\quad\quad\quad\quad\quad\quad\quad\quad\quad 72.3415 \text{ m}^3$
   Weight of concrete $= 72.3415 \times 2.40 = 173.62 \text{ T}$
   Volume of the fill $= 2 \times 6.50 \times 1.40 \times 1.34 = 24.40$
   $\quad\quad\quad 2 \times 2.90 \times 1.40 \times 1.34 = \underline{10.80}$
   $\quad\quad\quad\quad\quad\quad\quad\quad = 35.20 \text{ m}^3$
   Weight of backfill $= 35.29 \times 1.76 \quad = 62.20 \text{ T}$
   Total weight of foundation and backfill $= 235.82 \text{ T}$
   Total mass $m = \dfrac{235.82}{9.81} = 24.0 \text{ T s}^2\text{m}^{-1}$
2. *Natural frequencies of foundation—hammer system*
   The modulus of elasticity of the pad $E = 5 \times 10^4 \text{ T/m}^2$
   Thickness of the pad $b = 0.61 \text{ m}$
   Coefficient of rigidity of the pad $k_2 = \dfrac{EA_2}{t} = \dfrac{5 \times 10^4 \times 2.73}{0.61}$
   $\quad\quad = 22.4 \times 10^4 \text{ T/m.}$
   Mass of the anvil and frame $m_2 = \dfrac{34.3}{9.81} = 3.5 \text{ T s}^2\text{m}^{-1}$

Limiting natural frequency of anvil on pad is

$$\omega_{na}^2 = \frac{k_2}{m_2} = \frac{22.4 \times 10^4}{3.5} = 6.4 \times 10^4 \, \text{s}^{-2}$$

Now, $C_u = 1.1325 \times 10^3 \, \text{T/m}^3$ for an area of $10 \, \text{m}^2$

$$C_{u'} = 2C_{u1} = 2 \times 1.1325 \times 10^3 = 2.265 \times 10^3 \, \text{T/m}^3$$

Coefficient of rigidity of the soil

$$k_1 = C_{u'} \times A_1 = 2.265 \times 10^3 \times 37.05 = 8.4 \times 10^4 \, \text{T/m}$$

The limiting natural frequency of the whole system ω_{nl} is

$$\omega_{nl}^2 = \frac{k_1}{m_1 + m_2} = \frac{8.4 \times 10^4}{3.5 + 24.0} = 0.305 \times 10^4 \, \text{s}^{-2}$$

and
$$\mu = \frac{m_2}{m_1} = \frac{3.5}{24.0} = 0.1458$$

The two natural frequencies of the combined system are given by Eq. (9.87)

$$\omega_n^4 - (0.305 + 6.4) \, 1.1458 \times 10^4 \omega_n^2 + 1.1458 \times 0.305 \times 6.4 \times 10^8 = 0$$

$$\omega_n^4 - 7.69 \times 10^4 \omega_n^2 + 2.24 \times 10^8 = 0$$

$$\omega_n^2 = \tfrac{1}{2}\left[7.69 \pm \sqrt{(7.69)^2 - 4 \times 2.24} \right] \times 10^4$$

$$= \tfrac{1}{2}\left[7.69 \pm \sqrt{59 - 8.96} \right] \times 10^4$$

$$= \tfrac{1}{2}[7.69 \pm 7.10] \times 10^4$$

If $\omega_{n1} > \omega_{n2}$

$$\omega_{n1}^2 = \tfrac{1}{2} \times 14.79 \times 10^4 = 7.395 \times 10^4 \, \text{s}^{-2}$$

$$\omega_{n2}^2 = \tfrac{1}{2} \times 0.59 \times 10^4 = 0.295 \times 10^4 \, \text{s}^{-2}$$

$$\omega_{n2} = 54.3 \, \text{s}^{-1}$$

3. *Velocity of dropping parts at the beginning of impact*

$$V_{Ti} = \eta \sqrt{\frac{2g(W_0 + A_c p)h}{W_0}}$$

Therefore,

$$V_{Ti} = 0.65\sqrt{\frac{2 \times 9.81 \times (1.55 + 0.129 \times 70)0.9}{1.55}} = 7.13 \, \text{m/s}$$

4. *Velocity of anvil motion*

$$V_a = \frac{1 + e}{1 + \mu} V = \frac{1 + 0.5}{1 + \dfrac{34.2}{1.55}} \times 7.13 = 0.463 \text{ m/s}$$

5. *Amplitude of vibration of foundation*

$$z_1 = A_z = \frac{\left(\omega_{na}^2 - \omega_{n2}^2\right) \times \left(\omega_{na}^2 - \omega_{n1}^2\right)}{\omega_{na}^2\left(\omega_{n1}^2 - \omega_{n2}^2\right)\omega_{n2}} V_a = 1.14 \text{ mm}$$

and that of anvil

$$z_2 = A_a = \frac{\left(\omega_{na}^2 - \omega_{n1}^2\right) \times V_a}{\left(\omega_{n1}^2 - \omega_{n2}^2\right) \times \omega_{n2}} = 1.195 \text{ mm}$$

These are within permissible limits.
Dynamic stress in pad

$$= \frac{k_2(A_a + A_z)}{A_2} = \frac{22.4 \times 10^4(1.14 + 1.195)10^{-3}}{2.73} = 192 \text{ T/m}^2$$

This is also within permissible limits.

9.21 VIBRATION ISOLATION AND SCREENING OF WAVES

A machine foundation vibrating excessively may adversely affect its performance and cause distress to other machines and adjoining structures through transmission of energy associated with propagating waves. Reduction of vibration amplitude and prevention of damage to adjoining structures may therefore be necessary in many cases. This problem may be examined in two parts: vibration isolation and screening of waves.

Vibration Isolation

"Vibration isolation" implies reduction of amplitude of vibration of the machine. This may be necessary if it is not feasible to design a foundation for the limiting vibration amplitudes or in case excessive vibrations develop subsequent to installation of the machine. In Sec. 2.14, the principle of a vibration absorber has been explained. A vibration absorber, in practice, will consist of structural members designed to function as such. Barkan (1962) has also developed analysis for such a vibration absorber for a system undergoing rocking and sliding vibrations. Excessive vibrations in machine foundations may sometimes be reduced by suitable treatment of the soil below (Barkan, 1962). The efficiency of such remedial measures must first be ascertained through analysis. However, it is more convenient to mount the machine on antivibration mountings, made of steel springs, rubber, or cork. Such mountings are commercially available under different trade names and can also be fabricated to suit specific requirements.

Screening of Waves

Screening of waves by trenches has been investigated by Richart, Hall, and Woods (1970) and Woods (1968). The problem has been divided into two categories, active isolation (isolation at the source) and passive isolation (screening at a distance). Active isolation is the employment of trenches close to or surrounding the source of vibrations to reduce the amount of wave energy radiated away from the source (Fig. 9.34). Passive isolation is the employment of trenches at points away from the source of vibrations but near the object where the amplitude of vibrations must be reduced (Fig. 9.35).

In the tests for screening of vibrations, a source of vibration was set up at the center of a prepared site; the amplitude of vertical ground motion at selected points throughout the test site was determined for the "no-trench" (or "before") conditions; a trench was dug; and the amplitude of ground motion was measured at the same selected points after the trench was dug. A comparison was made of amplitudes of motion before and after the digging of the trench and was used in evaluating the effectiveness of the barrier. *Amplitude reduction factor*, defined as the ratio of amplitude after trench installation to amplitude before trench installation, was used to give a quantitative evaluation of the effectiveness of the trench on the amplitude of vertical ground motion at the point of measurement. If the amplitude reduction factor is 0.25 or less, the trench is considered effective in screening the vibrations.

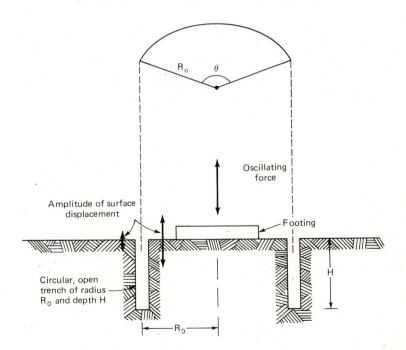

Figure 9.34 Schematic of vibration isolation using a circular trench surrounding the source of vibrations-active isolation. *(After Woods, 1968.)*

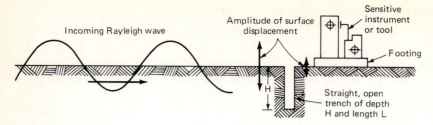

Figure 9.35 Schematic of vibration isolation using a straight trench-passive isolation. *(After Woods, 1968.)*

The soil at this site was uniform silty, fine sand (SM) up to 4 ft deep, with $\gamma_d = 104$ lb/ft³, $w = 7$ percent, $e = 0.61$ and $v_p = 940$ ft/s at surface, and sandy silt from 4 ft to 14 ft deep with $\gamma_d = 91$ lb/ft³, $w = 23$ percent, $e = 0.68$, and $v_p = 1750$ ft/s (at upper boundary). The water table was below 14 ft depth.

Wave length of the Rayleigh waves (λ_R) was determined at different frequencies as is listed in Table 9.4.

Critical dimensions of the trenches used in all tests were normalized on λ_R for the appropriate frequency when used to compare results of two or more tests at different frequencies.

In active tests, the depth of trenches was varied from 0.5 ft to 2 ft. The angular dimension θ of the trench was varied from 90° to 360° around the source of excitation in active tests. The radius R_0 (Fig. 9.34) of the trench varied from 0.5 ft to 1.0 ft.

On the basis of this study of active isolation it was found that for full-circle trenches ($\theta = 360°$) to be effective (that is, to achieve an amplitude reduction factor of 0.25 or less), and for R_0/λ_R from 0.22 to 0.910:

1. A minimum depth of $H/\lambda_R = 0.6$ was required.
2. The zone screened by a full-circle trench ($\theta = 360°$) extended to a distance of at least 10 wavelengths ($10\lambda_R$) from the source of excitation.

Table 9.4 Wavelength and wave velocity for the Rayleigh wave at the field site*

Frequency, Hz	λ_R, ft	v_R, ft/s
200	2.25	450
250	1.68	420
300	1.38	415
350	1.10	385

*After Woods (1968).

For partial-circle trenches at distance R_0/λ_R from 0.222 to 0.910, the zone screened by a partial-circle trench was defined as the area outside the trench, extending to at least 10 wavelengths ($10\lambda_R$) from the source, and bounded on the sides by radial lines from the center of the source through points 45° from the ends of the trench. It was found that

1. A minimum depth of $H/\lambda_R = 0.6$ was required for a trench to provide a screened zone with an amplitude reduction factor of 0.25 or less.
2. Partial-circle trenches of angular length θ less than 90 did not provide an effectively screened zone.
3. Amplification of vibratory energy occurred in the direction of the "open side" of the trench.

For passive isolation, in a semicircular area with radius of one-half the trench length ($L/2$) and center at the center of the trench, it was found that for the amplitude reduction factor to be 0.25 or less, the trench must be located between $2\lambda_R$ and $7\lambda_R$ from the source, and the depth of the trench H must be $1.33 \lambda_R$.

It must be recognized that the screening of waves is related to the wave-length of the Rayleigh wave, which depends upon the frequency of excitation. Therefore, no simple dimensions of trench would work in all cases. Also, in this study, the water table was at great depth. If the water table is close to the ground level, the dimensional criteria described above may need modification. Also, it may not be possible to keep vertical open trenches in stable condition on a long-term basis. If the trench is filled with slurry or is lined with steel sheet pile or similar material, its efficiency is reduced.

In partial trenches in both active and passive isolation, the amplitude of motion is increased on the opposite side of the trench. This amplification must be considered in evaluating the overall performance of the system.

9.22 OVERVIEW

The problems of analysis and design of foundations for reciprocating machines and impact machines have been discussed with two distinct approaches: the theory of linear elastic weightless spring, and the elastic-half-space theory. Vibrations in the mass of soil, the effect of embedment, nonlinearity of soil, and pile-supported foundations have not been included.

The analysis based on linear elastic massless spring does not consider damping. In the elastic-half-space theory, radiation damping affects the amplitudes, particularly at resonance.

When a plate of uniform thickness t, area $A = a \times b$ (Fig. 9.36) is subjected to a uniform pressure intensity p, then compression of the plate Δt

$$\Delta t = \frac{p}{E} \times t \qquad (9.101)$$

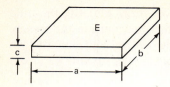

Figure 9.36 Computation of equivalent spring constant of an elastic plate.

where E is Young's modulus of the plate material. If the plate is now regraded as a spring of stiffness k and is subjected to a load $P = p \cdot A$, then by definition

$$k = \frac{P}{\Delta t} = \frac{EA}{t} \tag{9.102}$$

Thus we have established an "analogy" between the plate and the spring. In the more complex problem of the elastic half-space, it is no wonder that the analogues have been established as spring constants, and the damping has been treated in terms of elastic constants of the material, geometry of the problem, and the mode of vibrations of the foundation. And, fortunately enough for the practicing engineer, the analogues give satisfactory answers.

For four principal modes of vibrations, the mass ratio, damping factor, and equivalent spring constants are summarized in Table 9.3.

Also simultaneous sliding and rocking have not been considered based on analogues and from the theory of elastic half space. However, if the maximum sliding and rocking response frequencies differ by a factor of three or more, the two motions can be analyzed independently and the amplitudes of motion superposed (McNeill, 1969).

Table 9.5 Mass ratio B, damping factor ξ, and spring constant k for rigid circular footing on the semi-infinite elastic half space*

Mode of vibration	Mass (or inertia) ratio	Damping factor	Spring constant
1	2	3	4
Vertical	$B_z = \dfrac{(1-\nu)}{4}\dfrac{m}{\rho r_0^3}$	$\xi_z = \dfrac{0.425}{\sqrt{B_z}}$	$k_z = \dfrac{4Gr_0}{1-\nu}$
Sliding	$B_x = \dfrac{(7-8\nu)}{32(1-\nu)}\dfrac{m}{\rho r_0^3}$	$\xi_x = \dfrac{0.2875}{\sqrt{B_x}}$	$k_x = \dfrac{32(1-\nu)}{7-8\nu}Gr_0$
Rocking	$B_\phi = \dfrac{3(1-\nu)}{8}\cdot\dfrac{M_{m0}}{\rho r_0^5}$	$\xi_\phi = \dfrac{0.15}{(1+B_\phi)\sqrt{B_\phi}}$	$k_\phi = \dfrac{8Gr_0^3}{3(1-\nu)}$
Torsional	$B_\psi = \dfrac{J_z}{\rho r_0^5}$	$\xi_\psi = \dfrac{0.5}{1+2B_\psi}$	$k_\psi = \dfrac{16}{3}\cdot Gr_0^3$

* After Richart, Hall, and Woods (1970).

The mass of the soil spring has not been considered in the analysis presented in this chapter. The mass-spring system in Fig. 2.18 is considered to have a weight w per unit length. Considering the length of the spring ℓ, Chap. 2 shows that the natural frequency is given by the equation (p. 32)

$$\omega_n = \sqrt{\frac{kg}{W + \frac{1}{3}wl}}$$

that is, one-third of the mass of the springs can be assumed to be concentrated at the center of the vibrating mass.

Hsieh (1962) worked out the effective soil masses (or mass moments of inertia of soil) (Table 9.6).

However, Richart et al. (1970) recommended that even if the "in-phase mass" could be determined satisfactorily, this information would not lead directly to an evaluation of the vibration amplitude. Also, in fixing the quantities of analogue, the in-phase soil mass (or mass moment of inertia) has not been considered. Therefore, in-phase soil mass may not be considered at this stage in the analysis. However, future realistic analysis may consider this question.

It is a matter of general observation that both the equivalent spring constant and the apparent soil mass participating in vibrations increase when the foundation is embedded. The resulting natural frequency of the system is increased and the motion amplitude, both at resonance and at operating frequency, are reduced.

Anandkrishnan and Krishnaswamy (1973) considered an increase in effective damping force, due to skin friction mobilized between the vertical surface of the footing and the surrounding soil, as a Coulomb damper and obtained solutions for natural frequency. For an infinite medium, Lysmer and Kuhlemeyer (1969) proposed a finite dynamic model enclosed by a boundary subjected to a condition which assumes that all energy arriving at the boundary is absorbed.

Table 9.6 Effective mass and mass moment of inertia for soil below a vibrating footing*

Mode of vibration	Effective mass or mass moment of inertia of soil		
	$\nu = 0$	$\nu = 1/4$	$\nu = 1/2$
Vertical translation	$0.5\rho r_0^3$	$1.0\rho r_0^3$	$2.0\rho r_0^3$
Horizontal translation	$0.2\rho r_0^3$	$0.2\rho r_0^3$	$0.1\rho r_0^3$
Rocking	$0.4\rho r_0^5$	not	computed
Torsion (about vertical axis)	$0.3\rho r_0^5$	$0.3\rho r_0^5$	$0.3\rho r_0^5$

† After Hsieh.

An approximate analytical approach was formulated by Baranov (1957), who assumed that the soil underlying the footing base is an elastic half space and that the overlying soil is an independent elastic layer composed of a series of infinitesimally thin independent elastic layers. Compatibility conditions between the elastic half space and the overlying elastic layer were only satisfied at the body and very far from it. Nevertheless, the solution seems to yield reasonable results in closed form, and is very versatile and easily applicable to any vibration mode (Beredugo and Novak, 1972; Novak and Beredugo, 1971).

Novak and Beredugo (1972) extended Baranov's (1967) solution for vertical vibrations, compared it with the finite-element solution, and completed experiments to verify its applicability.

It was observed that, in the case of embedment in a half space, the resonant amplitude was practically independent of the mass ratio, whereas resonant frequency greatly depends on it.

In a stratum, increasing embedment reduces dependence on stratum thickness considerably.

In any case, if the effect of embedment is neglected, the design will be conservative. However, it is expected that, in another decade or so, simplified solutions for embedment effects will be available.

If a machine foundation is supported on piles, the vertical stiffness lies between

$$\frac{EA}{L} \text{ and } \left(\frac{EA}{L}\right)\frac{1}{2}$$

for bearing and friction piles, respectively,

in which $E=$ Young's modulus of the pile material
$A =$ area of cross section of the pile
$L =$ length of the pile

However, lateral pile stiffness needs to be worked out from principles discussed in Chap. 7.

The problem of analyzing and designing machine foundations has attracted the attention of several groups of investigators. Books by Major (1962) and Barkan (1962) represent the work of their lifetime. The book by Richart, Hall, and Wood (1970) is also a classical work in the same direction. Several reviews have been prepared on the subject (Prakash and Bhatia, 1964; Prakash and Gupta, 1966; McNeill, 1969). Therefore, it is no wonder that more up-to-date reviews will become available in the future.

REFERENCES

Anandkrishnan, M., and N.R. Krishnaswamy: Response of Embedded Footing to Vertical Vibrations, *J. Soil Mech. Found. Div.*, *ASCE*, vol. 99, no. SM 10, p. 863–883, October, 1973.

Arnold, R.N., G.N. Bycroft, and G.E. Warburton: Forced Vibrations of a Body on an Infinite Elastic Solid, *J. Appl. Mech.*, vol. 22, no. 3, pp. 391–400, 1955.

Barkan, D.D.: "Dynamics of Bases and Foundations," McGraw-Hill Book Co., New York, 1962.

Baranov, V.A.: On the Calculation of Excited Vibration of an Embedded Foundation (in Russian), *Voprosy Dynamiki Prochnocti* no. 14, Polytechnical Institute of Riga, pp. 195–209, 1967.

Beredugo, Y.O., and M. Novak: Coupled Horizontal and Rocking Vibration of Embedded Footings, *Can. Geotech. J.*, vol. 9, no. 4, pp. 477–497, November, 1972.

Bycroft, G.N.: Forced Vibrations of a Rigid Circular Plate on a Semi-Infinite Elastic Space and on an Elastic Stratum, *Philos. Trans. R. Soc. London, Ser. A*, vol. 248, pp. 327–368, 1956.

Chae, Y.S.: Vibrations of Non-Circular Foundations, *J. Soil Mech. Found. Div., ASCE*, vol. 95, no. SM 6, pp. 1411–1430, November, 1969.

Crandell, F.J.: Ground Vibrations due to Blasting and its Effects on Structures, *J. Boston Soc. Civ. Engin.*, April, 1959.

Hall, J.R., Jr.: Coupled Rocking and Sliding Oscillations of Rigid Circular Footings, in *Proceedings of the International Symposium on Wave Propagation and Dynamic Properties of Earth Materials*, University of New Mexico Press, Albuquerque, pp. 139–148, 1967.

Hertwig, A., G. Früh, and H. Lorenz: "Die Ermittlung der für das Bauwesen Wichtigsten Eigenschaften des Bodens durch Enzwungene Schwingungen", DEGEBO, vol. 1, Julius Springer, West Berlin, 1933.

Hsieh, T.K.: Foundation Vibrations, *Proc. Inst. Civ. Engin.* vol. 22, pp. 211–226, 1962.

Indian Standard Code of Practice for Plain and Reinforced Concrete, IS 456–1964, 2d rev., Indian Standards Institution, New Delhi.

Indian Standard Code of Practice for Use of Structural Timber in Building (Material, Grading and Design), Revised IS 883–1961, Indian Standards Institution, New Delhi.

Indian Standard Code of Practice for Design and Construction of Machine Foundations: IS 2974, Part I, 1970, Foundations for Reciprocating Machines: IS 2974, Part II, 1966, Foundations for Impact Machines, Indian Standards Institution, New Delhi.

Lysmer, J., and R.L. Kuhlemeyer: A Finite Dynamic Model for Infinite Media, *J. Engin. Mech. Div., ASCE*, vol. 95, no. EM 4, pp. 859–877, August, 1969.

―――― and F.E. Richart, Jr.: Dynamic Response of Footings to Vertical Loadings, *J. Soil Mech. Found. Div., ASCE*, vol. 92, no. SM 1, pp. 65–91, January, 1966.

McNeill, R.L.: Machine Foundations, Soil Dynamics Specialty Session, *Proc. Seventh Int. Conf. Soil Mech. Found. Engin.*, Mexico, August, 1969.

Novak, M., and Y.O. Beredugo: Effect of Embedment on Footing Vibration, *Proc. First Canadian Conf. Earthquake Engin.*, pp. 111–125, May, 1971.

―――― and ――――: Vertical Vibration of Embedded Footings, *J. Soil Mech. Found. Div., ASCE*, vol. 98, no. SM 12, pp. 1291–1310, December, 1972.

Prakash, S.: "Analysis and Design of Vibrating Footings: Soil Mechanics, Recent Developments"-Proceedings of the General Session of the Symposium, University of New South Wales, Sydney, pp. 295–326, July 14–18, 1975.

――――, S.L. Agarwal, and D.C. Gupta: "Report on Bearing Capacity and Dynamic Soil Constants for Forging Hammer of Jamuna Auto Industries, Yamuna Nagar," Earthquake Studies, Roorkee, India, 1966.

―――― and U.K. Bhatia: A Review of Machine Foundation Behavior, *Bull. Indian Soc. Earthquake Tech.*, Roorkee, vol. 2, no. 1, pp. 45 – 64, 1969.

―――― and D.C. Gupta: Annotated Bibliography of Machine Foundations, Earthquake Engineering Studies, Roorkee, India, 1966.

―――― and ――――: Soil Investigations and Design of a Forging Hammer Foundation, *Bull. Indian Soc. Earthquake Tech.*, Roorkee, India, vol. 5, no. 1–2, pp. 43–54, March–June, 1968.

―――― and V.K. Puri: Critical Evaluation of IS 5249–1969, *J. Indian Geotech. Soc.*, vol. 7, no. 1, pp. 43–56, vol. 7, no. 2, pp. 191–193, 1977.

Quinlan, P.M.: "The Elastic Theory of Soil Dynamics," Special Technical Publication No. 156, American Society for Testing and Materials, pp. 3–34, 1956.

Reiher, H., and F.J. Meister: "Die Empfindlichkeit der Menschen gegen Esschiiherungen" Forsch. Gebiete Ingenieurwesen, vol 2, no. 11, pp. 381–386, 1931.

Reissner E.: Stationare Axial Symmetriche durch eine Schuttiond Masse Erregte Schwingiuingen eines Homogenen Elastischen Halbraumes, *Ingenieur-Archiev*, vol. 7, no. 6, Berlin, pp. 381–396, 1936.

_____ : Freie und Erawungene Torsions Chwiugungen des Elastichen Halbraumes, *Ingenieur-Archive*, vol. 8, no. 4, Berlin, pp. 229–245, 1937.

_____ and H.F. Sagoel: "Forced Torsional Oscillations of an Elastic Half Space" *J. App. Physics*, vol. 15, pp. 652–662, 1944.

Richart, F.E., Jr.: Foundation Vibrations, *Trans. ASCE*, vol. 127, part 1, pp. 863–898, 1962.

_____ , J.R. Hall, Jr., and R.D. Woodes: "Vibrations of Soils and Foundations," Prentice-Hall, Inc., Englewood Cliffs, NJ, 1970.

_____ and R.V. Whitman: Comparison of Footing Vibration Tests with Theory, *J. Soil Mech. Found. Div.*, *ASCE*, vol. 53, no. SM 6, pp. 143–168, November, 1967.

Sung, T.Y.: "Vibrations in Semi-Infinite Solids due to Periodic Surface Loading," Special Technical Publication No. 156, American Society for Testing and Materials, pp. 35–63, 1953.

Taylor, D.W.: "Fundamentals of Soil Mechanics" John Wiley & Sons, New York 1948.

Whitman, R.V., and Richart, F.E., Jr.: Design Procedures for Dynamically Loaded Foundations, *J. Soil Mech. Found. Div.*, *ASCE*, vol. 93, no. SM 6, pp. 169–193, November, 1967.

INDEXES

SUBJECT INDEX